KT-379-224

THE
EARTH REPORT 3
AN A-Z GUIDE TO ENVIRONMENTAL ISSUES

THE
EARTH REPORT 3

AN A-Z GUIDE TO ENVIRONMENTAL ISSUES

GENERAL EDITORS

EDWARD GOLDSMITH AND NICHOLAS HILDYARD
(The Ecologist)

MITCHELL BEAZLEY

THE EARTH REPORT 3 was edited and designed by Mitchell
Beazley Publishers, part of Reed International Books, Michelin
House, 81 Fulham Road, London SW3 6RB

Editor John Morton
Assistant Editor Simon Ryder
Art Editor Jean Jottrand
Production Sarah Schuman

Copyright © Mitchell Beazley Publishers 1992
All rights reserved
No part of this work may be reproduced or utilized in any form by any
means, electronic or mechanical, including photocopying, recording,
or by any information storage and retrieval system, without the prior
written permission of the publishers.

A CIP catalogue record for this book is available from the British
Library

ISBN 0-85533-926-8

Note: Although all reasonable care has been taken in the preparation
of this book, neither the publishers nor the contributors or editors can
accept liability for any consequences arising from the use thereof or
from the information contained herein. The Publishers will be
grateful for any information that will assist them in keeping future
editions up to date.

Photoset in Great Britain by Bookworm Typesetting, Manchester
Reproduction by M. and E. Reproductions, North Fanbridge, Essex
Printed in Great Britain by Butler & Tanner Ltd., Frome, Somerset

Contents

How to use this book   6

Foreword   7
by Nicholas Hildyard

A-Z   10

Organizations   169

Index   172

Acknowledgements   175

Entries are in alphabetical order and carry both internal cross-references to other, relevant entries (which are indicated by *qv* in parentheses) and "see also" cross-references, set at the end of each entry, that refer to entries containing additional material. The "see also" references carry the following symbols:

Ⓐ agriculture
© conservation
Ⓔ energy
Ⓕ foundations of ecology and basic concepts
Ⓛ lifescan — entries relating to health and nutrition
Ⓝ nuclear
Ⓟ pollution
③ Third World

The symbols enable the reader to follow a specific theme.

Measurements Both metric and imperial measurements are given. See below for conversion factors.

Currency Is given in United States dollars ($), Australian dollars ($A) or pounds sterling (£).

Billions Traditionally, billions in the UK have been 1,000,000 million. US usage of a billion as 1,000 million, however, is more useful, is becoming common usage in the UK and is followed in this book.

Abbreviations and conversions

Bq	becquerel
cm	centimetre (0.393701 inch)
cu m	cubic metre (35.3146 cubic feet)
ft	foot (30.48cm)
gm	gramme (0.035273 ounce)
kg	kilogramme (1,000 grammes, 2.204 pounds)
km	kilometre (0.62137 mile)
kph	kilometre per hour
lb	pound (0.4536kg)
mph	miles per hour
MW	megawatts (a million watts)
microgramme	a millionth of a gramme
milligramme	a thousandth of a gramme
mol	mole (the SI unit of amount of substance)
mSv	millisieverts
tonne	1,000kg (2,204lb)
oz	ounce (28.35gm)
sq	square
ha	hectare (2.47105 acres); 100ha = 1 sq km

On June 1 1992, over 100 heads of state will gather in Brazil for the United Nations Conference on Environment and Development (UNCED). Few international gatherings have been so heavily promoted as "Earth Summit". Billed as the "last chance to save the Earth", politicians wax enthusiastic about it. But those looking towards UNCED for action will be sorely disappointed. Commercial self-interest and nationalism have already brought a proposed climate convention to a halt, whilst a proposed convention to safeguard world forestry has been jettisoned in favour of "a non-legally binding authoritative statement of principles for a global consensus on the management, conservation and sustainable development of all types of forests", the draft of which is as vague as its title.

Indeed, as delegates wrangle, millions whose fate and livelihoods will be debated may ask: what lies behind the razzmatazz? Are the delegates genuinely concerned for the environment and equity? Or are they simply jockeying to avoid erosion of their own power?

Few doubt the serious environmental threats facing humanity. From pole to pole, the growth of industrialism and the demands it stimulates are destroying the environment, undermining the livelihoods of millions in the interests of a tiny minority. Toxic wastes discharged into waterways have contaminated rivers and lakes, polluting water supplies and destroying fisheries. Forests, wetlands, grazing lands, and oceans are all threatened. Meanwhile, by polluting the atmosphere, depleting stratospheric ozone and accumulating greenhouse gases, industrial activity is destabilizing the global climate to a point where severe global warming appears unavoidable.

Paralleling this destruction is increasing impoverishment as more and more people's lives are devastated by the pursuit of short-term economic goals and political gain. Dispossessed of land, millions now live wretched, inhumane existences. The sense of oppression is poignantly expressed by an angry New Guinea villager threatened with resettlement for a dam: "We have become rubbish people." The same may be said for many in the North.

The issues are not new: on the contrary, from Victorian Britain's factory chimneys to the logged-out moonscapes of British Columbia, environmental degradation and impoverishment have gone hand in hand with economic expansion, as local livelihoods and environments are sacrificed in the quest for raw materials and waste dumping grounds. But the destruction is not unchallenged. In the South, local people have fought successive attempts, first by colonial regimes and then by their own post-independence governments and commercial interests, to transform them and their homelands and workers into "resources" for a global economy they cannot control. Likewise, the North has a long history of protest.

Where environmental vandalism was purely local – a razed forest here, a leaking toxic dump there, a polluted river here – parochial protest posed little threat to the status quo and could be easily contained. Commercial and industrial interests simply denied the existence of a problem or justified it in the name of "progress". Opposition could be forcibly subdued or denigrated as "Luddite". But as wanton destruction spreads, protest groups are taking common cause with other activists to create an increasingly powerful international political force.

Confronted by the growing strength of the environmental protest, business interests have been forced to address the environmental impact of their activities. Land-filling toxic wastes in the US is now being phased out, for example, but not because US companies regard it as environmentally unacceptable (they are quite willing to "export" wastes to countries with laxer controls) but because popular protest and possible consumer boycotts at home threaten their profits.

But threats posed by "green" activism go deeper than simply upsetting corporate apple carts. Tighter environmental standards and environmental degradation themselves now threaten to deny the global economy resources for expansion, simultaneously depriving it of cheap, readily available opportunities to dispose of industrial effluent. As soils are eroded, so land is removed from production; as seas are over-fished and rivers polluted, so catches plummet; as forests are razed or are ravaged by air pollution, so timber supplies dwindle; and as the economic costs of mitigating damage rise, so the global economy is sapped of capital it could use for production. In a world in which the ability to sustain productive growth determines economic clout, such constraints, exacerbated by grassroots pressure for change, pose a direct threat to established patterns of power.

It is not the first time commercial and political élites have been threatened by demands for social change. However, these élites have not only usually contrived to survive challenges to their hegemonies, but have generally managed to extend their domains. Their success has depended partly on a willingness to sacrifice individual "players" whose interests jeopardize the system as a whole, partly on their willingness to cede political power to new players with similar interests, and partly by using new "ideologies" to disguise old exploitative patterns.

The power-brokers' policy is thus not outright resistance to change but more one of *managing* change. At one level this is simply "damage limitation", with industrial interests attempting to head off costly measures, either by playing down their malign role (as the coal industry does with respect to global warming) or by exaggerating the importance of what they are doing to mitigate environmental degradation. At another level, however, more imaginative industrialists and politicians recognize the need to "capture" the environmental debate and frame it in terms that minimize changes to the status quo. This is the agenda at UNCED.

Firstly, and most obviously, governments and industry studiously avoid discussing the destruction resulting from economic growth, technology transfer and capital flows from northern to southern countries (and vice versa) and instead blame "poverty", "population growth" and "underdevelopment" without revealing their root causes. Predictably, the proposed "solutions" are more economic growth, increased capital flows and more technology transfer.

Secondly, there is an attempt to deny the many conflicts of interest underlying the crisis. Instead, UNCED promotes a rosy-tinted world where all humanity is united by a common interest in survival, in which conflicts of class, race, culture and gender are characterized as of secondary importance to humanity's supposedly common goal. But while a Bihari peasant shares the same planet as a corporate executive, to suggest they share a common future is farcical. Constant references to "humanity's common resources", for example, obscure the fact that the vast majority of people have no access to those resources, which they neither own nor control, and which are selfishly exploited for the narrow ends of a few individuals and institutions. In Brazil, for example, multinational companies own more land than all the peasants put together In Britain, just 9% of the population owns 84% of the land.

In addition, the flow of resources from the "common resource base" is grossly unequal. In the last 50 years, the US has single-handedly consumed more fossil fuels and minerals than the rest of humanity has consumed in all recorded history. The US beef industry alone consumes as much food as India and China's combined populations, an orgy of consumption dependent on starving other people.

Similarly, attempts to portray environmental problems as problems of "mismanagement" detract from the deep structural roots of the crisis by suggesting a solution of *more* management. Faced with pollution from chemical plants or toxic waste dumps, with soil erosion or the salinization of land through irrigation schemes, politicians and industrialists blame inefficient production processes, lack of technical expertise, corruption, governmental or market failure, and so on – anything to obscure the real causes. The proposed "solution", popularized as "sustainable development", is seen to lie in optimizing rather than maximizing production through making technologies more efficient and safeguarding overexploited resources by limiting access to them.

Whilst few question the need to husband carefully resources, many question the end result of the "managerial solutions" proposed by those in power. Quite apart from their viability (for example, less than 0.001% of the world's commercial tropical timber production is logged on a sustainable basis, despite years of research into "sustainable management" practices), many would ask: *whose* environment is to be managed by *whom* and in *whose* interests?

Rather than examine the forces undermining the ability of local people to husband their own environments, global "managers" consider how best to secure that environment for the global economy. Armed with their new-found "concern" for the environment, global managers threaten a new colonialism, in which the management of people, even whole societies, for the benefit of commercial interests is justified in the name of environmental protection.

Carbon-dioxide-absorbing tree farms will supplant peasants' fields, inhabitants of tropical forests will lose control of their environment, which will be used to service the industrialized nations, and population control efforts will be intensified to reduce pressure on resources. Leaders of southern nations eager for compensation from the industrialized nations for environmental damage are likely to play the global "green game" with resources as bargaining chips. Where such negotiation fails,

"resource wars" may well be supplemented by "conservation wars" in which the industrialized nations' "strike forces" intervene in the southern countries in the name of environmentalism.

In effect, what is to be "managed" are those *aspects* of the environment of value to the global economy – from germ-plasm for biotechnology, to pollution "sinks" and any other tradable commodities. Increasingly the environmental managers assume the right to protect the environment from "demands" that conflict with commercial "needs", a formula that labels local people, the main "competitors" for resources, as primary agents of environmental destruction. Once that premise is accepted, it is easy to demean the ways local people traditionally care for their environment. The way is thus opened for new institutions, administered for the needs of trade and commerce, to assume environmental management at all levels.

Instead of "saving the Earth", UNCED thus looks set to perpetuate exploitation for a minority. Small wonder that environmental concerns have been steadily marginalized as the conference approaches. At best, lip service is paid to demands of popular movements for agrarian reform, local control of local resources and a decisive voice in decision-making. The greatest task facing environmentalists is to place these demands at the very heart of the debate.

Acceptable daily
    intake (ADI)
Acid rain
Additives
Advanced gas-cooled
    reactor
Agent Orange
Aid
Air pollution
Alar
Alaska
Aldicarb
Aldrin
Algal blooms
Alpha radiation
Alternative
    technology
Amaranth
Amazonia
Americium
Antarctica
Antibiotics
Antioxidants
Appropriate
    technology
Aquaculture
Aquifer
Aral Sea
Artificial fertilizer
Artificial sweeteners
Asbestos
Aswan Dam
Atomic tests

Acceptable daily intake (ADI)

The number of milligrammes of a chemical that can safely be consumed every day by an average human, for each kilogramme (2.2lb) of body weight.

There are three major institutions setting ADIS, and the numbers they set often, but not invariably, coincide: the Joint Expert Committee on Food Additives of the United Nations Food and Agriculture .Organization (FAO) and the World Health Organization (WHO); the EEC's Scientific Committee for Food; and the US Food and Drug Administration (FDA).

The label of ADI is inappropriate for any chemical that causes cancer by a mutagenic (see *Mutagen*) route – and perhaps by other routes too – because with those chemicals we cannot assume that there is any threshold level below which they can safely be used. (See also: *Additives*ⓁⓅ, *Cancer*Ⓛ, *Carcinogen*Ⓛ, *Junk food*Ⓛ, *Teratogen*Ⓛ.)

Acid rain

Term used to describe the fallout of industrial pollutants, chiefly sulphur dioxide, nitrogen oxides and volatile hydrocarbons, which react with water and sunlight to form sulphuric and nitric acids, ammonium salts and other mineral acids. These then fall to earth, often thousands of miles from their source, as dry particles or as acidified rain, snow or fog.

The main sources of "acid" pollution are fossil fuel power stations and industrial processes which burn fossil fuels, with vehicle exhausts being a major source of nitrogen oxides. After two decades of intensive scientific research, it is clear that acidification of the environment remains one of the industrialized world's most intractable problems: indeed, acidification has variously been described as "an insidious malaria of the biosphere" and an "ecological holocaust". According to the Brundtland (*qv*) report, acidification may now be so advanced in Europe as to be "irreversible", the remedial costs being "beyond economic reach".

At times more acid than vine-gar, acid rain has corroded buildings, rendered lakes devoid of fishlife, and led to the decline and death of millions of trees. In Greece, acid rain, along with other pollutants, is eating away the marble of the Parthenon, while in India, the Taj Mahal is now succumbing to its ravages. In Scandinavia, 20,000 of Sweden's 90,000 lakes are acidified to some degree, 18,000 of them to the point where they are incapable of supporting fish, and in Norway, 80 per cent of the lakes and streams in the southern half of the country are either "dead" or on the critical list.

Researchers in the Federal Republic of West Germany have identified acid rain as one of the prime causes of *Waldsterben* – the West German term for the epidemic of tree deaths which has claimed more than 70,000sq km (27,000sq miles) of forests in 15 European countries. In 1989, a study by the UN Economic Commission for Europe found evidence of forest damage, measured in terms of needle loss or leaf damage, in 25 countries in Europe, including the Baltic states of the USSR. In West Germany, 52 per cent of the country's forests (some 38,000 sq km or 23,000sq miles) were affected; in Switzerland, 43 per cent; and in Sweden, 38 per cent of trees. According to the study, Britain was one of the worst affected countries, with 64 per cent of all trees showing some degree of damage, and 25 per cent having "moderate to severe" damage. Only Czechoslovakia, with 70.5 per cent of its trees damaged, and Greece, level pegging with 64 per cent, fared as badly or worse.

On the other side of the Atlantic, the picture is not much different. Acid rain, in combination with other airborne pollutants, has stricken the Canadian Parliament building in Ottawa and acidified more than 300 lakes in the province of Ontario – with a further 48,000 lakes now designated as "acid sensitive". In Nova Scotia, nine rivers are too acid to support salmon or trout hatcheries. Across the border in the USA, scientists claim that thousands of lakes on the eastern seaboard, especially in the Adirondack Mountains, are so acidic as to be virtual "fish graveyards". The US National Surface Water Survey discovered that at least 10 per cent of the lakes in the Adirondack region have pH values below 5.

Salt-water organisms have also been affected, according to a recent study by the US Environmental Defense Fund. The group cites evidence of damage to fish along the Atlantic coast of the USA, in particular to the spawning grounds for east coast fisheries. The study claims that acid rain contributes 25 per cent of the nitrogen entering Chesapeake Bay and other Atlantic coastal waters – a figure which the group says could rise to 40 per cent if current acid emissions are allowed to continue.

The effects of acid rain on North America's forests has been devastating, particularly for the conifer forests stretching up the Appalachian Mountains from Georgia to New England. A recent study by the World Resources Institute reports, "On the mountains where the trees are dying, the acidity of the cloud moisture is about 10 times greater than that at low elevations and about 100 times greater than that of unpolluted precipitation". In Vermont, New Hampshire and New York, 60 per cent of high-elevation red spruce are reported dead, while, in Southern California, 87 per cent of the Ponderosa and Jeffery pines in the San Bernardino Forest are damaged. In Canada, sugar maples are dying over wide areas, due in large part to the increasing acidification of soils in eastern Canada.

One of the main reasons that acid rain is so widespread is due to the policy "mind-set", prevalent in the 1960s and 1970s, which saw "dilution as the solution to pollution". Consequently, over the past three decades, power stations and industrial plants built their smokestacks higher and higher in order to disperse the pollutants farther afield so that they would not pollute the immediate environment. Carried by prevailing winds over considerable distances – there are documented cases of sulphur dioxide compounds being transported 1,000-2,000 kilometres (600-1,200 miles) in a period of three to five days – the pollutants were simply "exported" to other regions. Thus, almost 90 per cent of the sulphur deposited on Sweden comes from abroad, while Sweden in turn exports two-thirds of its own emissions. In Europe alone, the UK exports 3,750,000 tonnes. In North America, the USA "exports" 24,600,000 tonnes of sulphur dioxide.

Acid rain is not an entirely industrial phenomenon. In nature, it can be produced through such events as volcanic eruptions and forest fires. Nonetheless, nature's own "emissions" of sulphur and nitrogen oxides are dwarfed by those from industry. Every year, somewhere between 110 and 115 million tonnes of sulphur dioxide are spilled across Europe and North America, while the countries that make up the Organisation for Economic Co-operation and Development (OECD) as a whole generate about 37 million tonnes of nitrogen oxides. On a global basis probably 50 per cent of atmospheric sulphur is of natural origin: but in industrialized regions like Europe and eastern North America, more than 90 per cent of the deposited sulphur results from human activity.

Since full-scale liming began in 1982, Sweden has treated 5,500 acidified lakes.

Acid rain does not kill fish or trees directly but as a result of a number of inter-related processes. Scientists investigating *Waldsterben* have discerned three ways in which acid rain affects forests: through foliar leaching of nutrients; from the leaching of nutrients out of the root zone; and through the mobilization of phytotoxic concentrations of aluminium. In water courses, increased levels of acidity are now associated with elevated concentrations of such heavy metals as mercury, aluminium, lead, zinc and even cadmium. It is aluminium – the most common metal found in soils – that delivers the *coup de grace*. Precipitated as aluminium hydroxide, it coats the gills of fish, reducing the oxygen content in the blood and causing internal salt imbalances.

Only concerted international action will reduce acid rain. In 1984, Norway and Sweden were instrumental in forming the so-called "30 per cent club", initially consisting of 10 countries, which called for the reduction of sulphur dioxide levels by at least 30 per cent by 1993 (using 1980 emissions as a baseline). By April 1985, 19 countries had pledged themselves to achieving this reduction. In 1987, the Convention on Long-Range Transboundary Air Pollution (LRTAP), first drawn up in 1979, was finally ratified by enough countries to come into force. The convention requires signatory nations to reduce sulphur dioxide emissions by 30 per cent by 1993. However, two of the largest emitters of both sulphur and nitrogen oxides – the UK and the USA – refused to sign on the grounds that scientific uncertainty about the benefits made further reductions problematic.

Britain also blocked an EC attempt to reduce sulphur dioxide emissions in member states by 60 per cent by 1995. After lengthy negotiations, it finally agreed to cut emissions by 20 per cent of 1980 levels by 1993, followed by a further cut to 40 per cent by 1998, and to 60 per cent by 2003. Like Britain, the USA has also baulked at taking action over acid rain. In 1989, however, President Bush announced a programme to reduce sulphur dioxide emissions by 10 million tonnes (a 50 per cent reduction on current levels) by the year 2000. By contrast, 10 of the countries which have joined the "30 per cent club" have already cut emissions by 30 per cent, and 11 more are expected to have halved their emissions by 1995. Four countries predict that 1995 will see their emission cut even further – by 65 per cent.

Progress on reducing emissions of nitrogen oxides had also been hampered by political stonewalling. In 1989, a Protocol to the LRTAP Convention was signed by 25 nations, under which it was agreed to freeze nitrogen oxide emissions at 1987 levels – but not until 1994. Reductions in emissions (still to be discussed) would only be introduced under a second phase of the programme. More stringent measures had been proposed but had been blocked by the USA and Britain, together with Italy, Spain, Czechoslovakia and the USSR. The weakening of the protocol led 12 countries to sign an independent declaration binding them to reduce their emissions by 30 per cent by 1998. Britain, Italy, Spain and France also successfully watered down an EC directive aimed at imposing strict new regulations on nitrogen oxide emissions from small cars (less than 1,200cc). A compromise was eventually reached in 1989, under which emissions would be cut by 60 per cent by 1992 – far below the level originally proposed.

Environmental groups are concerned at the slow pace of international action on acid rain and have called for greater reductions in acid emissions. In 1989, a statement signed by 25 groups from 15 European countries warned: "If we are to save our natural environment, European emissions of sulphur and nitrogen oxides will have to be reduced by at least 90 per cent". (See also: *Air Pollution*℗©.)

Additives
Chemicals that are deliberately added to food products in the course of industrial processing. They are distinct from the chemicals of which foods are composed, the chemicals introduced deliberately in farming, or the contaminants that may inadvertently enter the food supply.

Food technologists identify at least 23 different sorts of additives, but they can conveniently be grouped into five major types.

First, there are the preservatives (*qv*) that inhibit or prevent the growth of micro-organisms which would otherwise cause the food to rot and become poisonous.

Secondly, there are antioxidants (*qv*) that prevent oils and fats from turning rancid, and thereby extend the shelf lives of products containing those ingredients.

While those two groups are important, they together account for less than one per cent of the total use of chemical food additives. The largest single group of chemicals is the cosmetics. These are additives that modify the taste, appearance and texture of food products. About 88 per cent of the money spent on all additives is spent on cosmetics. Another eight per cent is accounted for by processing aids, which are as useful in the processing as in the products. Nutrients such as vitamins, calcium and minerals account for the remaining fraction.

In 1986, the UK food industry spent about £225 million ($380 million) on more than 200,000 tonnes of additives – equivalent, per person, to about 8g (0.3oz) of chemicals in a kilogramme (2.2lb) of food – while the industry in the USA spent $2,250 million buying 1,250,000 tonnes of additives, which corresponds to 9g (0.3oz) per person in a similar quantity of food. There are about 3,850 additives in use in the UK, 3,500 of them being designed to enhance taste. Only 300 of these additives are covered by regulations requiring manufacturers to list additives on the labels of food and drink products. As from the end of 1992, however, new EC regulations will require 500 additives to be so listed.

The British government says

that it approves additives only if they are needed and safe. In recent years, the application of both these criteria has been challenged. While the usefulness of preservatives is generally agreed, the need for cosmetics, especially food dyes, is far more controversial. No one doubts that they can be useful for industry, but many argue that consumers have no need for them. The standards by which safety has been judged have also been challenged. There is increasing evidence that some additives are provoking acute intolerance in a small but indeterminate proportion of the population. For example, some food dyes (*qv*), preservatives, artificial sweeteners (*qv*) and monosodium glutamate (*qv*) have been implicated as causes of symptoms of intolerance such as hyperactivity and asthma.

The use of additives is defended by industry and government on the grounds that they can be used to reduce the incidence of bacterial food poisoning, lengthen shelf lives, and make food products more attractive and cheaper. Consumer groups have criticized their use not just because they may pose a hazard to health, but also because they can be used to embellish cheap or inferior ingredients and enable them to be presented as premium quality goods, and because their use can contribute to the over-consumption of fats, sugars and processed starches. (See also: *Cancer*Ⓛ, *Coal-tar dyes*Ⓛ, *Emulsifiers*Ⓛ, *Junk food*Ⓛ.)

Advanced gas-cooled reactor

The UK is the only country in the world that operates advanced gas-cooled reactors (AGRS), having seven stations with twin reactors in operation. The AGR uses carbon dioxide gas as coolant and has a moderator (*qv*) made up of a loose assembly of graphite bricks.

From an economic point of view the building of the first series of AGRS was an unmitigated disaster, brought about by intrinsic design problems not foreseen when scaling up from the prototype. All the AGR stations underwent long delays in construction.

Dungeness B, which opened in 1985, took just less than 20 years to come into service, instead of the five years projected.

When all the costs are taken into account, including excess construction costs and interest charges, the AGR is proving to be between 40 and 70 per cent more expensive to operate than a coal-fired plant of similar vintage.

The CEGB now admits that the operating performance of its AGRS has been much worse than previously acknowledged. The performance of three of the stations brought on stream since 1984 has been particularly poor. In the three years 1987-89, their annual "availability" (that is, the proportion of time in which power could be produced) was 43 per cent for Heysham 1, 27 per cent for Hartlepool and only 15 per cent for Dungeness B. The huge costs incurred by the AGR programme were the reason given by the CEGB for raising its electricity prices in 1987.

A problem in the AGR is that the steam generators are subject to corrosion, both from the hot carbon dioxide gas and from water getting into the steam "super-heat" section of the reactor. Should a number of boiler tubes fail simultaneously, then considerable quantities of water and steam will flow under pressure into the pressure vessel.

If that happened, a potentially dangerous situation would be created. The pressure vessel might become over-pressurized and breach, thus letting the coolant escape, or steam explosions might occur, through the reaction of hot fuel and water. Hydrogen might also be generated, as a result of the interaction of steam and graphite, again leading to the risk of an explosion. Finally, water and steam might bring about a sudden surge in reactivity similar in many respects to that which caused the Chernobyl (*qv*) explosion. Explosions of the size that destroyed the Chernobyl containment would be more than enough to burst apart an AGR.

Despite the problems, Nuclear Electric (the successor company to the CEGB), which took over five

of the AGRS in 1990, has announced it would like to extend the operating life of two of them, at Hinkley Point (*qv*) and Heysham, from 25-30 years. Meanwhile, the UK nuclear industry has shifted its allegiance to the American Pressurized Water Reactor (PWR), the first of which is under construction at Sizewell (*qv*) in Suffolk. (See also: *Nuclear accidents*Ⓝ, *Pressurized water reactor*Ⓝ.

Agent Orange

The code name given to a herbicide used extensively by US forces during the Vietnam War in order to defoliate the jungle and deprive the North Vietnamese of cover.

An equal mixture of 2,4,5-T (*qv*) and 2,4-D (*qv*), Agent Orange was heavily contaminated with dioxin (*qv*). Hospitals in North Vietnam reported that the rate of birth defects in sprayed areas had risen by 50 per cent. They also reported a significant increase in the rate of Down's Syndrome.

In the early 1980s, 2,500,000 Vietnam veterans sued both the US Government and the seven manufacturers of Agent Orange for alleged physical and psychological damages. The veterans reported illnesses ranging from chloracne – a disfiguring skin disease – to liver cancer, reproductive defects, genetic damage and mental disorders. The case was eventually settled out of court, with the manufacturers of Agent Orange agreeing to pay $180 million. The companies did not admit liability.

In Australia, where Vietnam veterans had also sued for injuries, a Royal Commission ruled that Agent Orange was not guilty of causing any adverse health effects among those who had served in Vietnam. (See also: *Biocide*ⒶⓅ, *Cancer*Ⓛ, *Phenoxy herbicides*ⒶⓅ.)

Aid

Transfers of capital – generally in the form of loans or grants – from governments and public institutions of the industrialized world to governments of the Third World. Where such capital transfers contain an element of "con ditionality", they are recorded by the Development Assistance Committee (DAC) of the Organization for Economic Cooperation and Development (OECD). The same applies if the money is provided as grants rather than loans. Aid is also provided in the form of "technical assistance", notably by various specialized agencies of the United Nations.

Three-quarters of all "official aid" registered with DAC is "bilateral aid", provided directly from one government to another. Much of this takes the form of grants. The rest is channelled through the World Bank (qv), the International Monetary Fund (qv) and regional banks, together with various funding institutions set up by the European Community. Such transfers are referred to as "multilateral aid" in that the funds are derived from different countries. Of the capital sent out as bilateral aid, well over 50 per cent is provided to finance specific projects, ten per cent as food aid and two per cent as disaster relief.

Between 1970 and 1980, the total amount of official aid rose from $7,000 million to $35,000 million, an increase of 50 per cent in real terms. In 1988, the figure was $51,000 million. On the other hand, by 1989 the volume of aid as a proportion of gross national product had declined in many countries to below levels in 1970.

Since 1982, the Third World has received less money in aid from the developed world than it has paid out in interest on loans already contracted. In 1989, Third World countries paid banks $20,000 million more in interest than they received in new loans. In the same year, the total transfer of capital from the Third World to the industrialized countries, including repatriation of profits by Western companies and other forms of capital flight, was $51,000 million, exactly the amount handed out in foreign aid the previous year. The gap is even greater if all financial flows – including the repatriation of profits by Western companies operating in the Third World and capital flows, whether legal or illegal – are taken into account.

The net flow of funds from the Third World to the industrialized world has embarrassed the main aid agencies, in particular the World Bank. Various plans for reversing the trend have been formulated, notably by the former US Senator Howard Baker, but none has yet been adopted.

In recent years, the value of aid for fighting poverty and malnutrition in the Third World has increasingly been questioned, the principal argument being that aid has been used as a political and economic weapon in the interests not of the Third World but of donor countries.

Thus most aid is "tied aid" – that is, it is conditional on recipient countries buying goods and services from the donor countries. Eighty per cent of Canadian aid is tied aid, while two-thirds of British aid is said never to leave Britain (some put the figure as high as 98 per cent). Such aid is in effect little more than an export subsidy.

Similarly, much of the aid given to Third World countries is given in order to enable them to export foodstuffs and raw materials to the industrialized world. In effect, it acts as an import subsidy for donor countries. The loans incurred to permit the modernization of Third World agriculture under the green revolution (qv) come under this category, since they serve largely to permit the large-scale production of cash crops (qv) for the industrialized world.

Aid is also used as a blatant political tool. The bulk of US aid has gone to strategically important countries, while the world's ten poorest countries received less than five per cent of the total of US bilateral aid supplied.

Another reason for doubting the value of aid as a means of fighting poverty and malnutrition in the Third World is that much of it takes the form of arms. Military aid is one of the biggest categories of US aid, having increased from 22 per cent of the total budget in 1980 to 37 per cent in 1985. During the same period, US military aid to sub-Saharan countries rose by more than 40 per cent – this despite the region

being ravaged by the greatest famine in human history.

In many cases, military aid is sent to blatantly oppressive governments – often dictatorships – whose lack of concern for the poor is well documented.

Corruption ensures that as much as 20-30 per cent of aid never reaches the poor, but is instead siphoned off into private bank accounts and slush funds.

As presently constituted, aid projects rarely improve the welfare of the poor and the hungry. Instead, they serve largely to satisfy the economic, political and strategic interests of industrialized countries and the financial interests of the ruling elites of the Third World.

It is worth considering, too, that without aid the vast development projects that have led to so much environmental degradation in the Third World would never have been initiated. (See also: *Food Aid, Cash crops*Ⓐ③, *Dams*③, *Deforestation*③, *Develop ment*③, *Third World debt*.)

Air pollution

Every year, thousands of millions of tonnes of pollutants enter the atmosphere from industry, vehicles, households and other sources – at enormous cost to the environment. Quite apart from the threat posed by greenhouse gases (qv) and the damage done by acid rain (qv), air pollution takes a massive toll on human health.

In the USA, a 1989 report by the Environmental Protection Agency estimated that more than 900,000 tonnes of toxic chemicals are pumped into the air every year – a figure which some argue is three times too low since the EPA study did not include emissions from vehicles or from companies emitting small volumes of pollutants. The EPA report surveyed 320 chemicals, only 7 of which were subject to emission standards. Sixty of the chemicals in the survey were known carcinogens. The 313 uncontrolled chemicals included butadiene, carbon tetrachloride, cadmium and acrylonitrile, all of which are widely used in manufacturing.

In the UK, Friends of the Earth

(FOE) estimate that one in five people are at risk from air pollution, the most sensitive groups being infants, the elderly, pregnant women and those with respiratory problems. Levels of sulphur dioxide, particulates, nitrogen dioxide, carbon monoxide and tropospheric ozone (*qv*) in Britain regularly exceed the "safe" levels as laid down by the World Health Organization. In a 1989 report, FOE concludes: "For some pollutants, the UK has no air quality standards, for others only lax European Community ones. During periods of particularly high pollution, all the government appears to do is keep quiet and wait for the problem to go away". At present, Britain spends some 1.5 per cent of its gross domestic product on air pollution control. (See also: *Acid Rain* ℗, *Cancer* ℗, Dilution and Dispersal℗, *Greenhouse Effect* ℗.)

Alar

Alar, the trade name for daminazide, is a pesticide which, until 1988, was used on about 10 per cent of the apple crop in the UK. In the early 1980s, the US Environmental Protection Agency (EPA) assessed studies indicating that dimethylhydrazine (UDMH), a breakdown product, caused tumours in mice. By 1987, the EPA had classified daminazide as a probable human carcinogen and, in 1989, announced its intention to ban it within 18 months. The UK reviewed daminazide in 1989. It was given a clean bill of health, based on a review of the evidence from the US.

Alaska

Since the territory received its statehood in 1959, Alaska's history has been characterized by a dramatic struggle between powerful, determined conservation and development lobbies. Many have regarded the state, an area one-sixth of all the other 49 US states put together, as America's last great wilderness, offering a last chance to achieve balance with the environment.

In 1968, 10,000 million barrels of oil and 736,000 million cubic metres (963,000 million cubic yards) of gas (25 per cent of proven US crude oil reserves and ten per cent of gas reserves) were discovered in Prudhoe Bay on Alaska's north shore. Extensive oilfields have been discovered elsewhere in the state.

In 1980 the Senate passed a bill closing 429,000sq km (165,000sq miles), in varying degrees, to development. But early in 1987 the then US Secretary for the Interior, Donald Hodel, recommended to Congress that oil development be permitted on 6,000sq km (2,300sq miles) of the Arctic National Wildlife Refuge (ANWR).

The plans for further development in Alaska have rekindled the controversy between conservationists and pro-oil boomers. The conservationists' case was considerably strengthened by the release in 1987 of a US Fish and Wildlife Service report documenting the extent of environmental damage caused by oil exploration. The report stated that the development of the Prudhoe Bay oilfield and the Trans-Alaskan pipeline had caused far greater damage than predicted in the original environmental impact statements. According to the report, construction and development activities destroyed the habitats of more than 20,000 birds, resulting in a marked decline in bird populations. Almost 4,500 hectares (11,000 acres) of wilderness have been lost to development at Prudhoe Bay, double that predicted in the original assessment. In addition, the area has seen a dramatic decline in such predators as bears and wolves.

In March 1989, some of the worst fears of environmentalists became reality when a supertanker, the *Exxon Valdez* (*qv*), struck rocks and went aground in Prince William Sound, releasing 12 million gallons of crude oil. The scale of the disaster was sufficient to put an end to any further talk of further development.

Two years later, however, the Gulf War (*qv*) brought the issue back on to the agenda. Concerned about its dependence upon oil from a region as unstable as the Middle East, the USA is once again looking at its home reserves. In June 1991, a Senate committee approved a new US Energy Bill that would permit exploratory drilling through all 19 million acres of the ANWR. The bill has the support of President Bush and of most Alaskans, who received annual cash dividends of up to $1,000 per person from the Prudhoe Bay field. If the ANWR is opened up to the oil industry, it will set a precedent for the exploitation and despoilation of some of the world's last remaining areas of protected wilderness. See also: *Development*©, *Extinction*©, *Oil*©.)

Aldicarb

A highly toxic insecticide of the carbamate (*qv*) group. Like other compounds in the group, aldicarb is a suspected carcinogen (*qv*). It is also a cholinesterase inhibitor, some people being especially sensitive to its effects.

Aldicarb is not selective and can harm non-target species. Gulls and stone curlews have died from aldicarb poisoning after consuming residues in earthworms.

Aldicarb is persistent in water. In 1983, the detection of aldicarb (known as Temik in the USA) in drinking water wells led to a year-long ban on its use in parts of Florida. In Long Island, New York, aldicarb in 1,000 wells was linked to a 46 per cent rise in spontaneous abortions.

In Britain, aldicarb is classed as a poison and is subject to special rules regarding protective clothing, which must be worn when it is used in concentrated form. In the Philippines, aldicarb is classified as too dangerous for general use.

The use of aldicarb is now restricted in the USA. Nonetheless, there is evidence that aldicarb has been sprayed illegally. Following a spate of unexplained illnesses in the mid-1980s, the public health authorities in California analysed locally grown watermelons and found high levels of aldicarb residues – despite aldicarb being restricted for use on watermelons. Growers argued that the residues resulted from the previous spraying of aldicarb on cotton crops – but both the state authorities and the manufacturers deny that aldicarb persists in the soil longer than six months. A recent report by two researchers in Wisconsin has suggested that exposure to aldicarb may be linked to the spread of the AIDS virus. Aldicarb is known to interfere with the immune system and this, they argue, may leave people more vulnerable to AIDS. (See also: *Biocide*Ⓟ, *Cancer*ⓁⓅ, *Groundwater*Ⓟ, *Pesticides*ⒶⓅ.)

Aldrin

A toxic chlorinated hydrocarbon (*qv*) insecticide. A suspect carcinogen (*qv*), teratogen (*qv*) and mutagen (*qv*), it is classified by the World Health Organization as "highly hazardous". Once in the environment, aldrin is converted into dieldrin (*qv*).

Banned in Sweden, the use of aldrin has been severely restricted in the USA since 1976. In 1979, the EC issued a directive to all member states banning the marketing and sale of aldrin in plant protection products. However, the commission agreed to permit certain "derogations" on uses. In May 1989 Britain banned all pesticides containing aldrin with immediate effect. Aldrin continues to be widely used in the Third World. (See also: *Biocide*Ⓟ, *Cancer*Ⓛ, *Insecticides*Ⓟ, *Pesticides*ⒶⓅ.)

Algal blooms

In recent years, many coastal areas, particularly in the northern North Sea, have suffered severe algal blooms, the result of massive population explosions of phytoplankton. The cause of the blooms has been pinned primarily on pollution by sewage, the run-off of artificial fertilizers (*qv*) and the discharge of phosphate (*qv*) detergents, all of which add nutrients to the receiving waters, causing their eutrophication (*qv*). In 1980, some 100,000 tonnes of phosphorus and one million tonnes of nitrogen entered the North Sea via rivers, quadrupling the sea's natural nitrogen load and increasing its phosphate load sevenfold. In many areas the impact of the resulting algal blooms

has been devastating. In May 1988, the western coast of Sweden was invaded by *Chrysochromultina polylepsis*, a yellow algae that suffocates fish by forming a slimy skin around their gills. Thousands of fish were killed and the Swedish National Natural Reserve Board reported that some areas were rendered completely devoid of marine life. Another algae, *Gonyalaux*, invaded Danish waters with equally devastating consequences. In Norway, algal blooms have threatened to ruin the country's 747 coastal fish farms and 659 hatcheries. Norway provides about 80 per cent of world salmon sales. The blooms have also been implicated as a cause of acid rain (*qv*). Phytoplankton growing in the open ocean release the gas dimethyl sulphide, which is transformed into sulphuric acid and sulphur dioxide acid in the Earth's atmosphere. Recent research by the ocean chemists Meinrat Andreae and Peter Liss has shown that the emission of dimethyl sulphide from algal blooms in Western Europe may be comparable in volume to the total industrial emissions of sulphur. (See also: *North Sea* Ⓟ.)

Alpha radiation

Positively charged particles released when one element transforms into another.

Compared with gamma (*qv*) and beta radiation (*qv*), alpha particles are heavy and slow moving with poor penetration. A sheet of paper or the outer layers of skin are enough to stop them.

Nonetheless, alpha particles can cause intense biological damage – possibly 10-20 times more than gamma radiation. The danger lies when alpha emitters are either inhaled or ingested with food, since they tend to accumulate in specific organs and tissues such as the lung and bone. (See also: *Cancer*Ⓛ, *Carcinogen*ⒻⓁ, *Plutonium*Ⓝ, *Radiation and health*ⓁⓃ.)

Alternative technology

Technology designed to use resources more efficiently and cause less environmental damage than

technology in more widespread use but serving similar ends. Given this broad definition there are few technologies for which alternatives cannot be devised, and the pursuit of such alternatives has inspired many people within the ecological movement in many industrial countries.

The small-scale use of moving water in rivers, windmills, heat pumps, solar-energy collectors, and other devices to generate electricity for domestic use provide examples of alternative technologies. These alternatives have found application in many rural areas in industrial countries and are no longer considered strange. (See also: *Energy*, *Soft energy paths*Ⓔ, *Solar energy*Ⓔ, *Tidal power*Ⓔ, *Wave power*Ⓔ, *Wind power*Ⓔ.)

Amaranth

A widely used red coal-tar dye (*qv*), known in the USA as Red 2 and in the EC as E123. It was first synthesized in 1878, and first produced on a large scale in the USA in 1914.

There are about 18 manufacturers in Western Europe, producing more than 300 tonnes a year. Amaranth is used not merely in food products, but also in drug preparations, cosmetics and inks.

It is one of the most widely used food dyes (*qv*) in the UK, and the most widely used red food dye. It can generally be found in soft drinks, sweets, and especially in products imitating cherries, strawberries, raspberries, or blackcurrants. In 1983, the British food industry incorporated about 50 tonnes of amaranth into their products. It can also be found in toothpastes and is available from British retailers as a food dye.

The doubts about the long-term safety of amaranth became particularly severe in 1970 when some work in the Soviet Union suggested that it was carcinogenic (see *Carcinogen*). This provoked an extensive discussion, and amaranth was banned in the USA in January 1976.

Amaranth is also banned in the USSR, Greece, Yugoslavia, Norway, Finland and Austria, but permitted and used in Britain and at least 63 other countries. (See also: *Additives*Ⓛ, *Cancer*Ⓛ.)

Amazonia

Stretching from the Atlantic coast of Brazil to the foothills of the Peruvian Andes, the Amazon Basin – better known as Amazonia – covers an area larger than the entire continent of Australia.

The world's largest tropical rainforest, Amazonia has a vital role to play in regulating the Earth's climate. It is also a biological treasure trove, providing a habitat for millions of animal and plant species including 2,500 species of trees, 1,800 species of birds and 2,000 species of fish. A hundred sq metres of forest can contain as many as 230 different tree species – as against a mere ten to 15 species in a typical temperate forest. In addition, Amazonia is the homeland for numerous tribal groups.

Since World War II, the Amazonian states have been intent on exploiting Amazonia's vast natural wealth and on "opening up" the forest to settlers. The destruction caused by development programmes is described in the accompanying illustration.

Satellite photographs reveal that the area of cleared land in Brazilian Amazonia more than doubled between 1975 and 1978 – from 28,600sq km (11,000sq miles) to 77,000sq km (30,000sq miles). Despite a 1977 resolution committing all eight Amazonian states to the "sustainable" development of the Amazon Basin, the destruction continues apace. The latest satellite photographs reveal that some 48,000sq km (18,500sq miles) of primary rainforest, an area the size of Belgium, disappeared in smoke during the 1988 burning season. If the area of *cerrado* (or savannah) forest burned is also included, the total figure exceeds 120,000sq km (46,000sq miles). The State of Mato Grosso was worst affected, losing some 21,700sq km (8,000sq miles) of rainforest and 27,600sq km (10,600sq miles) of *cerrado*. Official figures put the total area already lost at four per cent of the forest domain: independent experts, however, say the real figure is closer to 15-20 per cent. If the destruction were to continue at its current exponential rate, then, predicts Jose Lutzenberger, one of Brazil's leading ecologists, "by the year 2000, everything will be gone". Mining, dam projects, log-

ging, ranching, road projects and colonization programmes pose the greatest threats. Ranching projects alone were responsible for the destruction of 38 per cent of the forest lost between 1966 and 1975, with road and highway operations accounting for 25 per cent.

Amazonia has immense mineral resources, Brazil earning some $9,000 million a year from mining operations. Gold, diamonds, uranium, titanium and tin have all been discovered on the Brazilian-Venezuelan border, threatening to devastate the homeland of 20,000 Yanomami Indians.

In north-western Amazonia, on the upper reaches of the Rio Negro, a gold rush has already led to the area being invaded by thousands of prospectors. For local Indians, the experience has proved catastrophic. Recently, the Brazilian Government awarded mining concessions totalling 2,000sq km (770sq miles).

The environmental impact of the Grande Carajas (*qv*) project in north-eastern Brazil will be enormous. Some 15,000sq km (5,800sq miles) of forest will be cut simply to supply charcoal for the smelting of pig iron.

In the last decade 10% of the Amazon rain forest has been cleared for cattle ranching.

Some 30,000sq km (11,500sq miles) in Grande Carajas will be cleared for cattle ranching, all in pursuit of Brazil's ambition to become the world's largest producer of beef. Almost all of the meat produced will be exported.

Dam projects, too, are a major threat to the forests of Amazonia and its peoples. Some 68 large dams are planned for Brazilian Amazonia alone under the country's 2010 Plan (*qv*): if built, they could flood an area the size of Great Britain.

Dam projects, mines, road projects and ranching have all brought encroaching cultivators (*qv*) in their wake. Though just two per cent of Amazonian soils are reckoned fertile enough to be farmed on a sustainable basis, the Brazilian Government has long encouraged settlers to colonize the rainforest under the slogan "Land without men for men without land."

The result has been catastrophic – both for the environment and for the landless peasants who seek a living in the forests. In Western Amazonia, the $1,600 million Polonoroeste road-building project has opened up the state of Rondonia to settlers, most of whom have been displaced from the fertile lands of southern Brazil in order to make way for vast government-backed plantations. The soils of Rondonia are so poor that many settlers have no option but to abandon their farms after the first harvest, forcing them to clear yet more forest in order to survive. An estimated 70,000 to 80,000 settlers arrive in Rondonia every year.

For the indigenous tribes of the Amazon, the development of Amazonia has proved nothing short of disastrous, 130 tribes having been wiped out in this century alone through disease, resettlement and the effects of culture shock.

In October 1988, President Sarney of Brazil announced a package of measures to combat deforestation, including a total ban on log exports, a three-month suspension of ranching subsidies (since extended indefinitely) and environmental controls on future agricultural and industrial projects. And in 1990, newly elected President Collor surprised the world by appointing the respected environmentalist Jose Lutzenberger as Environment Secretary. The success of these seemingly vigorous measures is uncertain. The number of trees felled in the Amazon in 1991 was 27 per cent less than in 1989, but some observers attribute this to an unusually heavy rainy season and to economic recession. Law enforcement in the region is difficult, and over 10,000 cubic metres of illegally logged timber are still being exported every month. (See also: *Deforestation*③, *Development*③, *Greenhouse effect*Ⓕ, *Hamburger connection*③, *Tribal peoples*③, *Tropical forests*③.)

Americium

A radioactive element that does not exist naturally on Earth, but is created in nuclear reactors.

Three different radioisotopes of americium can be formed. In terms of quantities generated, the most important is americium-241, itself a breakdown product of plutonium-241. Americium-241 has a half-life of 458 years. Once created, it will thus remain a potential pollutant for several thousand years.

Americium, an alpha emitter (see *Alpha radiation*), is at least one-third more radio-toxic than plutonium-239. The "safe" body burden is less than 0.04 microcurie.

Americium is a major constituent of the alpha wastes discharged from the Sellafield (*qv*) reprocessing plant in Cumbria.

In all, between 1968 and 1978 some 27,478 curies of alpha emitters were discharged into the Irish Sea via a pipeline from the Sellafield works. Forty-five per cent of that volume was made up of americium-241. Since October 1983, BNFL has embarked on a $240 million programme to reduce alpha discharges to 20 curies a year, the level achieved by Cap de la Hague (*qv*) in Normandy.

Contrary to expectations, both plutonium and americium are now coming ashore, thus contaminating the area around Sellafield. Hot spots of americium and plutonium have been found along the saltmarshes adjoining the Ravenglass estuary. Sheep grazing along the saltmarshes have been found with up to 100 times more plutonium in their livers than found in sheep from uncontaminated areas. (See also: *Plutonium*Ⓝ, *Radiation and health*Ⓝ.)

Antarctica

Antarctica is one of the last untouched wildernesses on Earth. The continent is the size of the United States and Mexico put together, around 14 million sq km (5,400,000sq miles). Most of the land mass is covered in ice with an average thickness of 1,600m (5,250ft), though this can extend in some parts to a thickness of 4,000m (13,000ft). Though pack ice is present in the sea all year round, in the winter the ice expands to cover 200 million sq km (77 million sq miles) and prevents access to parts of the coastline normally accessible in the summer months.

Fin fish, such as the Antarctic cod, had been so overfished by the early 1970s that the catches declined to a fraction of their previous levels. Today, the Russian, and to a lesser extent Japanese, Polish and German fishing fleets, are concentrating their efforts on fishing for krill (*qv*), a small shrimp-like creature that exists in enormous quantities in the Antarctic seas.

There is clearly tremendous interest in Antarctica's huge mineral and marine resource potential. However, the potential for irreversible environmental damage is very high. The pesticide DDT (*qv*) has already been found in penguin fat and eggs, though the nearest inhabited continent is 1,800km (1,100 miles) away. Biological processes operate only slowly and intermittently. The terrestrial ecosystem is particularly fragile and has little capacity to withstand physical, chemical or biological changes without itself being altered. Though there are more than 500 different species of lichen, 70 species of mosses, and two types of flowering plants, such vegetation is sparse and vulnerable. A human footprint in a bed of moss can remain for several years. Some damage has already occurred because of the research stations there.

The greatest threat, however, lies in commercial exploitation of Antarctica's resources. Oil is particularly menacing. The Antarctic seas are the roughest in the world and this, coupled with the extreme temperatures, would make the extraction and transportation of oil a hazardous enterprise at the best of times.

Oil pollution would cause a variety of disasters. It would threaten most of the animal life that depends on the marine environment, such as seals and penguins. An oil spill on ice would increase its capacity to absorb heat and would cause it to melt, with potentially disastrous consequences. Oil, in such a cold environment, would also take longer to decompose than in temperate areas.

Since 1961 a number of important protective conventions have been adopted by the member nations of the Antarctic Treaty. Most important among these is the Convention on the Conservation of Antarctica Marine Living Resources (CCAMLR), which is particularly interested in ensuring that the effects of krill fishing will not threaten other species in the ecosystem, though the establishment of krill quotas has been hampered by the fact that three of the parties to the convention, Japan, Poland, and the Soviet Union, are major krill-fishing nations.

In 1977, the consultative members of the treaty agreed not to proceed with any kind of commercial exploitation of Antarctica's mineral resources until a general agreement had been reached. Four years later, in October 1991, a treaty banning mining for the next 50 years was signed. Any move to lift the ban would now require approval by 75 per cent of the 26 "voting nations" of the Antarctic Treaty Body. The campaign for the ban had been led by Greenpeace and the World Wide Fund for Nature.

Antibiotics

Drugs used to combat bacterial infections. Mass-produced, synthesized antibiotics first became widely available after World War II and have undoubtedly saved many lives. But their abuse has led to many strains of bacteria becoming resistant to them, particularly to penicillin.

According to the World Health Organization (WHO), the number of intestinal bacteria showing signs of resistance to antibiotics tripled in the five years between 1976 and 1981. WHO warns that the general development of bacterial resistance could lead to a resurgence of such infectious diseases as pneumonia, meningitis, cholera, salmonella and sexually transmitted disease. Ironically, the problem of resistance is particularly severe in hospitals: 90 per cent of the staphylococcal infections found in hospitals are resistant to penicillin.

The use of antibiotics plays havoc with the body's own ability to fight infections. For that reason, practitioners of homoeopathy and other forms of alternative medicines eschew the use of synthetic antibiotics, stressing the importance of a healthy diet and lifestyle as the first line of defence against infections.

Antioxidants

A group of chemicals that are added to oils and fats to inhibit oxidation and thereby slow down the rate at which foods become rancid and unpalatable. Oils and fats in food products oxidize from normal contact with atmospheric oxygen. In extreme cases they can become toxic, though they develop an unacceptable taste long before that happens. The effect of antioxidants is therefore to extend the shelf-lives of products to which they are added.

There are two broad groups of antioxidants, the natural ones and the synthetics. Some oils such as cold-pressed olive oil contain naturally occurring constituents that act as antioxidants, but most commercially used oils and fats do not enjoy such protection. Antioxidants are added to a wide range of fat-containing food products, such as fried snack foods, breakfast cereals, baked goods, cured meats, margarine and dessert products. In the EC, all permitted antioxidants have been allocated E numbers, ranging from E300 to E321.

Unlike most groups of additives, the levels at which antioxidants can be used in particular types of products are stipulated in regulations, because their excessive use would constitute a health abuse. While some antioxidants such as ascorbic acid (E300) and the ascorbates (E302-E304) are accepted as being safe, the safety of the synthetic antioxidants butylated hydroxyanisole (E320) and butylated hydroxytoluene (E321) is a matter of dispute. (See also: *Additives* ©.)

Appropriate technology

Technology that uses tools, machinery, and methods that can be applied readily by the people for whom they are intended, and can then be sustained and maintained by them without recourse to imported supplies that may be difficult to obtain. (See also: *Alternative technology* ©.)

Aquaculture

The farming of fish, mussels, oysters and other aquatic organisms. Aquaculture is now being actively promoted by the UN Food and Agriculture Organization (FAO) (*qv*) in many Third World countries as a new source of fish supplies.

At present, marine fisheries provide the bulk of world fish production, yielding 76.8 million tonnes in 1983. By the year 2000, however, FAO predicts that world demand for fish will have outstripped marine catches by between 20-30 million tonnes a year. In reality, the shortfall is likely to be even higher since fish stocks are increasingly threatened by pollution and overfishing.

Great hopes have been pinned on aquaculture as the solution to the expected shortfall in fish supplies. At present, it accounts for about ten per cent of world fish production. FAO would like to increase that by five to ten times by the end of the century – a goal that seems unrealistic.

The bulk of current production from aquaculture comes from smallholders using traditional methods of fish farming. But FAO has been seeking to change this, promoting large-scale projects designed to maximize production. Unfortunately, FAO's plans are likely to make less (rather than more) fish available to the rural poor.

Indeed, traditional systems of aquaculture are highly sophisticated, reflecting the role that fish farming has played for centuries in the cultures of many peasant societies, particularly in South-East Asia. They are cheap to run, employ local technology and use existing sites, such as village ponds, paddy fields and irrigation canals. Aquaculture is thus complementary to other activities rather than competitive with them. In addition, the fish reared under traditional systems are readily available to local people.

By contrast, the prestige operations being promoted by FAO make use of expensive technology, require the clearance of new land and have high costs – not least the "opportunity cost" of the valuable land they take over.

Those high costs provide one reason why the "Blue Revolution", like the "Green Revolution" (qv) before it, cannot serve to feed the world's poor. To service the loans used to set up modern fish farms, their produce must necessarily be sold for urban consumption or for export.

FAO's plans to expand aquaculture have already hit problems. Attempts to set up modern fish-farms in the Nile Delta have failed, largely because no account was taken of local soil conditions. The sodic montmorillonite clay of the area is entirely unsuited to fish farming since, under water, it turns to a slurry and collapses.

Aquaculture requires a fertile clay soil and a reliable gravity-fed supply of uncontaminated water – itself an increasingly rare commodity. Such sites are scarce and, because they tend to be valuable for agriculture, are generally already in use. It is only in rare instances that converting them to aquaculture can help feed the hungry. In 1988, FAO carried out a reappraisal of its own aquaculture activities. The results of the report have not been released, but there does seem to have been some change in FAO's view. The World Bank has withdrawn support for large-scale aquaculture projects. But enthusiasm lingers on in the private sector, and massive fish farms are still being set up in countries such as Thailand, Ecuador and the Philippines. (See also: *Development* ③.)

Aquifer

A geological term that refers to a permeable formation of rock, gravel or soil through which water may percolate. When the underlying rock is impermeable, an aquifer acts as a groundwater reservoir.

By drilling wells or boreholes, engineers can tap the waters in an aquifer. More than 100 million Americans rely on aquifers for their drinking water and 40 per cent of the water used by US farmers for irrigation (qv) comes from groundwaters.

Aquifers can vary from being a few centimetres below the surface to being many hundreds of metres below. Their waters are recharged by the downward seepage of surface waters. They are therefore susceptible to pollution by contaminants within surface waters.

The pace at which groundwaters travel through an aquifer is snail-like, generally moving at less than a metre a month. The dark, lifeless environment of groundwaters makes the degradation of pollutants extremely slow. Once contaminated, therefore, pollutants can remain in an aquifer for hundreds of thousands of years. (See also: *Groundwater* ℗, *Ogallala Aquifer* ℗.)

Aral Sea

Situated in Soviet Central Asia, the Aral Sea was once the fourth largest lake in the world. Today, the Sea is less than half its former size. Overextraction of water for irrigation (qv) from the Amu Dar'ya and Syr Dar'ya rivers has led to large areas of the Sea drying out altogether. In places, the water has receded by up to 60km (35 miles), leaving ships stranded on newly created sand dunes.

In 1960, the Soviet Ministry of Water initiated a plan to take massive quantities of water from the Amu Dar'ya and Syr Dar'ya in order to transform the arid plains of Soviet Central Asia into productive cotton fields. It was recognized that such exploitation would dry out the Aral Sea, but there was another grandiose scheme – since shelved – which would have reversed the flows of the great Siberian rivers to the north in order to replenish the depleted rivers of the Aral Basin.

For the people of the Aral Basin, the project has brought misery. Two-thirds of the land under irrigation is now affected by salinization (qv), and much of it can no longer support crops. Dust storms whip up the dried-out bed of the Aral Sea, carrying millions of tonnes of salt on to the land.

In areas that have been spared salinization, the land is so overexploited that crops will only grow if massive amounts of chemical fertilizers are applied. Pest epidemics are only kept at bay by spraying tonne after tonne of pesticides (qv). Local drinking water is now heavily contaminated with pesticides and herbicides.

The impact on the health of those who still live and work in the region has been devastating. One in ten children die in infancy and there has been a sharp rise in the incidence of typhoid, stomach and respiratory problems, and throat cancer. Malnutrition is also rife.

Artificial fertilizer

Compound salts of nitrogen (N), phosphorus (P) and potassium (K) added to the soil to increase crop yield. Most artificial fertilizers used today consist of different proportions of N, P and K.

The use of artificial fertilizers had enormous impact on agriculture worldwide, especially after Haber in Germany developed his process for capturing nitrogen from the air and converting it into ammonia (NH_3). Farmers no longer had to leave their fields fallow to regain fertility or to follow crop rotations with the use of nitrogen-fixing legumes; nor did they need to keep animals to provide farmyard manure; instead they began growing the same crops year in and year out.

The long-term effect of reliance on artificial fertilizers is soil degradation. Soil needs more than additions of N, P and K. Without organic waste, many problems arise. The soil cannot support the microorganisms that produce humus; and without humus, the population of nitrogen-fixing bacteria declines. The number of earthworms decreases (a problem made worse by pesticide spraying) and the soil becomes less well aerated, reducing the supply of oxygen available to soil organisms. The roots of plants become shallower as the nutrients in the soil become scarcer, thus weakening the plants. The soil's capacity to store water is also affected and the structure of the soil begins to break down, leaving the land prone to erosion and compaction.

To compensate for the soil's dwindling natural fertility, farmers must apply more and more fertilizers – often with diminishing returns. Twenty years ago, farmers in the US corn belt could have expected a tonne of fertilizer to add 15-20 tonnes to their grain harvest. Today the same tonne can only increase production by about 5-10 tonnes.

Crops grown with artificial fertilizers tend to be poor in nutritional quality, to have a poor storage life, to be lacking in variety and to be contaminated with the residue of agrochemicals.

The use of nitrogen fertilizers has led to the pollution of surface waters and groundwaters (qv) with nitrate (qv), causing many drinking water (qv) supplies to be a health hazard. Fertilizer run-off to surface waters has also led to the eutrophication (qv) of rivers and to algal blooms (qv) in coastal areas. In addition, artificial fertilizers are a source of atmospheric nitrous oxide, one of the major causes of the greenhouse effect (qv) and a possible cause of stratospheric ozone (qv) depletion.

An EC commission has announced plans to impose strictly enforced controls on the use of artificial fertilizers over the next few years. Denmark has stated its intention to cut its use of nitrogen fertilizers by 25 per cent. However, these measures do not go far enough. The pollution that is caused by artificial fertilizers (and, in particular, the part played by nitrogen fertilizers in augmenting the greenhouse effect (qv)), necessitates that they be phased out as soon as possible in favour of a return to organic methods of farming. (See also: *Eutrophication*©℗, *Green Revolution*Ⓐ③, *Greenhouse Effect* ℗, *Groundwater*Ⓛ℗, *Nitrate*Ⓛ℗, *Organic farming*Ⓐ©, *Post harvest losses*Ⓐ③, *Traditional agriculture*Ⓐ.)

Artificial sweeteners

Compounds that contribute sweetness, but no bulk, to food and drinks. They are to be distinguished from sugar and other sweeteners such as Mannitol, Sorbitol and Xylitol which provide both bulk and sweetness. Those taken voluntarily are most often used by diabetics or people wishing to lose weight.

In 1988 six artificial sweeteners were being sold in industrialized countries. The two main ones are saccharin (qv) and Aspartame (qv). Another group, cyclamates, are permitted in 16 countries but banned in the UK and USA. Acesulfame-K is permitted in nine countries. Thaumatin is permitted in Britain and Switzerland, while Belgium and the UK permit neohesperidin dihydrochalcone. There are at least seven other compounds that firms in the chemical and food industries wish to market.

In 1987, the British market for artificial sweeteners amounted to approximately $40 million, accounting for approximately 20 per cent of total European sales, while the American market was almost $150 million. In the late 1980s and early 1990s, the UK market for artificial sweeteners grew at a rate of more than 10 per cent a year. Worldwide sales of Aspartame amounted to about $600 million in 1984 and have subsequently grown considerably.

It is almost invariably assumed that artificial sweeteners help consumers to lose weight because they contain fewer calories than sugar, despite the fact that there is no evidence to support that belief. In 1986, new research suggested that using them may actually stimulate the appetite for carbohydrates and thus even be counter-productive. Their usefulness, in principle, to diabetics is less often questioned, but the levels at which diabetics have been consuming artificial sweeteners has given cause for concern.

There have been, and continue to be, arguments over the safety and acceptability of artificial sweeteners. From an economic point of view, their increased use has generally contributed to the fall in the price of sugar, which, in turn, has severely damaged the economy of sugar-producing countries in the Third World. (See also: *Additives*Ⓛ, *Cancer*Ⓛ, *Cyclamates*Ⓛ.)

Asbestos

The generic name for a group of fibrous mineral silicates, consisting of crocidolite ("blue" asbestos), chrysotile ("white" asbestos) and amosite ("brown" asbestos).

Once mined, the asbestos fibres are separated out from the rock in which they are embedded. They are then spun into a cloth, which can be mixed with cement or resin to give it shape. Because it is both highly resistant to heat and a poor conductor of electricity, asbestos has been used in a wide range of materials – from roofing slates to fire-fighting suits.

The dangers of asbestos lie in its fibres, which can range in length from one four-hundred-thousandth of a centimetre to more than 30cm (1ft). If inhaled, the fibres lodge in the lungs and the tissues of the bronchial tubes. The result is a crippling lung disease called asbestosis. In the final stages of the disease, victims can be so breathless that they are unable even to climb stairs. Asbestos also causes lung cancer, cancer of the gastro-intestinal tract and mesothelioma, a malignant cancer of the inner lining of the chest.

In the USA, official statistics put the potential death toll from exposure to all forms of asbestos at two million people. According to the US Environmental Protection Agency (EPA), 65,000 Americans currently suffer from asbestosis, a further 12,000 dying every year from asbestos-related cancers.

Many of those suffering from asbestosis have now sued the major US asbestos companies for damages. In 1982, inundated by claims, the Manville Corporation filed for bankruptcy, thus freezing all future suits against the company but allowing it to continue operating. At the time, Manville faced 100,000 suits.

In early 1987, Manville proposed a settlement whereby it would set up a trust fund to pay out $2,500 million over the next 30 years. The proposal has been opposed by both Manville's shareholders and those who have sued the company. The latter have demanded punitive damages on the grounds that Manville continued to sell asbestos without warning labels even after the dangers were fully appreciated.

The EPA has now proposed a total ban on the production of all asbestos products within the USA, arguing that "there is no level of exposure without risk." The ban would phase out all asbestos products within ten years.

In Europe, the Swiss Eternit group has agreed to eliminate asbestos from all cement products for sale in Switzerland and Germany, except asbestos piping.

In Britain, both blue and brown asbestos have been officially banned since January 1986. White asbestos continues to be sold, despite numerous case studies linking its use to mesothelioma.

With tighter controls being imposed on the use and production of asbestos products, many companies have simply "exported" their factories to the Third World – in particular to India, South Korea and Mexico – or to countries where regulations are less strict, such as South Africa.

A 1987 US study has suggested that most common asbestos substitutes, such as glass fibre, may also be a cause of lung cancer. (See also: *Cancer*①, *Carcinogen*⑥①, *Export of pollution*℗③.

Aswan Dam

Opening Egypt's Aswan Dam in 1970, President Nasser promised that the dam would prove "a source of everlasting prosperity". Today, Aswan has become a symbol of all that can go wrong with big water development projects.

The dam has caused a dramatic increase in waterborne disease. Schistosomiasis (*qv*), a parasitic disease, has rocketed in villages close to Lake Nasser, behind Aswan, some communities suffering 100 per cent infection rates.

The perennial irrigation projects fed by Aswan have caused widespread salinization (*qv*). Prior to the dam, the accumulated salts had been flushed out of the land by the Nile's annual flood. Now 35 per cent of irrigated land is affected.

In addition, the fertility of downstream farmland has been badly affected by the reduced silt-load of the Nile. Before Aswan, the Nile deposited 100 million tonnes a year of organically rich sediment on nearly 10,000sq km (3,800sq miles) of land. Today, it deposits a few tonnes a year, the remainder being trapped behind the dam. To compensate for the loss of nutrients, Egypt must apply artificial fertilizers – at huge cost.

The reduction of silt has also led to coastal erosion and the loss of sardine shoals along the eastern Mediterranean. Before Aswan, sardine catches amounted to some 18,000 tonnes a year. After the dam opened, catches fell to 500 tonnes a year. This loss has been partly compensated for by the development of fishing in Lake Nasser and the setting up of an ocean-going fleet. (See also: *Dams*Ⓐ©①③, *Development*③, *Resettlement programmes*③, *Waterborne diseases*①.)

Atomic tests

The world's nuclear powers have carried out regular nuclear weapons tests ever since 1945. In 1963, atomic testing went underground when the USA, UK and USSR signed the Limited Test Ban Treaty, banning atmospheric tests. More than 100 other nations acceded to the treaty, with the notable exceptions of France and China. France continued with atmospheric testing until 1974 with a further 37 tests, while China only began atmospheric testing after the treaty had been signed.

In 1985 the USSR adopted a self-imposed moratorium on testing, but the initiative came to naught when the USA refused to reciprocate. The moratorium ended after 19 months.

Bitter controversy still surrounds the ecological and medical effects of the atmospheric tests conducted from 1945 to 1963. More than 250,000 US troops took part in the US atmospheric tests. Many were exposed to very high levels of radiation without any warning about the dangers. Some troops were positioned as close as 2,280m (2,500yd) from ground zero, the aim being to test their reactions in the wake of an atomic blast. The leukemia rate among veterans of one test – Operation Smokey – has since been found to be double the national average.

About 170,000 civilians living downwind of the main US test site in the Nevada desert were exposed to fallout from the tests. A 1979 study revealed the cancer rate among exposed children in southern Utah to be three times higher than normal: 500 adult and child cancer deaths are alleged.

Several test sites – most notoriously Maralinga (*qv*) and Emu Fields in Australia and the Marshall Islands (*qv*) in the Pacific – are now known to have been thoroughly contaminated by radioactive fallout.

In the USA, Australia and the United Kingdom, servicemen and civilians exposed to radioactive fallout have sued their respective governments for compensation, alleging cancers and other health effects. In April 1987, a $2,600,000 award to nine civilian cancer victims of the US atomic tests was overturned by the Federal Appeals Court.

Little information exists on the ecological and medical damage caused by the Soviet· Union's atmospheric tests – or on those conducted by China. (See also: *Mururoa* , *Nuclear proliferation* ℕ.)

Balance of nature
Baltic Sea
Barnett Report
Basel accident
Basel Convention
Becquerel
Benzene
Beta radiation
Bhopal
Bikini Atoll
Bilateral aid
Bioaccumulation
Biochemical oxygen demand
Biocide
Bioconcentration
Biodiversity
Biological control
Biological diversity
Biosphere
Biotechnology
BOD (Biochemical oxygen demand)
Bovine growth hormone
Bovine somatotrophin
Bovine spongiform encephalopathy
Breeder reactor
Browns Ferry
Brundtland Report
BSE
BST

Balance of nature

A basic concept of ecology, regarded by Dr. Frank Egerton, a leading historian of ecological thought, as "the oldest ecological theory".

The idea greatly pre-dates the term "ecology", having been entertained by all known tribal peoples since time immemorial. In such societies, "natural" disasters – epidemics, floods, drought and the like – are traditionally regarded as divine retribution for the violation of basic cultural norms and, thus, the disruption of the natural order or "balance of nature". Only when that balance is restored by reverting to "the old ways" – ways that embody a respect for nature and that help to maintain ecological harmony – can order be restored.

In modern times, the concept of the "balance of nature" played a central role in the thinking of George Perkins Marsh, a 19th-century American diplomat who was the first US minister to the kingdom of Italy and one of the most important ecological thinkers. Marsh believed that "All nature is linked together by invisible bonds, and every organic creature, however low, is necessary to the well-being of some other among the myriad forms of life with which the creator has peopled the Earth."

The notion of the balance of nature is very much part of the "organismic" or "holistic" view of the world promoted by such early academic ecologists as F.E. Clements, V.E. Shelford and C. Forbes at the beginning of this century. Clements and his colleagues stressed the equilibrium and stability to be found in nature, introducing such concepts as the "unity of nature", "mutualism" (qv), "stability" and "ecological climax".

But their ideas found no place in a society committed to development and "progress" (which Marsh described as a "war against the order of nature"). Indeed, other academic ecologists actively sought to discredit Clements. In an effort to gain scientific respectability and to make "ecology" more acceptable to mainstream society, the old "holistic" concepts, including that of "the balance of nature", have been abandoned. Today, most academic ecologists reject the notion altogether, seeing perpetual flux and change where their predecessors saw balance and stability.

Nevertheless, the concept of the balance of nature has been revived within the ecological movement (*qv*) by deep ecologists (see *Deep ecology*), as indeed have its associated concepts of mutualism, ecological climax and so on. Their rehabilitation is playing a critical part in the development of a new ecological world view. (See also: *Biosphere*Ⓕ, *Ecological succession*Ⓕ, *Gaia*Ⓕ, *Holism*Ⓕ.)

Baltic Sea
See: *Regional seas.*

Barnett Report
In 1987, after allegations of corruption in the timber industry, the Papua New Guinea government commissioned a report from Judge Thomas Barnett. It was, and still remains, the only thorough investigation into illegal operations of the timber industry in a tropical country.

The report uncovered corruption on a massive scale, and emanating from the highest echelons of society. Logging companies, many Japanese owned, were able to extract massive profits through bribery, illegal concessions, tax-avoidance, and false declaration of output and sale price. The monitoring of timber operations was almost non-existent, and damage to the environment and to local habitats was extensive and sometimes catastrophic.

The Barnett report was never officially published. None of the incriminated concession owners and government officials were prosecuted, and one of them, Ted Diro, went on to become acting Prime Minister. Judge Barnett was stabbed, almost fatally, by an unknown assailant, and much of the evidence was destroyed in a mysterious fire in government offices. Although promises were made to clean up the industry, few were put into effect. (See also: *Tropical timber trade* ©③.

Basel accident
See: *Sandoz fire.*

Basel Convention
See: *Export of pollution.*

Becquerel
Measure of radioactivity, named after A.H. Becquerel (1852-1908), who discovered the phenomenon in 1896. One becquerel (bq) is one disintegration per second. The unit is replacing the curie (ci), which is equivalent to 37,000,000,000bq. (See also: *Radiation and health*ⓁⓃ, *Radioactivity*Ⓕ.)

Benzene
A volatile and inflammable chemical, normally produced from petroleum but also obtainable from coal. It is used widely in industry as a solvent and as a raw material in the manufacture of chemicals. Benzene is also a component of petrol.

Benzene is highly poisonous with serious acute and chronic effects. Exposure to a high concentration of the vapour causes confusion, dizziness, unconsciousness and respiratory failure leading to death. If the affected person is moved to a clean air zone before serious damage occurs, recovery is possible. Because benzene is absorbed through the skin, this can add to the inhaled dose and aggravate the symptoms.

More serious and more widespread is chronic poisoning by benzene, whereby smaller quantities are absorbed frequently over a long period. Benzene has a cumulative effect and repeated exposure causes mounting damage. Its chronic effects are on the blood-forming tissues, progressively reducing the numbers of white and/or red blood cells present. Most serious is its ability to cause leukemia, a form of cancer, which may not be identified before it reaches an untreatable stage. For this reason, workers exposed to benzene should be medically examined on a regular basis. Industrial safety limits for benzene have recently been revised downward in many countries in view of its ability to cause

leukemia. (See also: *Cancer*Ⓛ, *Carcinogen*ⓁⓅ.)

Beta radiation
Fast-moving energetic electrons, shed from the nucleus of atoms undergoing spontaneous radioactive transformation. The negatively charged beta particles are able to penetrate several centimetres of living tissue, which they damage by disrupting the electrons orbiting around the atoms making up the cells. Like other forms of radiation, beta particles form ions in the cell, which then interact with other atoms in aberrant ways. If the cell is not killed by such radiation, but continues to reproduce itself, it may form a malignant line of cells that ultimately grows into a cancer.

In sufficient intensity, beta radiation can burn the skin and other tissues. Marshall Islanders who were covered in fall-out from US atmospheric weapons testing suffered severe beta burns, as did a number of the firemen who fought the Chernobyl blaze during the accident of April 1986. (See also: *Radioactivity*Ⓝ, *Radiation and health*ⓁⓃ.)

Bhopal
The site of a major chemical accident in Central India, involving a pesticide plant belonging to Union Carbide. A chronology of the accident is given in the accompanying illustration.

Any accurate measure of the number of casualties is impossible for a number of reasons. Many of the bodies were cremated, destroying crucial evidence of the cause of death. Many died some time later and in a different locality, so their deaths were not registered with the Bhopal authorities. Many are still dying today.

Thousands are now suffering from a host of ailments including lung damage, vomiting blood, conjunctivitis, damaged eyesight, pains in the abdomen, lassitude and depression. Women are suffering from similar problems, and on top of these there seem to be gynaecological complications such as menstrual disorders, a white vaginal discharge and some evidence of reproductive disorders. The overwhelming impression is that the victims of Bhopal have lost their hold on health, already tenuous due to poverty and malnutrition, and that this, combined with the symptoms of lassitude and breathlessness, has seriously affected their capacity to work.

Immediate emergency relief was plagued by lack of funds and by bureaucratic delays. One year after the disaster, less than 1,400 people had received the maximum government compensation grant of $830 for each life lost in the family. This means that the number of people compensated was below the official tally at the time, a gross underestimate anyway. A tortuous legal battle over compensation for the victims, fought out in the US and Indian courts, ended in February 1989 when the Indian government agreed to accept a $470 million settlement from Union Carbide. The settlement, which amounted to just $793 for each of the 592,000 who had filed claims, was met with outrage in India and condemned as derisory. One of the five Supreme Court judges who had accepted the settlement subsequently withdrew his support. In March 1989, several new claims were submitted, thus re-opening the case. The last of the appeals was heard by the Supreme Court in August 1990. The court subsequently confirmed the original settlement, but left the door open for further claims.

At a local and individual level the Bhopal disaster is still very much a reality. At a more general level, the accident seems to have achieved little in the way of making the chemical industry either more accountable or safer.

Other companies have also suffered major accidents, the most notorious being the pollution of the Rhine by a spill from a Sandoz (see *Sandoz fire*) warehouse at Basel. Such events suggest that many more Bhopals lie in store. (See also: *Development③*, *Export of pollution③*, *Pesticides℗*.)

Bikini Atoll
See: *Atomic tests, Marshall Islands.*

Bilateral aid
See: *Aid.*

Bioaccumulation
See: *Bioconcentration.*

Biochemical oxygen demand
See: *BOD.*

Biocide
"Life-killing" – a term applied to those chemicals used to destroy living organisms that also interfere with, or threaten, human health and activities. They include herbicides (used against weeds), insecticides (used against insect pests), nematicides (used against eelworms and similar animals), acaricides (used against mites), fungicides (used against plant diseases and moulds), and rodenticides (used against rats).

Chemicals such as antibiotics, used in medicine to kill harmful organisms, are not generally included in this group. Some biocides are selective, being most potent against a small number of species, while others are more generally toxic. A wide-spectrum biocide is formaldehyde (*qv*), poisonous to all forms of life and used to sterilize soil in greenhouses before crops are planted. The term pesticide (*qv*) is more generally used in place of biocide. (See also: *Cancer①, Carbamates①℗, Chlorinated hydrocarbons①℗, Herbicides④℗, Insecticides④℗, Mercury④℗, Organophosphates①℗.*)

Bioconcentration
Once in the environment, many pollutants tend to accumulate within the tissues of living organisms, reaching higher and higher concentrations as they move up the food chain. As each creature eats its prey, it takes in a large part of the pollutants that are locked in the prey's bone and fat. A predator eats many times its own body weight in prey during the course of its life. As a result, a predator ends up with a much higher concentration of pollutants in its own body than was in the bodies of its prey. The more stages there are in a food chain, the greater is the increase in concentrations from the bottom

to the top of the chain. In an environment like the North Sea (*qv*), for example, a seal may carry 80 million times the PCB (*qv*) level found in the seawater in which it swims. This process is known as bioconcentration and can have macabre consequences. The biologists Anne and Paul Ehrlich recall the experience of a village in Borneo:

"Some years ago, large quantities of DDT were used by the World Health Organization in a programme of mosquito control in Borneo. Soon the local people, spared a mosquito plague, began to suffer a plague of caterpillars, which devoured the thatched roofs of their houses, causing them to fall in. The habits of the caterpillars limited their exposure to DDT, but predatory wasps that had formerly controlled the caterpillars were devastated.

"Further spraying was done indoors to get rid of houseflies. The local gecko lizards, which previously had controlled the flies, continued to gobble their corpses – now full of DDT. As a result, the geckos were poisoned, and the dying geckos were caught and eaten by house cats. The cats received massive doses of DDT, which had been concentrated as it passed from fly to gecko to cat, and the cats died. This led to another plague, now of rats. They not only devoured the people's food but also threatened them with yet another plague – this time the genuine article, bubonic plague. The Government of Borneo became so concerned that cats were parachuted into the area in an attempt to restore the balance." (See also: *Balance of nature℉, Dilution and dispersal℗.*)

Biodiversity
The variety of biological forms within an environment. See: *Genetic diversity.*

Biological control
A general term describing a variety of biological techniques used as substitutes for the chemical control of pests.

In nature, many potential pests are controlled biologically. Thus birds, bats, fish and amphibians consume vast quantities of insects. Birds, reptiles and mammals, such as hedgehogs and moles, consume ground-dwelling invertebrates such as slugs.

Biological control by humans can take several forms. It may mean using a natural predator to control the pest. For example, red spider mite in greenhouses can be prevented from causing economic damage to crops by using a predatory mite. The pest is introduced first, deliberately, and allowed to breed. When its population density reaches an appropriate level, the predator is introduced. The two species maintain a balance so that the pest is always present but causes no harm.

Of course, this does not always work as planned. Introduced predators have often failed to reduce the populations of target species and have themselves proliferated, eventually becoming pests in their own right. Ferrets introduced into New Zealand to control rabbits, for example, proved more interested in native ground-nesting birds, whose numbers they decimated.

Another method of biological control involves disrupting the breeding of pest species. Where females mate only once in each breeding cycle, this may be achieved by breeding a captive population of the pest, separating the sexes, sterilizing the males chemically (or, more usually, by subjecting them to low doses of ionizing radiation), then releasing them at an appropriate time into the wild. There, males and females still mate, but a proportion of the matings are unproductive and an increase in population growth is prevented – or, at least, limited. However, this, too, can go wrong, the classic case being the release of supposedly sterile medflies in California – the result was a medfly epidemic (*qv*).

A third method of biological control involves synthesizing chemical substances called "pheromones", which many insects release to attract mates. The synthesized pheromones are then used to attract individuals of one or other sex to sterilize or kill them.

(See also: *Balance of nature*©Ⓕ, *Biocide*Ⓐ①Ⓟ, *Pesticides*ⒶⓅ.)

Biological diversity
See: *Extinction*©, *Genetic diversity*©.

Biosphere
The global ecosystem, the constituent parts of which are all of Earth's living organisms together with their terrestrial environment – including the hydrosphere (Earth's water), the atmosphere and the upper lithosphere (rock and soil near to Earth's surface).

The term "biosphere" was first coined in 1875 by the Austrian geologist Edward Suess. The concept was later refined by the Russian geologist Vladimir Vernadsky, who published a monograph entitled *The Biosphere* in 1926. Vernadsky presented a dynamic view of the Earth as a living planet in which organisms play an active role in the natural cycles of the Earth. He also drew attention to how such cycles could be altered by human activities.

The concept has recently been resurrected by Professor James Lovelock and Lynn Margulis, who have accentuated the self-organizing nature of "Gaia" (*qv*), the name they give to the biosphere and its ability to control its own physical and biological balance in the face of potentially disruptive change. Mainstream science shows little interest in the concept of the biosphere as a functioning unit, the structure and function (and indeed the very existence) of which is difficult to establish on the basis of reductionist scientific method. (See also: *Ecology*Ⓕ, *Ecosystem*Ⓕ, *Holism*Ⓕ, *Mutualism*Ⓕ).

Biotechnology
Generic terms for those technologies that seek to use living organisms (or parts of living organisms) to modify existing forms of life or to create new forms of life.

As such, biotechnology presents both a benefit and a threat to both humanity and the environment. At its most benign, it consists of nothing more harmful than, say, fermentation or the cross-breeding of plants and animals. At the other end of the spectrum lie genetically engineered organisms, potentially the most dangerous scientific development yet known. Many large firms in the agriculture and food industries now see developments in biotechnology as the key to their future. From the genetic manipulation of plants through to the development of new types of foodstuffs, large companies are increasingly investing in ways of using biotechnology to increase their control over the food chain. (See also: *Genetic engineering*Ⓟ.)

BOD (Biochemical oxygen demand)
One of the official measures of how polluting a substance is when it is discharged into a living watercourse. A substance is said to have a high BOD if, when it is discharged into a waterway, it provides the bacteria and other microorganisms living there with a rich food source, allowing them to reproduce rapidly. The increasing numbers of bacteria use up the oxygen in the water. If the BOD of the effluent is too high, or the receiving waterway is unable to dilute it to a safe level, the amount of oxygen falls to such an extent that fish and other aquatic organisms suffocate.

One of the main aims of sewage treatment is to reduce the BOD of the liquid so that it can be discharged into a river without causing serious pollution. Regulatory authorities concerned with water pollution normally set limits on the volume and BOD of an effluent before it is permitted to be discharged.

Organic matter is present in healthy streams and lakes and this will give the water a BOD of a few parts per million, a load which the system has no difficulty in handling.

Thanks to stricter pollution controls – principally on discharges of sewage – BOD levels in some of the major rivers in Western Europe and North America have been reduced dramatically in recent years. The most publicized success story is that of London's River Thames, which, in the late 1950s, was so polluted with sewage that no fish could survive in the 100-odd kilometres (60 miles) from Richmond to the sea. During the 1960s, new sewage works were built and many old ones were modernized. Gradually, the fish began to return to the river: by 1969, more than 50 species had been identified. Ten years later, the number was closer to 100. Birds, too, began to flourish – the numbers of swan, pochard, teal, shelduck, dunlin and tern have all risen since the 1960s.

But BOD levels are only part of the story. Organic matter is not the only form of pollution entering water courses: pesticides (*qv*) and nitrates (*qv*) from farmland, leachate (*qv*) from toxic waste dumps and chemicals discharged by industry are among others. As a measure of pollution, BOD can give no indication of the extent to which a waterway may be contaminated with such harmful chemicals – unless, of course, they raise the oxygen demand of the receiving waters. Nonetheless, those chemicals pose a potent threat to public health and the environment – many of them being suspected or proven carcinogens (*qv*). (See also: *Eutrophication*Ⓒℙ, *Hazardous waste*ℙ, *Landfill*ℙ, *Micropollutants*Ⓒℙ.)

Bovine growth hormone
See: *Bovine somatotrophin*.

Bovine somatotrophin
A genetically-engineered version of the natural Bovine Growth Hormone (BGH), bovine somatotrophin (BST) is claimed by its manufacturers to boost milk yields by up to 20 per cent. Permission is now being sought to market BST in both the USA and the EC. Although BST has never been properly tested on humans, unlabelled milk and meat from BST-treated cows has already been sold to consumers in Britain and the USA, where the synthetic hormone is currently undergoing secret field trials.

Contrary to repeated assurances from industry and government that BST poses no public health risks, there remain a wide range of unresolved questions on

its human and veterinary health effects. Field trials reveal that, while increasing yields, BST causes cows to lose much of their body fat, resulting in increased stress and susceptibility to infectious disease. There is also evidence that BST reduces fertility and renders cows more intolerant to heat.

Claims that BST dramatically increases milk yield are also suspect, the results from field trials being highly variable, with some herds actually reducing their yield. "Lactational crash" – a severe reduction in milk yields, due primarily to stress – has also been noted in some cows.

The health effects of biosynthetic milk hormones on humans is also a cause for concern. Industry's claim that BST is a "natural" hormone is false, the synthetic hormone having eight more amino acid residues than the natural bovine growth hormone. As such, BST is not a compound which is found in nature, and human exposure to it should therefore be a matter of extreme caution, particularly since BST is known to affect species other than cows. Fears have been expressed that BST could suppress the human immune system. In addition, BST could trigger premature growth in babies, breast growth in young children and breast cancer in adults. Treatment with BST may also mobilize some of the pesticides (many of them carcinogenic) which are stored in body fat.

In the EC, a moratorium has been called on the use of BST to boost milk yields. However, drug companies are making vigorous attempts to have the moratorium lifted. Mr John Gummer, the British Minister of Agriculture, has given an unequivocal assurance that BST is safe. However, according to Professor Richard Lacey, a member of the Ministry of Agriculture's Advisory Group on Veterinary Products (AGVP), scientists who were involved in assessing the BST field trials have been unable to challenge Gummer's statement because of the threat of prosecution under the Official Secrets Act and the Medicines Act if they reveal the actual conclusions of the AGVP. Lacey also

alleges that a Ministry statement on the safety of BST, purporting to reflect the views of the AGVP, was in fact drawn up by ministry officials in consultation with the drug companies prior even to the AGVP meeting.

In the USA, the Food and Drugs Administration (FDA) decided – on the basis of allegedly confidential data – to exempt BST and met-BST from its "Investigation New Animal Drug" (INAD) procedures. In granting the INAD exemption, the FDA is in apparent violation of Section 512 of the 1968 Animal Drug Amendments to the 1938 Federal Food Drug and Cosmetic Act (FFDCA). The FFDCA amendments require the agency to have a "prescribed and approved" test method for determining whether the drug is being improperly used with resulting illegal residues in food. At present, such a test is not available. (See also: *Genetic engineering* ℙ.)

Bovine spongiform encephalopathy
Bovine spongiform encephalopathy (BSE) – popularly known as "mad cow disease" – affects the brains of cattle causing them to stagger about uncontrollably. It was first diagnosed in late 1985, but by the end of 1986 the disease was being reported from many parts of the UK. Since then, the number of reported cases has grown rapidly.

A favourite theory about BSE, although not a proven one, is that it was transmitted to cattle from sheep as a result of the "recycling" of sheep remains into animal feed. Another theory is that the use of chemicals in agriculture, particularly the use of organophosphorus compounds to eradicate the warble fly, has weakened the immune system of large numbers of cattle. It is not known with any certainty whether the disease can be passed from cow to calf, or from one member of a herd to another.

It is known that BSE, like other transmissible spongiform encephalopathies (TSEs), has a relatively long incubation period, which may account for the fact that it is much more prevalent in dairy cows (which have a typical lifespan of 8-10 years) than in beef cattle (which are normally slaughtered when 2 or 3 years old). Other forms of TSE are found in humans (Creutzfeldt-Jacobs disease) and in sheep (scrapie), and TSEs can be transmitted to mice and pigs. The infective agent is extremely difficult to destroy, and can survive very high temperatures.

Because of its long incubation period, it is not known how many cattle in Britain are infected with BSE. A Ministry of Agriculture working party, headed by Sir Richard Southwood, was set up to advise on BSE. Since the publication of the Southwood report in 1989, the Government has persistently quoted one statement from the report, which asserts that it is "most unlikely that BSE will have any implications for human health." This claim is contested by others. Significantly, the Southwood report warned that "if our assessments of these likelihoods are incorrect, the implications would be extremely serious". The Government continues to insist on the slaughter of all cattle diagnosed to have BSE, but insists that the risk to human health is almost non-existent.

Breeder reactor
See: *Fast reactor*.

Browns Ferry
Site of a near-disastrous nuclear accident in 1975. At the time, Browns Ferry, in Alabama, was the world's largest nuclear power station, consisting of two 1,065-megawatt boiling water reactors.

The accident occurred when two electricians were checking the air flow through cable passages beneath the control room with a candle. The candle ignited some foam packing and the fire spread along the cables into the Unit 1 reactor building.

Both reactors were shut down, and the fire burned for seven hours. The station was out of action for 18 months.

Browns Ferry, rather than Three Mile Island (*qv*), marks the beginning of US disenchantment with nuclear power. The decline

was sudden. 1974 was the peak year for US reactor order: the last order that has not subsequently been cancelled was placed in 1975. (See also: *Nuclear accidents*Ⓝ.)

Brundtland Report
The report of the World Commission on Environment and Development, chaired by Gro Harlem Brundtland, was published in 1987. It remains the best example at an international level of a growing recognition in parts of the business, scientific, academic and political "establishment" that the world is in a state of crisis. The report documented the interlocking threats confronting humanity – from global poverty to environmental destruction.

The report, also known by its title "Our Common Future", reflects a desire to accommodate demands for social justice and environmental conservation within the existing framework of society. It argues for "sustainable growth" and that a combination of economic incentives, better management and improved technologies could provide a "development that meets the needs of the present without compromising the ability of future generations to meet their own needs". It envisages "an expanding world economy", with a "five-to-tenfold increase in manufacturing", with even the already affluent countries growing by 3-4 per cent a year.

The report describes the problems that humanity faces well, but confines itself to a call upon those in power to reform their ways. It does not propose radical changes to the institutions that have brought the world to its present parlous condition, such as the transnational corporations and the financial system.

Nor does the report attack the basic values of industrial society. It still treats the environment as a warehouse of resources, put there to satisfy open-ended human demands. The Brundtland Commissioners realize that mismanagement is interfering with production, but do not envisage a concept of sustainability based on a deeper rapprochement between

human wants and the needs of other species.

Thus, although the Brundtland report identifies many signs of bad development, it fails to address the issue of overdevelopment. Equally serious, it avoids altogether the issue of power, preferring to give the impression that because humanity shares a common globe, all humans must therefore share the same common interests. Yet there is little community of interests between, say, the director of a major chemical company and a peasant in India. (See also: *Sustainable development*③.)

BSE See: *Bovine spongiform encephalopathy*.

BST See: *Bovine somatotrophin*.

Cadmium
Cancer
Cancer research
Candu reactor
Cap de la Hague
Captan
Car emissions
Carbamates
Carbon cycle
Carbon dioxide
Carbon taxes
Carcinogen
Caribbean Sea
Carrying capacity
Cash crops
Catalytic converter
CFCs
Chernobyl, USSR
Child labour
Chipko movement
Chlordane
Chlorinated
    hydrocarbons
Chlorinated solvents
Chlorination
Chlorofluorocarbons (CFCs)
Chlorofluorocarbon
    substitutes
Circle of poison
Climate change
Co-disposal
Co-generation
Coal
Coal-tar dyes
Codex Alimentarius
Colourings
Combined heat and
    power (CHP)
Community supported
    agriculture
Containment
Contraception
Convenience food
Conversion products
Coral reefs
Coronary heart disease
Creys Malville
Cyclamates

Cadmium

A toxic heavy metal that has had serious effects on human health in a number of incidents around the world. If cadmium compounds are swallowed their irritant and emetic action usually results in the material being expelled from the body before fatal poisoning occurs. If dust or vapours are inhaled, however, pulmonary oedema and death can occur.

Chronic cadmium poisoning causes damage to the kidneys and heart. Prolonged exposure also results in a loss of calcium from the bones, which then become brittle and break easily. In Japan, for example, a whole village was stricken by cadmium poisoning – known as "itai-itai" disease, meaning "it hurts, it hurts" – after industrial effluent contaminated rice supplies. One victim died as a result of 57 fractures, the last one occurring when she was covered by a sheet. Cadmium poisoning has also occurred when people have consumed food or drinks stored in cadmium-plated vessels.

Cadmium is used in metal plating, in certain plastics as a pigment and in some rechargeable batteries. It is naturally present in phosphate fertilizers and is discharged to the environment when they are refined. Zinc and lead (qv) smelting also results in cadmium pollution since the metal is usually present in zinc and lead ores. Because of its widespread use, cadmium frequently occurs at high levels in sewage sludge, as domestic wastes are rarely separated from industrial wastes that contain heavy metals. This limits its use as a fertilizer and can cause the metal to bioconcentrate (see *Bioconcentration*) in marine life if the sludge is dumped at sea. Incinerating refuse also disperses cadmium into the environment.

To reduce pollution by cadmium, restrictions on its use are being imposed in Sweden. Germany has banned the use of cadmium in pesticides. In Britain, a ban on cadmium plating in food utensils has been in force since 1956. Tough new controls on the use of cadmium are being contemplated by the EC. (See also: *Heavy metals*Ⓕ Ⓟ.)

Cancer

A disease caused by a breakdown in the mechanisms governing cell division, organs and tissues with rapid cell division (such as the liver) being particularly susceptible.

Cancer is a "disease of civilization" (qv). Its incidence among tribal people living in their natural environment is usually extremely low, often indiscernible. Cancer is also rare in countries that are in the early stages of economic development. Thus, according to the World Health Organization (WHO), the crude rate of cancer in 1985 in West Africa was 94, and in Micronesia and Polynesia 151. By contrast, it was 638 in North America, 748 in Australia, New Zealand and Melanesia and more than 1,000 in Europe. The worldwide incidence of cancer in 1985 was 5,900,000 and the number of deaths was 4,300,000. In the USA, there were 900,000 new cases in 1986, with 450,000 deaths – an incidence of one in three, and a mortality rate of one in four.

Deaths from cancer continue to increase from year to year. According to WHO, between 1960 and 1980 they rose in 28 industrial countries by 55 per cent among men and 40 per cent among women. A five per cent decline in deaths from cervical cancer and a 12 per cent decline in stomach cancer among men (15 per cent among women) were more than made up by a 60 per cent increase in breast cancer and a 116 per cent increase in lung cancer among men (200 per cent among women).

In the USA, the incidence of cancer has increased steadily since the 1930s by about some two per cent a year and the mortality rate by some one per cent. For white males born in 1985, the probability of developing cancer is 36 per cent, and of dying from it, 23 per cent. For those born ten years earlier the probabilities are lower – 30 per cent and 19 per cent respectively.

The increased incidence of cancer is officially attributed to increased longevity, smoking and the consumption of fats and alcohol. Environmental pollution has been consistently played down as a cause of cancer. The chemical industry in Britain, for example, argues that only five per cent of cancers are caused by occupational exposure to carcinogens.

That view, however, is contested by a number of scientists, notably Professor Samuel Epstein of the School of Public Heath, University of Illinois. "Increased longevity is certainly a factor to take into account, but it must not be exaggerated since the cancer rate has seriously increased among children and is now an important cause of their deaths. So, too, diet and tobacco are important causes of cancer, but to single them out as the primary causes is to detract from the lethal impact of everyday exposure to carcinogenic chemicals."

Support for the view that pollution is a major cause of cancer comes from a variety of studies. In 1978, a US commission, appointed by the Secretary of Health, Education and Welfare, estimated that 38 per cent of all future cancers would reflect exposure to just six widely used occupational carcinogens. Some experts suggest that 80 per cent of cancers may have an environmental cause.

Studies show significant clusters of cancer in areas with a high density of chemical factories and toxic waste dumps. The Chesapeake Bay area is a case in point. In one locality, where the per capita level of toxic waste generated is 46 times greater than the national average, deaths by cancer are several times higher than the US average.

The cancer rate on the Chicago south side, a highly polluted area containing 22 chemical plants in addition to 31 operating or closed chemical waste dumps, was found by the Illinois Environmental Protection Agency in 1984 to be 20 per cent higher than in the rest of Chicago.

In the UK, the incidence of cancer of the lung and stomach is particularly high in northern industrial cities such as Liverpool, Southport, Manchester and Jarrow.

The carcinogenicity of chemic-als and heavy metals such as radon gas, nickel ores, chromium, arsenic, mustard gas, vinyl chloride and asbestos has been well established by epidemiological studies among workers exposed to these carcinogens at their place of work. The carcinogenicity of a large number of the 9,000 or so synthetic organic chemicals, in which category most modern pesticides must be included, has also been established by the US Environmental Protection Agency (EPA) and other regulatory agencies.

A further consideration is that at least 20 per cent of the 100,000 people who die from lung cancer in the USA are non-smokers, among whom the lung cancer rate doubled between 1958 and 1969 and continues to increase.

Studies among animals also show pollution to be a cause of cancer. Extremely high rates of cancer have been found, for instance, among fish living in waters contaminated with agricultural and industrial pollutants. Thus, recent research shows that 40 per cent of the flat fish in certain parts of the North Sea now have cancer. Studies have shown that the incidence of cancer among tomcods more than two years old in the highly polluted Hudson River is 80-90 per cent, whereas among tomcods living in a clean environment it is less than 2.5 per cent.

The official view is that considerable progress has been made in the treatment of cancer. This, too, is contested by many critics. The overall cancer "cure" rate in the USA, as measured by survival for more than five years after diagnosis, is at present 50 per cent for whites and 38 per cent for blacks. It does not seem to have increased in the last decades, even though some progress has been made in the treatment of cancer of the cervix and a few rare cancers such as those of the testes, Hodgkin's disease and childhood leukaemia. The generally accepted treatment – chemotherapy – has serious side effects, and even when effective can increase the subsequent risk of developing a second cancer by up to 100 times. (See also: *Additives*ⓁⓅ, *Biocide*ⓁⓅ, *Carcinogen*Ⓟ, *Cancer research*ⓁⓅ, *Junk food*ⓁⓅ.)

Cancer research

In 1971, the US Government, by an Act of Congress, declared war on cancer. Researchers were confident that, with sufficient funds, they could establish the exact mechanism of carcinogenesis (see *Carcinogen*), and that with a budget of just $1,000 million a year for ten years, they could find a cure.

Funding for cancer research was thus increased from $230 million a year in 1971 to $815 million in 1977 (from £144 million to £509 million), and, at one time, some 7,000 scientists were employed on the programme.

However, despite 25 years of research, only moderate progress has been made either in understanding carcinogenesis or in the treatment of cancer. Meanwhile, the incidence of the disease, except in cases of stomach cancer and cancer of the cervix, has continued to increase.

This would suggest that the research has been misdirected. Much of it has been concentrated on the role played by viruses in carcinogenesis, on the development of a vaccine, and on chemotherapy.

On the other hand, little effort has been made to prevent cancer by reducing the public's exposure to carcinogenic chemicals and low-level radiation – the two principal known causes of cancer. Indeed, until the passing of the Toxic Substances Act of 1976, which was long delayed by chemical industry lobbying, there was no requirement in the USA for chemical companies to test any chemical before it was put on the market. Even today, the number of chemicals that have been seriously screened for their possible carcinogenic effects is a minute proportion of those that have been sold commercially.

Research on a cure is more glamorous and carries greater scientific kudos – Nobel prizes for example – than research on prevention. It also leads to the development of marketable products – such as anti-cancer drugs. Prevention does not. But most important of all, a policy of prevention, if actively pursued, would seriously compromise the viability of many industries by requiring a ban on the production, sale and use of carcinogenic substances. Among those that would be jeopardized are the chemical industry, the asbestos (*qv*) industry, the food-processing industry and the tobacco (*qv*) industry. Small wonder that they are most active in lobbying against such efforts at establishing a policy of cancer prevention. (See also: *Cancer*Ⓛ, *Delaney Amendment*Ⓛ, *Proposition 65*Ⓛ, *Radiation and health*ⓁⓃ.)

Candu reactor

A type of nuclear reactor developed by Canada. After World War II Canada decided not to manufacture atomic weapons, but continued work on power reactors using natural (unenriched) uranium, which it has in abundance, and heavy water as moderator (*qv*) and coolant. The result was the Candu reactor, the first units becoming operational in 1971 at Pickering, near Toronto. By 1990, there were 18 reactors in operation with a total capacity of 12,000MW. Candu reactors have been exported to India, Pakistan, South Korea and Argentina. Thailand is also expected to order Candu reactors.

The design of the reactor is unusual in that fuel is contained in a large number of pressure tubes, rather than in a single pressure vessel. These are enclosed in a large steel tank, called a calandria. Heavy water under pressure passes through the tubes, and then to steam generators. Like Magnox reactors (*qv*), Candu reactors can be refuelled on load.

A British 100MW prototype pressure tube reactor, called a steam generating heavy water reactor (SGHWR), closely similar to Candu, except that it uses enriched uranium, was operated at Winfrith from 1967-90. It almost became the basis for a modest programme of commercial heavy water reactors, because by 1974 it was apparent that the advanced gas-cooled reactors (AGRS) (*qv*) were proving difficult to build. The government, unwilling to order American pressurized water reactors (PWRS) (*qv*), decided on SGHWRS instead. In 1976 the decision was reversed, and two more AGRS were ordered instead.

Cap de la Hague

Nuclear reprocessing plant, situated on the coast of Normandy, and used to reprocess spent fuel from France's civil nuclear programme and from other countries, such as Japan.

Known officially as UP2, or Usine Plutonium 2 (UP1 is a military plant at Marcoule), Cap de la Hague opened in 1966, reprocessing Magnox (*qv*) fuel.

In 1969, France opted for pressurized water reactors (PWR) (*qv*) and built a new plant, known as the HAO plant, to enable Cap de la Hague to handle the higher burn-up oxide fuel from PWRS. The HAO plant began operating in 1976.

Initially, it was intended that the plant should reprocess 800 tonnes a year, but this target was deemed impractical and the plant was finally designed for a throughput of 400 tonnes a year. Even so, the plant had considerable spare capacity. This allowed COGEMA, the company that runs Cap de la Hague, to bid for reprocessing contracts from abroad. In this they had some success because the only competition – the B204 Head End plant at Sellafield (*qv*) in the UK – had been closed following an accident in September 1973.

Within months of opening, the HAO plant was closed following a strike by process workers demanding better radiological protection. Ironically, workers at Cap de la Hague are exposed to far lower levels of radiation than workers at Sellafield – this despite the great difficulties of handling oxide fuel. Discharges to the sea from Cap de la Hague are also lower than from Sellafield. There have, however, been serious incidents at the plant; notably, two fires (in 1980 and 1981), the second of which involved a waste-storage silo.

The HAO plant has also been plagued by technical problems. By 1985, only 1,000 tonnes of PWR fuel had been reprocessed. Ignoring the first two years of operation (which suffered teething problems), an average of 140 tonnes a year were reprocessed from 1978 to 1985. A 1982-83 report by the Castaing Commission – a government-appointed group of independent experts – came to the unequivocal conclusion that reprocessing in France was in a state of crisis.

Since then, little has happened to alter the commission's conclusions. Though two new plants, UP3-A and UP2-800, both with a planned throughput of 800 tonnes a year, are coming on stream, a third, UP3-B, was cancelled when the expected volumes of foreign business failed to materialize.

In 1990, a government-commissioned report by the Commisseriat à l'Energie Atomique (CEA) questioned the whole rationale behind reprocessing at Cap de la Hague. The report pointed out that both uranium and plutonium were being stockpiled at a rate that far outstripped demand. One suggestion is to use some of the plutonium in MOX (mixed oxide) fuel, which can be utilized in existing reactors. But the eventual aim of using plutonium in a new generation of "fast breeder reactors" looks like becoming an increasingly remote possibility. (See also: *Fast reactor*Ⓝ, *Reprocessing*Ⓝ.)

Captan

A fungicide used as a spray, dip or seed treatment against a variety of plant diseases, including those found on garden plants. Rooting compounds used for plant propagation sometimes contain it.

It is not an acute poison, but it is an irritant to the skin, lungs and eyes. More seriously, captan has been shown to cause mutations in bacterial and several other types of cells, including human cells. It has also been shown to be carcinogenic (see *Carcinogen*) in mice and teratogenic (see *Teratogen*) in rats, rabbits and hamsters. There are few specific controls on its use in Britain. Captan is banned, however, in Finland and Germany. (See also: *Biocide*Ⓛ Ⓟ, *Cancer*Ⓛ, *Mutagen*Ⓕ Ⓛ Ⓟ, *Pesticides*Ⓛ Ⓟ.)

Car emissions

The internal combustion engine produces many different substances in its exhaust, several of which are serious pollutants. Carbon monoxide, an odourless and highly poisonous gas, can build up to dangerous concentrations if a car engine is run in confined spaces or if the car's windows are closed and a leak in its exhaust system allows fumes to enter it. Unburned hydrocarbons give motor exhausts their unpleasant smell and, with particles of incompletely burned fuel, form part of the visible smoke. Both these groups of substances are carcinogenic (see *Carcinogen*). Nitrogen oxides are emitted by all car engines, but those operating at higher temperatures produce most. They are irritant and poisonous gases, and are a major cause of acid rain (*qv*).

The compounds listed above are known as primary pollutants, since they are polluting when produced. But hydrocarbons, nitrogen oxides and other components of the atmosphere combine, under the influence of sunlight, to form the secondary pollutant ozone (*qv*), which is a major greenhouse gas (*qv*). Ozone is extremely poisonous and a powerful irritant in the lower atmosphere. Ozone, and the compounds it forms when it reacts with other pollutants, is one of the main ingredients of the damaging photochemical smogs afflicting heavily trafficked sunny cities such as Los Angeles, Athens and Sydney.

Diesel engines, largely because they consume less fuel than petrol engines of equivalent power, emit less carbon monoxide, carbon dioxide and unburned hydrocarbons. On the other hand, they give off more nitrogen oxide and a greater quantity of soot particles. On balance, a long-distance lorry is better fuelled by diesel, while a bus – which remains stationary for long periods with its engine running – may pollute less when it is powered by petrol.

In an attempt to reduce photochemical smog, California's state pollution authorities have proposed a ban on the use of petrol as a fuel for cars in southern California by the year 2007. The cars would instead be run on electricity or methanol, which burns more cleanly than petrol. By 1993, all office and rented cars would have to be converted to clean-burn fuels; by 1998, 70 per cent of trucks and buses would have to be converted and 90 per cent of private cars; and by 2007, all vehicles would be covered. Other states could follow suit. Under a new air pollution control programme announced by President Bush in 1989, the worst polluted cities in the USA – Los Angeles, New York and Houston – will be required to cut car emissions by 40 per cent by 2010. In the USA, new legislation has been passed to reduce car pollution in towns by 70 per cent over the next 15 years.

Many car engines still emit a dangerous additional pollutant, lead. This is added to gasoline to improve its performance and is dispersed as fine particles in the exhaust. High levels of lead are now found in the environment as a result of the use of leaded fuel.

Although unleaded fuel is now being increasingly used in many Western countries – notably the USA, where leaded fuel is being phased out – the switch to unleaded fuel has brought its own environmental problems. In the USA, the volatile aromatic hydro-

A traffic jam in Bangkok, where car exhaust pollution is near that of Mexico City.

carbon content of petrol – benzene, toluene, and xylene – has been doubled to more than 40 per cent to improve performance, and is particularly high in high octane grades. Benzene, toluene and xylene are established carcinogens. Exposure to such pollutants is severe at filling stations and in traffic jams. (See also: *Acid rain*Ⓕ, *Catalytic converter*Ⓕ, *Lead*Ⓕ.)

Carbamates
Organic nitrogen compounds, many of which are used as pesticides. The commonest types are the carbamate insecticides, which were developed in the 1950s and onward, providing new chemicals to be used against a wide variety of insect pests, including those that had become resistant to DDT (*qv*) and organophosphates (*qv*). Resistance to carbamates, however, has now become a problem.

Carbamate insecticides range in hazard from the moderately toxic carbaryl to the highly poisonous aldicarb (*qv*). They resemble organophosphorus compounds in that they attack the nervous system by inhibiting the substance acetylcholinesterase.

Some carbamates are used as fungicides, a notable example being zineb – zinc ethylenebis(dithiocarbamate). This is a recognized carcinogen (*qv*) and, like many compounds in this group, is a powerful skin irritant. Several other chemicals in the carbamate group are suspected of causing lung cancer.

They are unselective and can readily kill non-target organisms, especially bees, but most do not leave long-lasting residues.

Carbaryl is used in insecticidal shampoos to kill head lice as well as in gardening and agriculture. (See also: *Biocide*Ⓕ, *Cancer*Ⓛ, *Pesticides*ⓁⒻ.)

Carbon cycle
The circulation of carbon in the biosphere (*qv*). As a building block of the molecules that make up living cells, carbon is an essential element for life on Earth. Carbon is thus a basic ingredient of proteins, carbohydrates, hormones, bones, connective tissue and nerve cells. Equally important, as

a primary component of carbohydrates such as sugar and starch, carbon is directly involved in photosynthesis and respiration, the processes by which energy from the sun in the form of light is used to build up energy-rich molecules. These molecules are then used at a later date to release their energy to the cell. The fossil fuels – coal, petroleum and natural gas – are all carbonaceous compounds which at a previous time in the Earth's history have been built up by living cells through photosynthesis.

Carbon compounds, whether as gases, liquids or solids, move between the atmosphere, oceans, rivers and landmass through both geophysical and chemical processes and with living organisms acting as a powerful intermediary. Thus carbon in the atmosphere as carbon dioxide (*qv*) can get washed out as carbonic acid, which interacts with rocks to form bicarbonates, which flow into rivers and into the oceans. Equally, the oceans absorb carbon dioxide gas directly from the atmosphere.

Living organisms play an integral role in the carbon cycle, affecting the rate at which carbon dioxide interchanges between land, sea and the atmosphere. Marine algae such as coccolithophorids and other diatoms form elaborate limestone shells from bicarbonate, as do corals, and as solid limestone gradually sink to the ocean floor to form in time the limestone cliffs that are a prominent feature of both coastlines and inland hills. On land, the formation of peat, brown coal and black coal are also sinks for carbon dioxide. Meanwhile, if photosynthesis and respiration are in balance, there is no net change in the carbon dioxide balance in the atmosphere.

Geophysical processes such as volcanoes spew out carbon dioxide as well as other gases, and tectonic plate movements, which can thrust limestone deposits on the ocean floor up onto land, are means by which carbon returns into circulation, as is the burning of fossil fuels. (See also: *Balance of nature*Ⓕ, *Carbon dioxide*Ⓕ, *Gaia*Ⓕ, *Greenhouse effect*ⒻⓅ.)

Carbon dioxide
Carbon dioxide is a natural component of air and a vital part of the carbon cycle (*qv*). It is produced when animals breathe, when vegetation rots, and when any material containing carbon is burned. Plants use carbon dioxide as a food and, with the addition of water and sunlight, convert it into sugars during photosynthesis. Photosynthesis is ultimately the source of food for all but a few types of living organisms.

Carbon dioxide is not toxic but can suffocate since it cannot support life. It is used in fire extinguishers because it will not support combustion.

The build up of carbon dioxide in the atmosphere now threatens to destabilize the world's climate, precipitating the so-called greenhouse effect (*qv*). The principal causes of that build-up are industrial emissions resulting from the combustion of fossil fuel and the cutting down of the Earth's tropical rainforests. (See also: *Gaia*Ⓕ, *Greenhouse gases*Ⓟ, *Tropical forests*ⒸⒻ.)

Carbon taxes
The realization that the world will face severe problems from global warming if carbon emissions are not drastically reduced has coincided with a growing world-wide commitment to free market economics, and a widespread belief that economic incentives are more effective than state intervention. Governments and international bodies are therefore turning to various forms of taxation as a means of curbing carbon emissions. Europe in particular has led the way, with proposals in various countries for carbon taxes on fossil fuels such as coal.

But the idea has not been universally welcomed. In Britain both the Conservative and the Labour parties have rejected carbon taxes; the USA, which is responsible for 23 per cent of the world's carbon emissions, is still reluctant to admit that there is a global warming problem.

There is also considerable disagreement between the advocates of taxation as to whether it should be a strict "carbon tax", applicable only to fossil fuels, or whether it should be a broad spectrum "energy tax", with possible concessions for renewable energy sources.

Many politicians and economists fear that carbon taxes, by increasing the price of energy, will bring about a global recession, similar to that which occurred after the oil crisis of 1973, and, by the same token, that any nation that taxed energy unilaterally would put itself at a trading disadvantage. Most studies of the question have concluded that this fear, although real, is exaggerated, and that with the introduction of energy efficiency techniques any downturn in the economy should be slight.

It is also feared by some that it would be the poorer sections of society who would be forced to make cutbacks. For example, a large increase in fuel prices would be unlikely to persuade the well off to lower the temperature of their central heating, while for the old and the unemployed it would mean genuine hardship. Such effects could be mitigated by using the revenue from taxation to support the less well off, but governments would be tempted to use the money in other ways.

Another problem with this kind of tax is with the economies of Third World countries. For example, a blanket tax on carbon emissions would paralyse many Third World economies, which even now cannot afford to pay for the oil they buy on the international market. There have been suggestions that the proceeds of such a tax could be directed into a fund to assist poorer countries to develop alternatives. But the amounts of money involved are so high, and the attitudes of certain countries so intransigent, that any agreement of this kind seems highly unlikely.

Behind the economic and social problems associated with carbon taxes lies a more basic objection: that there is no way of anticipating how successful they will be in reducing emissions. Proponents of market mechanisms frequently cite the oil crisis of 1973 as evidence that rising fuel prices prom-

ote energy efficiency. But neither increased costs nor increased efficiency are a cast iron guarantee that consumption will drop. In Germany between 1973 and 1985, for example, the price of oil rose 500 per cent in real terms; but energy consumption remained more or less unchanged. (See also: *Tradable emissions*③.)

Carcinogen

Any agent that causes cancer (*qv*). Most carcinogens are also mutagenic (see *Mutagen*) and many are teratogenic (see *Teratogen*).

Even when a substance is supected of being carcinogenic, it is often hard to establish that it is indeed a carcinogen in the strict sense of the word. One reason is that many substances that are not carcinogenic in themselves can be transformed by living organisms into carcinogens – an example being the conversion of nitrite to nitrosamine in the human gut.

Equally, many substances act only as cancer promoters; that is, they do not cause cancers but instead promote the growth of tumours that have previously been triggered by other substances.

The long period – known as the latency period – between exposure to a carcinogen and the appearance of clinical symptoms of cancer also makes it hard to pin down a suspect substance as the cause of a cancer. For leukemia, the latency period is six to seven years, while for many other cancers it can be up to 40 years.

A further problem is that a carcinogen may cause clinical symptoms of cancer only in the offspring of those exposed. Thus, it was the daughters of women exposed during pregnancy to the hormone diethylstilbestrol (DES) (*qv*) who contracted vaginal cancer – not their mothers.

In addition, it is difficult to establish epidemiologically which substances have caused a cancer, when, in the highly polluted environment in which we live, the average person is exposed every day to a large number of known or suspected carcinogens.

The problem is compounded by

synergistic reactions between the different chemicals. It is known for instance, that uranium miners (who already suffer from a high incidence of lung cancer) have an eight times higher chance of contracting the disease if they also smoke.

A further difficulty is that many carcinogens are harmful at levels so low they are very difficult to measure, or – like dioxin (*qv*), for example – can be measured only at a prohibitive cost.

Finally, efforts to identify carcinogens have been hampered by the low priority given by governments to research into the possible carcinogenicity of chemicals in the environment.

Even when the carcinogenicity of a chemical has been established, it is difficult to have it removed permanently from current use, often because of the extremely strong pressure exerted on government by industry. Thus, though the carcinogenicity of various coal-tar dyes (*qv*) has been well established, their use (in many varieties of soft drinks for instance) is still tolerated in most countries.

Since indisputable scientific evidence for the carcinogenicity of a chemical is so difficult to obtain, the only responsible course of action must be to ban all suspect carcinogens unless their safety can be demonstrated by exhaustive tests (including tests for additive and synergic (see *Synergy*) effects), carried out over appropriate periods of time, on sufficiently large samples. Where a suspect substance forms part of a specific chemical group – the phenoxy herbicides (*qv*), for example – the entire group should be regarded as suspect. (See also: *Cancer research*①.)

Caribbean Sea

See: *Regional seas*.

Carrying capacity

Term derived from the biological sciences to denote the optimum population that an ecosystem can sustain without interfering with the ecosystem's basic structure and stability.

Because the term takes no

account of levels of technology or patterns of trade and consumption, however, it can be misleading when applied to human societies. A recent study by UN-ESCO, for example, examined the impact of modern agriculture on the world's arid land; it concluded that in every region the impact of human activity was greater than the land could support. But although such lands are undoubtedly under severe ecological stress, the cause may not be population pressure at the local level, as the notion of carrying capacity would imply. Where the areas are being used to grow export crops, for example, it is the demands of consumers in the importing countries that can be held responsible. Different forms of land use and changes in global patterns of trade could greatly reduce the pressure on these over-exploited areas.

Cash crops

Crops grown for sale on the urban market or for export. Cash crops have long been promoted as essential to Third World development. The crops grown include such foods as coffee, cocoa, and vegetables, and other non-food items such as tobacco or cotton.

In those countries lacking mineral or oil wealth, cash crops are a major source of foreign exchange, without which it would be impossible to import the technology deemed necessary for development.

Critics argue, however, that by using land that could otherwise be used to grow food for local consumption, cash crops are a major cause of world hunger.

Vast areas of the Third World have been turned over to growing cash crops. In West Africa, for example, 70 per cent of Gambia's arable land and 55 per cent of Senegal's is used to grow peanuts. In Niger, the amount of land used for peanuts expanded fivefold – from 730sq km (290sq miles) to 4,320sq km (1,670sq miles) – in the 30-odd years between 1934 and 1968, the eve of the Sahel famine.

In Africa as a whole, the production of coffee has quadrupled since the mid-1960s, while the output of sugar has tripled and that of cotton and cocoa doubled. The production of tobacco has risen by 60 per cent. Those increases were achieved by expanding the area under production rather than by increasing yields.

Significantly, a 1986 study reveals that despite food aid and cereal imports, the Third World as a whole was a net exporter of food to the industrialized world throughout the 1970s. The author of the report, Professor George Kent of the University of Hawaii, points out: "Of the food entering into international trade in 1976 ($123,650 million worth) 11.9 per cent went from richer to poorer countries, while 20.2 per cent went from poorer to richer." Moreover, the food exported from Third World countries was "on balance" of a higher quality than that imported by them.

Many cash crops are ruinous to the soil. Land used to grow peanuts, for example, typically requires a minimum of six years of lying fallow to recover its fertility. If that fallow period is not observed, the soil is quickly depleted of nutrients. One study in the Caramance region of Senegal found that land used to grow two successive crops of peanuts had lost 30 per cent of its organic matter by the end of the second year. Yields dropped by 20 to 40 per cent.

With the best agricultural land being used to grow cash crops, Third World peasants are increasingly forced to use marginal land to grow food for their own consumption. The result can be devastating to the environment. In the Sahel region of West Africa, the northward march of the peanut pushed local nomads onto desert margins, which could not sustain the increased grazing pressure.

Once locked into the cash economy, peasants are particularly vulnerable to the vagaries of the world commodities market. In Thailand, for example, thousands of square kilometres of forest have been cleared to grow tapioca for export to the EC as feed for pigs and cattle. With beef and pork surpluses in Europe forcing a cut-back in production, the tapioca market collapsed, forcing many Thai peasants into debt bondage. Many have literally sold their children into child labour (qv).

Much of the foreign exchange earned from growing cash crops is spent on huge development projects – large dams for example – that bring few rewards for Third World peasants, benefiting instead the small urban and rural elites. Vast sums are also spent on buying Western consumer goods and armaments – $165,000 million being spent on defence by Third World countries between 1972 and 1982. Egypt alone spends $800 million a year servicing its military debt, while Argentina's military spending ate up 61 per cent of its annual export earnings during the late 1980s.

Cash crops have also had a major adverse impact on women in Third World countries. Such crops were first established exclusively through male hands, that is, from male plantation owners or government officials to male farmers. Also, until quite recently, most agricultural development programmes, credit schemes and land privatization schemes were available only to men. Women were, and still are, increasingly burdened with the responsibility for producing all the food for household consumption on land rejected for cash crops.

Additionally, women are expected to help with the production of the cash crops and, in regions where male migration is prevalent, they become responsible for the family debt. This has resulted in intolerable workloads, less-nutritious meals and environmental degradation. In some regions of sub-Saharan Africa, women are now responsible for 80 per cent of agricultural production.

Many development activists in the Third World now argue that "delinking" from the cash economy is the only hope for improving the status of Third World peasants. A recent study from Tanzania reveals that the health of villagers improves dramatically when the national economy is depressed. The reason is clear enough: with the government having less money to spend on roads, the national distribution system breaks down. As a result, villagers can no longer sell their cash crops and grow food for their own consumption. (See also: *Dams*Ⓐ③, *Development*③, *Green Revolution*Ⓐ③, *Irrigation*Ⓐ③, *International Monetary Fund*③, *World Bank*③.)

Catalytic converter

A device fitted to motor vehicle exhausts to destroy some of the harmful gases produced by the vehicle's internal combustion engine. Expensive metals such as platinum are used to bring about this process, which takes place in two stages. First, nitrogen oxides are reduced to nitrogen (a normal constituent of air) and then carbon monoxide and unburned hydrocarbons are oxidized to harmless products.

For the system to work efficiently the proportion of air in the exhaust must be carefully controlled and electronic devices are used to ensure this. Some catalytic converters – known as oxidation catalysts – simply destroy carbon monoxide and unburnt hydrocarbons so that other techniques, such as lean-burn engines, are required in addition to the converter to control the release of nitrogen oxides.

Catalytic converters are poisoned by lead, so vehicles that are fitted with them must run on unleaded fuel. They are also fairly expensive to manufacture and need to be used properly, since poor maintenance reduces their efficiency. This is a serious problem as, in practice, necessary maintenance is not always done. Catalytic converters must be fitted to all new Japanese and US cars by law, and Germany is also introducing them. They are not required in the UK. However, from 1992, all new cars retailed in the EC with an engine capacity of more than 1,000cc will have to be fitted with a catalytic converter. (See also: *Acid rain*Ⓟ, *Car emissions*Ⓟ, *Lead*Ⓟ.)

CFCs

See: *Chlorofluorocarbons.*

Chernobyl, USSR

Site of the world's worst nuclear reactor accident. The accident occurred at 1.23am on Saturday, April 26 1986, when a powerful explosion inside the number 4 reactor at the Chernobyl nuclear power station in the Ukraine blew aside a 1,000 tonne, 60cm-thick steel lid and blasted through the surrounding concrete containment structure.

Two men were killed in the immediate blast, and 30 others (mainly firemen) died from subsequent radiation burns and sickness, following exposure to gamma and beta radiation from the exposed core. Initially, some 135,000 people living within a 30km (18-mile) radius of the plant were evacuated, as was local livestock. Later, however, the evacuation zone was extended as the extent of true contamination became known.

Three years later, a further 100,000 people had to be moved because decontamination procedures had not proved sufficiently effective. Gross deformities have developed among farm animals in the region and the level of disease amongst the human population, including cancers, has increased markedly. The genetic effects are not yet known.

According to the Soviet authorities, between 30 and 50 million curies of radioactive substances escaped during the accident, including 20 per cent of the radio-iodine in the reactor core and about 12 per cent of the radio-caesium.

Much of the radiation was carried west over Europe and, eventually, the eastern coast of the USA. Heavy rains over parts of Scandinavia and Western Europe washed out considerable quantities of radioactive substances, some areas receiving several hundred times the fall-out of those where it remained dry. Radio-iodine and caesium were by far the most important isotopes. Milk products and vegetables were quickly contaminated in such places as Gvle, some 100km (60 miles) north of Stockholm, and

several thousand kilometres away from Chernobyl, the fall-out levels were so high – up to 200,000 becquerels of caesium per square kilometre of soil – that livestock had to be kept in for several months right into the summer.

In Britain, heavy rains over North Wales, Cumbria and Scotland led to surprisingly high levels of radioactive caesium in animals. Sheep in particular became contaminated and hundreds of thousands of lambs that would otherwise have been marketed for their meat were found to have caesium levels greater than 1,000 becquerels a kilogramme, the level set by the British Government as the upper limit for sale and consumption. In June 1986, some 4,225,000 sheep were affected on almost 9,000 farms. The Ministry of Agriculture, Fisheries and Food (MAFF) predicted that levels of caesium would fall quickly during the 1986 growing season. This proved a miscalculation, and caesium has persisted in upland pastures for much longer than was expected. In 1991, 583,000 sheep on more than 700 farms, mostly in Wales, were still subject to restrictions on their movement and slaughter because of radioactive contamination.

Undoubtedly, those worst affected by the fall-out outside the USSR were the Lapps – the Sami people – living primarily off reindeer products in the northern parts of Norway, Sweden and Finland. In these countries, radiation levels rose more than sevenfold and many reindeer had to be slaughtered as a consequence.

Controversy has raged and will continue to rage over the number of people in the USSR and Europe who will die of cancer over the next 50 years as a result of radioactive contamination from Chernobyl. The UK Atomic Energy Authority has estimated that approximately 1,000 people in Western Europe will eventually die of cancer caused by Chernobyl fall-out, and that more than 8,500 people in Eastern Europe and the Soviet Union will die of the same cause. However, some US radiation experts have estimated that the final cancer toll may be more than one million.

As a result of the growing openness within Soviet society, new information has gradually emerged about Chernobyl. At the 1991 fifth anniversary of the accident, the environmental and health effects were revealed to be far worse than the authorities had predicted. According to newly published Soviet maps, about 7 million people are still living in areas where the contamination in the ground is at a higher level than that which led to the restrictions on British sheep farming. Even at a distance of 160km (100 miles) from Chernobyl, there are stretches of land where the caesium in the soil is as concentrated as in the immediate vicinity of the stricken reactor.

Because of the vast area affected, the lack of adequate official monitoring or guidance, the difficulties of bringing in "clean" food, and the unexpected persistence of the radioactivity, many people have continued to grow and eat their own produce in areas from which they should have been evacuated. Often they have been paid extra wages, known as "coffin supplements", as compensation. There are now plans for a fresh wave of evacuations to new towns and settlements outside the contaminated zone.

There has also been a marked deterioration in the health both of those people still living in the contaminated areas and those who have been evacuated to cities such as Kiev, capital of the Ukraine. The hospital in Poleske, just outside the 30km (18-mile) exclusion zone, for example, has recorded major increases in throat and stomach illnesses, anaemia and infant deaths. Kiev hospitals have registered an increase in leukemia cases and in thyroid cancer, the expected result of exposure to radioactive iodine. Some children have suffered an unexplained sudden loss of hair. Health workers claim that the accident has damaged people's immune systems, and talk about an epidemic of "Chernobyl AIDS".

A major study of the health effects of Chernobyl by the International Atomic Energy Agency (IAEA) (qv), published in 1991, disputed that the extent of illnesses could be directly attributable to radiation. It blamed the majority on the stress and trauma associated with the aftermath of a disaster, and said it was too early for many radiation-linked effects to have developed. Critics said the IAEA study was hasty and incomplete. It did not include many people who had been evacuated, or the 600,000 "liquidators" – an army of people who worked in hazardous conditions on the clean-up operation after the accident and are now dispersed throughout the Soviet Union.

The worsening situation has prompted calls for more effective measures to deal with the crisis, and for the punishment of those who covered up the true effects of the accident. In 1990, the Soviet government announced a 16 billion rouble emergency programme, including the evacuation of a further 200,000 people. The Ukrainian and Byelorussian parliaments have demanded more. European organizations have assisted in programmes to provide better medical facilities and health care, especially for what are now called the "children of Chernobyl".

At the Chernobyl plant itself, the most serious development is the discovery of cracks in the concrete tomb (the "sarcophagus") that was hastily built around the damaged reactor. Temperatures inside still reach 200°C.

Engineers now say that a new shelter will have to be placed over the top of the sarcophagus to avoid the escape of further radioactive material. The cost of building the sarcophagus is only part of the $170-215 thousand million figure that Soviet government economist Yuri Koryakin has set on the total bill for the Chernobyl accident.

The figure includes the economic effects of abandoned agricultural land and lost electricity, and dwarfs the net contribution of nuclear power to the Soviet economy since it was inaugurated in 1954. In Europe, the accident has also brought substantial costs: British farmers have received $15 million in compensation, and the German government has paid out over $240 million.

Chernobyl has had a profound effect on the nuclear industry around the world, which had stated that the chance of such an accident was remote. The Western nuclear industry has portrayed the Soviet RBMK design as being uniquely dangerous. Other experts claim, however, that the "positive void coefficient", whereby reactivity increases as coolant expands, and which was fundamental to the accident, is a problem shared by other designs, such as the fast reactor (qv). Fear of another accident like that at Chernobyl has prompted renewed international opposition to nuclear power, which has slowed expansion of nuclear power programmes in nearly every nation that has one. (See also: *Nuclear accidents*Ⓝ Ⓟ.)

Child labour

According to the International Labour Organization (ILO), some 75 million children between the ages of eight and 15 are forced to work for a living. In India alone, there are more than 16 million child labourers. In Thailand, where the figure reaches more than one million, the number grew by six per cent between 1983 and 1984.

Many children are forced to work, even as prostitutes, to help pay off their family debts. In most cases, their wages are paid in advance, so they are in effective "debt bondage" to their employers. Working conditions are generally atrocious and pay is minimal. Many children are treated as virtual slaves.

The problem of child labour has been exacerbated by the increasing indebtedness of Third World peasants – in many cases, the direct result of the modernization of agriculture through the Green Revolution (qv). The high costs of such agricultural inputs as fertilizers and pesticides, and the low prices commanded by their produce, have left peasants in debt to money-lenders for several generations. Environmental degradation – particularly deforestation – has compounded the problem, with droughts and floods causing crop losses and thus increasing indebtedness. (See also: *Cash crops*Ⓐ③, *Development*③.)

Chipko movement

A grassroots movement, principal activists of which have been village women, that sprang up in the 1970s to oppose deforestation in the Indian state of Uttar Pradesh. "Chipko" means "to embrace" in Hindi, and the movement is so called because women embrace trees to prevent their being felled. The movement draws on a long history of village-led opposition to commercial felling of both virgin and communal forest and to restrictions on villagers' access to these. It also owes a great deal to Mahatma Gandhi's philosophy, both in terms of its commitment to non-violent resistance and in terms of Gandhi's village-oriented approach to economic development.

The Chipko campaign resulted in some early success, culminating, in 1980, with the Indian government agreeing to a 15-year ban on commercial felling in the Himalayan forests of Uttar Pradesh. This gave the movement time to extend its support base and launch a massive tree-planting effort involving local people.

Initially, the Chipko movement was concerned with the just allocation of rights to utilize the forests. As time has passed, however, it has matured into a fully-fledged environmental movement. Underpinning the Chipko philosophy today is the recognition that forests are a fundamental resource, ensuring the viability of both human life and wildlife in the Himalayas. Their importance to humans lies in the fact that they prevent soil erosion, thus preserving precious agricultural land. They retain water, reducing fluctuations in the supply of water and preventing flash floods. They are also a crucial source of fuel and fodder for the villagers. In the words of one of the Chipko movement's basic slogans, "What do the forests bear? Soil, water and pure air." This important message is spreading to other parts of the Indian subcontinent, such as Karnataka, Rajasthan, and Orissa. Such success gives some substance to the hope that the rapid deforestation of India might also be checked and even reversed. (See also: *Eucalyptus*Ⓒ③.)

Chlordane

A toxic and highly persistent chlorinated hydrocarbon (*qv*) insecticide. It is readily absorbed through the skin and has caused fatal poisoning in humans as a result. The nervous system is the principal target, with respiratory failure being the cause of death. It is a carcinogen (*qv*) and teratogen (*qv*). Chronic chlordane poisoning causes damage to the liver and kidneys and the material has caused cancer in laboratory animals. An association between chlordane exposure and leukemia in humans has been demonstrated and evidence suggests that chlordane, in a mixture with the similar compound heptachlor, may cause brain tumours in children exposed to it before and after birth.

In the USA, chlordane was finally withdrawn from commerce in 1988, after a long-running legal battle between environmentalists and the Environmental Protection Agency. Previously it had been restricted from agricultural use but was permitted for termite treatment: tens of millions of homes were sprayed and millions of Americans exposed to the chemical. In Britain, chlordane was also banned in 1988, but its use on fine sports turf was permitted until 1992. Chlordane is banned in France, Germany and several other industrialized countries. Nonetheless, it continues to be used in agriculture in the Third World, which is contrary to the advice of the World Bank (*qv*).

Non-target organisms are harmed by chlordane, which accumulates in food chains through bioconcentration (*qv*). Groundwater contamination has also been reported. Heptachlor, another chlorinated hydrocarbon insecticide, resembles chlordane in its toxicological and environmental effects. (See also: *Biocide*Ⓟ, *Cancer*Ⓛ, *Export of pollution*Ⓟ③, *Groundwater*Ⓟ.)

Chlorinated hydrocarbons

Hydrocarbons are organic chemicals containing only carbon and hydrogen in their molecules. It is possible to replace one or more of the hydrogen atoms with atoms of chlorine to produce a chlorinated hydrocarbon. Some chlorinated hydrocarbons may also contain oxygen.

The simpler chlorinated hydrocarbons are almost entirely synthetic, rarely occurring in any quantity in nature. The bacteria involved in decomposing waste material, as part of the natural cycles of decay and recycling, cannot cope easily with these new synthetic substances. As a result, chlorinated hydrocarbons tend to persist in the environment.

The most notorious chlorinated hydrocarbon is the insecticide DDT (*qv*) which, together with other similar compounds such as dieldrin (*qv*) and hexachlorcyclohexane (HCH) (*qv*), has caused massive damage to wildlife due to its ability to persist in food chains. Chlorinated hydrocarbon insecticides are hardly soluble in water but dissolve readily in fat. This means that they are stored in the fatty tissues of the body. Consequently, small amounts eaten regularly build up to high levels in the tissues – a process known as bioconcentration (*qv*). If a predator eats several small animals with large amounts of chlorinated hydrocarbon insecticide in their tissues, it may absorb a fatal dose.

Insecticides are not the only chlorinated hydrocarbons capable of causing pollution. The contamination of water supplies by chlorinated solvents (*qv*) is a growing problem, as many of these materials are toxic and suspected carcinogens (*qv*). Where fluorine is included in the hydrocarbon molecule as well as chlorine, gases known as chlorofluorocarbons (*qv*) are formed: these are used as propellants in aerosol cans and may be destroying the protective ozone layer (*qv*).

If chlorinated compounds are burned at low temperatures – for instance around 500°C (930°F) – significant quantities of highly toxic dioxins (*qv*) are produced. When plastics such as PVC or any items containing chlorinated solvents are burned in waste incinerators, a health risk may thus be created. Serious dioxin contamination has resulted from fires involving electrical transformers containing PCBS (*qv*).

Because of the environmental problems they have caused, chlorinated hydrocarbon insecticides are banned or restricted for many uses or are being phased out in most developed countries of the world. However, controls in the Third World are not as strict and they are still sold, often by companies based in Western countries where these chemicals are banned. (See also: *Cancer*©, *Circle of poison*℗③, *Groundwater*©℗, *Hazardous waste*©℗.)

Chlorinated solvents

Solvents are liquids used to dissolve materials for a wide range of purposes. Chlorinated solvents – chlorinated hydrocarbons (*qv*), widely used in industry and a growing number of domestic products – are one group of solvents that are causing increasing environmental problems.

Some, such as perchlorethylene and trichlorethylene, are used for grease removal in dry cleaning establishments or industrial processes such as microchip manufacture. Chloroform has also been used industrially as a de-greaser, and the closely related carbon tetrachloride has been used as a fire extinguisher as well as a spot remover for clothing. Paint removers often contain methylene chloride, while thinners for typewriter correcting fluid are frequently based on trichlorethylene.

Most chlorinated solvents are poisonous to some degree. Inhaling them can produce drowsiness and unconsciousness, possibly leading to collapse. Placing recently dry-cleaned clothing in a warm, sealed car can lead to a dangerous build-up of solvent fumes, while the abuse of correct ing fluid by glue-sniffers has had fatal results. Prolonged exposure to these materials can cause damage to the kidneys, liver and, in some cases, the heart.

Several chlorinated solvents are proven or suspected carcinogens (*qv*). Chloroform has been withdrawn as an ingredient of medicines in North America and parts of Europe for this reason and question marks hang over methylene chloride and trichlorethylene.

Chlorinated solvents persist in the environment as they are not easily broken down by microorganisms. If dumped in landfills (*qv*) or lagoons, they may evaporate – which may lead to damage to the ozone layer (*qv*) – or percolate through the soil to groundwater (*qv*). Many wells in the USA have been badly polluted by carelessly dumped chlorinated solvents, and in some places taking a shower can cause an unacceptably high exposure to solvent fumes as the material evaporates from the heated water. Water supplies have been lost in Britain and the Netherlands through similar pollution. Other groundwater sources may be at risk since it takes a long time for the solvents to reach the water table from the surface.

In Britain, the Department of the Environment estimates that ten per cent of potable aquifers could be contaminated with concentrations of chlorinated solvents above the limits recommended as safe by the World Health Organization. The two solvents causing most concern are trichloroethane and tetrachloroethylene.

Chlorinated solvents cannot easily be burned since they form toxic partial combustion products. If their vapours are exposed to a naked flame, or drawn through a cigarette, the poisonous gas phosgene is formed. Combustion in an incinerator at too low a temperature leads to the formation of dioxins (*qv*).

Until such time as the carcinogenic pollutants can be phased out, waste chlorinated solvents are best recycled where possible or disposed of in specialist high temperature incinerators with stringent pollution controls. (See also: *Hazardous waste*©℗.)

Chlorination

Chlorination simply means "adding chlorine" and has two environmental contexts. In industrial chemistry, chlorination means adding chlorine atoms to other molecules, often hydrocarbons, to produce a wide range of new chemicals, including the chlorinated hydrocarbons (*qv*). Chlorination reactions can be hazardous, but the most dangerous aspect of this process is the bulk storage of chlorine gas on the factory site. Chlorine is highly toxic – it was used as a weapon in World War I – and a major leak from an industrial plant could have devastating consequences.

In gaseous form, chlorine is also used to disinfect water. It is a powerful germicide, killing most microorganisms. Concern has been expressed at the presence of chlorinated organic chemicals in treated water. These substances, known as micropollutants (*qv*), are formed when the chlorine reacts with traces of other chemicals – some of natural origin and some from industrial discharges – present in the raw water. Some of these substances are known or suspected carcinogens (*qv*). In laboratory tests, chlorinated drinking water samples have been shown to cause mutations in bacteria.

Further investigations are continuing into this problem, but some scientists are recommending the use of ozone for water disinfection, especially where levels of trace organic compounds in the raw water are high. Many swimming pools now use ozone for disinfection since it does not lead to irritant chlorination products being formed in the water and does not involve the storage of toxic chemicals.

Chlorofluorocarbons (CFCs)

Chlorine-based compounds used as aerosol propellants, refrigerants, coolants, sterilants, solvents and in the production of insulating foam packaging used by the fast food industry. CFCS have long residence times – of 100 years or more in some instances – in the lower atmosphere. There are no natural mechanisms for their removal and CFCS break down only under the action of ultraviolet radiation when they enter the upper atmosphere. Consequently, atmospheric levels are rising sharply and will remain high even if CFC releases cease immediately.

Concern has arisen because CFCS are implicated in two major threats to the global environment posed by air pollution. They are greenhouse gases (*qv*) – that is, they allow incoming solar radiation to pass relatively unhindered but trap outgoing terrestrial radiation before it can escape to space, heating the planet through the "greenhouse effect" (*qv*). CFCS are up to 10,000 times more effective as greenhouse gases than carbon dioxide, and are currently responsible for around 20 per cent of global warming.

CFCS, along with halons (*qv*), are also responsible for the rapid depletion of the stratospheric ozone layer (*qv*). Chlorine atoms are broken off from the CFC molecules by the action of ultraviolet light in the upper atmosphere. The free chlorine atoms then break down ozone molecules to ordinary oxygen but are not destroyed themselves so that one chlorine atom can destroy thousands of ozone molecules.

Concern over the threat of ozone depletion led to the Vienna Convention for the Protection of the Ozone Layer in 1985, established under the auspices of the United Nations Environment Programme. This was followed by the Montreal Protocol (*qv*), signed in September 1987 by the main CFC-producing and -consuming nations. The Protocol currently commits signatories in the developed world to phase out CFC production by the year 2000.

The huge amounts of CFCS in use which will inevitably be released into the atmosphere, and the time-lag of around 10 years between the release of a CFC and it reaching the stratospheric ozone layer, make immediate action imperative. Increasing evidence of

the seriousness of the problem has prompted several governments to go beyond the measures agreed under the Montreal Protocol. The EC intends to ban CFC production by 1997; Sweden, Austria, the Netherlands and Germany aim to phase out production by 1995.

The speed at which CFCS are phased out will largely be dictated by the speed at which industry comes up with alternatives. Although most CFC uses are either frivolous (fast-food packaging, for example) or, like spray cans, can be replaced with non-chemical alternatives, most governments have chosen to defend the interests of the chemical industry and opt for a phased withdrawal. Unfortunately the chemical substitutes so far offered are far from satisfactory. Although HCFCS, for instance, have a much lower ozone depletion potential, they are still ozone destroyers. HFCS which do not deplete ozone are potent greenhouse gases. (See also: *CFC substitutes, Montreal Protocol, Ozone layer*ⓟ.)

Chlorofluorocarbon substitutes

When it became clear in the late 1980s that ozone-depleting substances, such as chlorofluorocarbons (CFCS) (*qv*), would have to be phased out by the end of the century, chemical companies were quick to discover substitutes. The first of these to be developed was a group of chemicals known as HCFCS.

The US chemical group Dupont has invested heavily in HCFCS and at least one, HCFC22, is already on the market; the French firm Atochem is producing another, known as HCFC142b. These HCFCS have a considerably lower ozone depletion potential (ODP) than CFCS; for example, HCFC141b has an ODP that is only approximately one tenth of that of CFC11.

But given the extent of the damage that has been wrought by CFCS, this tenth is still significant. Many environmental groups campaign for all ozone-depleting chemicals, without exception, to be banned outright by the early 1990s. But the Montreal Protocol

(*qv*), the international treaty that supervises the phasing-out of ozone-depleting substances, sees HCFCS as a helpful palliative for industry, and has only recommended that they should be phased out by 2020 if possible, and 2040 at the latest.

A further disadvantage of HCFCS is that they contribute to the greenhouse effect (*qv*). Over a period of 20 years, HCFC22 has a global warming potential that is 90 per cent of that of CFC11, although over 100 years this figure drops to 45 per cent. Also, HCFC123 has been found to be carcinogenic, and there are fears that this may prove to be the case with some of the others.

Attention has therefore turned to another group of chemicals, HFCS, which contain no chlorine and so do not deplete the ozone layer. Dupont and ICI have both started to produce HFC134a. However, these chemicals also contribute to the greenhouse effect, although the extent of this contribution is disputed.

Circle of poison

The term "circle of poison" was coined by two American researchers, David Weir and Mark Shapiro, to describe the international trade in pesticides banned or restricted in the West. The complete circle is described in the accompanying illustration.

The victims of the circle of poison begin with Western chemical workers and end with Western consumers, who frequently eat imported food heavily contaminated with banned pesticides. In between lie the Third World peasants who use the chemicals. Examples of the chemicals involved include DDT (*qv*), hexachlorocyclohexane (HCH) (*qv*), and dieldrin (*qv*).

There are at least 3 million cases of acute pesticide poisoning in the world each year. These cases result in about 20,000 deaths – mostly in the Third World – and the majority of them involve banned chemicals. In Costa Rica, for example, farmhands using the chemical DPCP on banana plantations have been found to have a high rate of sterility.

Studies undertaken in America have consistently shown imported foods to be contaminated with pesticides. In 1983, the National Resources Defense Council (NRDC), an independent group, tested imported coffee beans for pesticides and found "multiple illegal chemical residues on every sample taken". One specimen was contaminated with DDT, BHC, lindane, aldrin and chlordane.

The true extent of the problem can only be guessed at since the USA and other authorities test only a minute fraction of imported foods. Of the 2,000 million oranges imported into the USA in 1982, only 14 were tested for pesticide residues by the Food and Drug Administration (FDA). Morever, says the NRDC, only a limited number of pesticides are tested. No tests, for example, are made for DBCP, a known carcinogen (qv) banned in the USA but widely used in the Third World.

In 1985, the UN Food and Agriculture Organization (FAO) issued a code of practice aimed at controlling the export of banned or restricted pesticides. The code requires prior notification to be given to the government of the importing country, which must give its explicit consent to the import. However, lobbying by Britain and other major exporters has ensured that the code has no legal force. Four years after the Code was introduced, a report in 1989 by the Pesticide Action Network detailed numerous infringements of the Code and demonstrated that unacceptable practices are still widespread. (See also: *Development*③, *Export of pollution*Ⓟ③.)

Climate change
See: *Greenhouse effect*.

Co-disposal
The process by which industrial wastes, usually in a liquid form, are disposed of on the same landfill (qv) site as domestic wastes. The reasoning is that the domestic wastes are capable of absorbing a reasonable volume of liquid, thereby preventing the run-off of effluent into streams or the excessive generation of leachate (qv). In addition, the biological processes that occur within a landfill site may help to break down some of the organic materials in the waste and render them harmless.

However, recent research shows that co-disposal is not as effective in breaking down or arresting the migration of wastes as previously thought, with the result that water supplies have frequently been polluted. Further problems have arisen through the absorptive capacity of the domestic wastes being exceeded, leading to the escape of leachates. In addition, the mixing of incompatible wastes has on occasion led to fires or to the release of toxic gases. The pollution record at co-disposal sites has led the USA to ban the practice. Its use is also being curtailed in many north European countries. However, it remains in use in Britain and in most other countries.

In 1989, Britain's Natural Environment Research Council, one of the country's most respected research bodies, described co-disposal as "an expedient response to an immediate problem which, unfortunately, takes no account of the potential long-term implications for public health and safety". It went on: "The assumptions that toxic materials are diluted in a much larger volume of wastes and that this mixture is then non-hazardous ... are suspect. First, the degradation products and leachates arising from domestic wastes can themselves be serious water pollutants. Second, many co-disposal waste substances are extremely long-lived and consequently will either remain exactly where they are buried, possibly as concentrated pockets, or will be dispersed through the nearby waste and surrounding rock formations." (See also: *Hazardous waste*Ⓟ.)

Co-generation
See: *Combined heat and power*.

Coal
A hydrocarbon "fossil" fuel formed when plant remains are buried under anoxic conditions. Peat forms the lowest rank, with most water and volatiles and least carbon per unit weight, followed by lignite ("brown coal"), then "hard coal" and ending with the highest rank, anthracite. In terms of the energy they yield when burned, one tonne of hard coal is equal to about three tonnes of lignite, these being the two coals in greatest use worldwide.

In 1986, world production of hard coal was a little more than 3,000 million tonnes, and production of lignite was just over 1,000 million tonnes. The largest producer is China, which doubled its output between 1973 and 1986 to 835 million tonnes. Total world reserves are vast; coal that is already accessible but unmined amounts to over 580 billion tonnes, which at current rates of use is at least 100 years' supply. Mining coal is a particularly hazardous activity, involving the risks of gas explosions and mine collapses. Thousands of mine workers have been killed in major accidents. It has become increasingly common to use "open cast" mining – digging up coal by stripping away the layers of ground above it. Worldwide, about 40 per cent of coal is excavated by this method. Open cast mining, however, is much more environmentally intrusive than deep mining. In Britain, deep mine pits have been closed because of economic pressures, and a fifth of the coal produced in Britain now comes from open cast mines.

Today, there is concern about the inevitable carbon dioxide (qv) emissions from the combustion of coal, which are increasing the carbon dioxide content of the atmosphere and threatening to cause climatic changes through the greenhouse effect (qv).

There is further concern about emission of sulphur dioxide and oxides of nitrogen from coal-fired power stations, as these are involved in the production of acid rain (qv). These emissions, however, can be greatly reduced by the use of scrubbers (qv) and also by fluidized bed technology.

They could be further reduced by switching to combined heat and power (qv) energy systems that would drastically reduce the amount of coal required to generate a given amount of energy, by making use of the waste heat for district heating programmes. The contention that coal-fired power stations are more expensive to build and to operate than nuclear power stations, with which they have recently been replaced in a number of countries, cannot be substantiated.

Coal-tar dyes

A group of synthetic food dyes (*qv*) used widely in food and drinks. First discovered during the late 19th century, they were used to dye fabrics. From the technical point of view, they are preferable to many natural vegetable dyes in that they are very strong, fast and chemically stable. At least 17 of them are in widespread use worldwide, though none is permitted in Norway. The best known of the dyes are amaranth (*qv*) and Tartrazine (*qv*).

There has been a long-standing controversy about the safety of coal-tar dyes. During this century, at least a dozen of them have been banned or withdrawn because they have been shown to cause cancer in laboratory animals. They have also been implicated in provoking acute intolerance among a small but indeterminate number of people. In particular, they have been shown to provoke a number of conditions including hyperactivity, asthma, eczema, urticaria and migraine.

Nonetheless, their use continues to be approved by the World Health Organization, the UN's Food and Agriculture Organization, the EC and numerous national authorities, including the US Food and Drugs Administration and Britain's Food Advisory Committee. (See also: *Additives©, Cancer©.*)

Codex Alimentarius

One of the objectives of the GATT (*qv*) Uruguay Round is to "harmonize" international regulations concerning food safety. At present every country sets its own standards for the levels of pesticides, hormones and other contaminants in food.

The organization charged with assessing this evidence is the Codex Alimentarius Commission, a joint body of the United Nations Food and Agriculture Organization (FAO) (*qv*) and the World Health Organization (WHO). The prominence of corporate interests on the Codex gives grounds to question its impartiality. For instance, the US delegation consists of 10 government officials and 18 representatives of the food industry, but no independent scientists or members of consumer groups.

If the harmonization proposals are accepted, no nation would be permitted to exceed the maximum levels of pesticides in food, as prescribed by the Codex. Nor would they be allowed to set stricter domestic standards, which would be interpreted as a form of trade protectionism because it would prejudice the importing of food from countries with lower standards.

There is a considerable anxiety among environmentalists that many of the regulations and restrictions upon pesticides that have been set recently in some industrialized countries will be overturned by Codex rulings. For example, Codex residue levels for pesticides such as DDT, aldrin, endrin and heptachlor on various crops are 5, 10 or even 50 times less stringent than those set by the US Food and Drug Administration. (See also: *GATT.*)

Colourings
See: *Food dyes.*

Combined heat and power (CHP)

Also known as co-generation. Most power stations, particularly the gigawatt-size ones used in the UK, produce electricity with an efficiency of around 35 per cent. The remainder of the heat energy is discharged into the environment as waste. Combined heat and power systems provide a means by which the "waste" heat is put to good purpose in providing hot water and space heating in domestic and industrial buildings. Through CHP schemes the efficiency with which energy is used can be as high as 75 per cent or more. Furthermore, the use of waste

heat will in itself tend to reduce electricity demand, particularly when used for heating. Studies for the British government have estimated that there is a potential market for providing heat from over 20 gigawatts of CHP capacity.

Many European cities – Copenhagen and Hamburg, for instance – have CHP schemes, and worldwide there are at present some 114 gigawatts of heat and power capacity. By improving energy use, CHP leads to fuel saving and reduced energy costs. It also tends to reduce the monopoly hold of the electricity supply industry, since CHP schemes can often best be operated by municipal authorities. (See also: *Energy conservation©, Soft energy paths©.*)

Community supported agriculture

Radical alternative to conventional systems of food production and marketing, now gaining an increasing number of supporters. Rather than a farmer buying or renting land, deciding what crops to grow for what markets, and then selling the produce through a series of intermediaries, community supported agriculture (CSA) involves direct contact between farmers and consumers. Instead of food production being the preoccupation of the farmer alone, the community (or a specific group of people from one area) agree to share the risks and responsibilities. This is done by drawing up a detailed farm budget for a year (including labour costs) and dividing this by the number of people, or households, that the farm will support. From this the cost of a "share" can be worked out, with each household committing itself to paying this amount.

The produce is then divided among "shareholders". When there is a bumper crop, each household receives a large amount, and when a crop does badly each household receives less. In this way the risks of farming are shared among a wider community, and the farmers, ensured of a guaranteed income, can grow the variety and quality of produce that the community wants rather than concentrating on the crops that generate good returns.

Farms in CSA schemes tend to be organic and have much greater crop diversity, operate at a reasonable cost because there are no intermediaries between grower and consumer, and re-establish a link between consumers and the land. Such farms tend to move towards the development of more sustainable food-production systems. In the USA, more than 200 farms operate in this way, with the number growing rapidly as more people hear about the concept. Similar schemes also operate in Europe and Japan – the Japanese having developed similar systems without knowledge of the CSA movement in the USA. (See also: *Organic Farming.*)

Containment

All nuclear reactors have a layer of concrete 2 to 5m (6 to 16ft) thick surrounding the pressure vessel. This is the primary containment, sometimes called the biological shield.

The pressurized water reactor (*qv*) primary containment encloses the entire primary circuit – steam generators, main pumps, etc. – as well as the core within its pressure vessel. The reactor building itself is designed to act as a further secondary containment, within which is the secondary circuit and the turbo-generators. Advanced gas-cooled reactor (*qv*) stations have a similar arrangement, but the steam generators and pumps of the Magnox reactors (*qv*) are outside the primary containment. Some Magnox stations do not have adequate secondary containment, which is a characteristic they share with the Soviet RBMK reactors, as was brought to light in the aftermath of the Chernobyl accident.

However, well-designed containment vessels do not provide fail-safe protection. Some experts dispute that the containment vessel at Three Mile Island (*qv*) could have withstood an explosion on the scale of Chernobyl. Even where the containment does not rupture, the radioactive material

it "traps" must eventually be released into the environment. In the case of Three Mile Island, trapped radioactive gas was vented directly into the atmosphere, despite public protests. (See also: *Chernobyl*Ⓝ, Nuclear accidents ⒫Ⓝ.)

Contraception

Contraception is perceived as an essential component of modern life and, in particular, as a solution to global population growth. Of all the contraceptive methods available in the West, two have become particularly popular: the pill and the coil (intra-uterine device or IUD). In Britain in 1983, 2,900,000 women used the pill and 600,000 the IUD. The figures for the USA in 1982 are 8,400,000 and 2,200,000 respectively. Unfortunately, both forms of contraception also appear to have serious health effects.

In 1983, two studies published in *The Lancet* established the dangers of using male and female hormones to block ovulation. One found large increases in cervical cancer in women using the pill and the other found significant increases in breast cancer in women who had been taking the pill before they reached 25 years of age. In general, it seems that the pill can be a contributory factor in the pathogenesis of a number of diseases ranging from headaches and migraines to cardiovascular diseases and cancer. There is also strong evidence to suggest that taking the pill during the first few weeks of pregnancy (which occurs in ten per cent of all pregnancies in the USA) has teratogenic (see *Teratogen*) effects on foetuses and may increase vulnerability to cancer.

In 1989, a re-analysis of data that had previously been used to discredit a causal link between breast cancer and the pill was carried out by Professor Julian Peto of the UK Institute of Cancer Research. It showed that in fact the risk of developing breast cancer increased with the number of years that a woman had taken the pill: women who had taken the pill for between 4–7 years have a 25 per cent higher chance of get-

ting breast cancer, while after 12 years the chances almost double.

The dangers of the coil have not been investigated as thoroughly as those of the pill, though it is clear that they exist. It is thought to work by causing an inflammation that either prevents the egg from implanting itself or interferes with spermatozoa in the uterus. The uterus is well protected, so it is not surprising that the insertion of a foreign body into it should lead to serious infections and other complications, such as miscarriages and perforation of the uterine wall. Some measure of the unpleasant side-effects of IUD use can be obtained by looking at the rate of removal during the first year of use. This varies from 30 to 40 per cent, according to the type of coil.

Both these methods of contraception are clearly unsatisfactory from the point of view of health. Yet there is tremendous official and unofficial pressure to adopt them at an early age. Many consider it deplorable that received opinion on sexual liberation should so endanger the health of women of all ages. It also must not be forgotten that in the promotion of modern contraceptives, natural and traditional methods of birth control have been ridiculed and replaced with artificial implants or products, which are available only through outside markets. Additionally, contraceptives such as long-lasting implants under the skin (notably Norplant) and the controversial injectable Depo-Provera are still being tested on and promoted among women in the Third World. Apart from the disgrace of experimenting on women who are provided with sparse information or follow-up health care and minimal choice, it appears that the long-lasting contraceptives are being favoured by international organizations –such as the United Nations Population Fund and the International Planned Parenthood Foundation – essentially because their use is out of women's control. (See also: *Cancer*Ⓛ, *Demographic transition*③, *Family planning*Ⓛ, *Population explosion*③.)

Convenience food

See: *Junk food*.

Conversion products

Chemicals entering the environment rarely remain in the same chemical form for very long. A wide range of processes acts on them, many involving living organisms, and the conversion products that result may be radically different from the original.

In many cases, a complicated substance is broken down into a range of simpler ones, a process known as biodegradation. Many organophosphorus pesticides, for instance, are broken down by the action of water, bacteria and other chemicals in the environment into, ultimately, carbon dioxide, phosphate and water – all of which are much less harmful than the original insecticide. Organic materials in domestic waste –such as proteins and cellulose –are broken down to nitrogen, carbon dioxide, fatty acids, water and methane.

In some cases, the conversion products may be more harmful than the original material. In certain conditions mercury (*qv*) compounds can be converted by bacteria into methyl mercury, a much more hazardous form. The pesticide heptachlor is converted first into heptachlor epoxide and then into heptachlor epoxide ketone, each of which is more toxic than the preceding form. Nitrogen oxides and unburned hydrocarbons from vehicle exhausts – themselves unpleasant air pollutants – are involved in the production of the toxic gas ozone and, when exposed to sunlight, a range of powerful irritants called PANS. (See also: *Bioconcentration*©®, *Cancer*©®, *Synergy*©.)

Coral reefs

Among the most diverse ecosystems in the world, coral reefs are produced in shallow warm seas by colonies of small marine organisms – known as polyps – that secrete limestone to form tubes within which they shelter and from whose open ends they feed. The myriad tubular skeletons left behind by the polyps build up into the reef. The polyps feed on tiny brown algae, known as Zooxanthellae, which colonize the inner surface of the polyps' tubes. The population is thus mainly fed from the reef itself rather than from the water, enabling reefs to survive in the marine equivalent of deserts. The relationship between the polyps and the algae is a perfect example of symbiosis.

The largest reef in the world is the Great Barrier Reef (*qv*), off the north-east coast of Australia. It extends for more than 3,000km (1,240 miles) and in terms of the number of species it supports is the richest ecosystem on Earth.

Coral reefs are among the most productive ecosystems in the world, their potential yield in fish being estimated at 9 million tonnes – about 12 per cent of the present world fish catch. However, overfishing is threatening many reefs, particularly those where dynamite is used to kill the fish.

Reefs are extremely vulnerable to changes in their environment. In particular, they cannot tolerate pollution that enriches the water but increases its opacity; they must have light to permit photosynthesis by the algae and thus require clear water, containing little nutrient or organic matter. They do not occur, for example, close to the mouths of large rivers because of the cloudiness of water carrying sediment. Many reefs are being destroyed by sewage pollution, which encourages the excessive growth of the algae, eventually smothering the polyps. Silt run-off into the sea – the result of deforestation (*qv*) and misguided agricultural practices – also poses a threat.

Coral reefs are subject to other forms of degradation. Many are threatened by the proliferation of the predatory Crown of Thorns starfish, which annihilate the polyp population, a phenomenon that is possibly related to pollution. Building booms in tropical islands have also led to the mining of reefs to obtain limestone, leading to coastal erosion and increased storm damage. Tourism has resulted in many reefs being depleted of their coral for sale in souvenir shops or to decorate aquaria; the sale of coral has grown enormously in recent years.

Coral reefs are almost certain to be affected by global warming. If the tropical oceans get warmer, the Zooxanthellae will disappear because they cannot tolerate waters above 30°C. The disappearance of Zooxanthellae causes reefs to bleach. The bleaching of many reefs occurred throughout the tropics in 1991. (See also: *Development*③, *Balance of nature*©.)

Coronary heart disease

A disease of the blood vessels of the heart. It is now one of the two principal causes of death among industrial populations, the other being cancer. About four out of ten men and two out of ten women alive today will die of it. As such, it has achieved the status of an epidemic.

In England and Wales alone, half a million people are diagnosed as suffering from heart disease. For 100,000 of them, it will prove fatal. In Britain as a whole, the disease affects 12 per cent of men between the ages of 50 and 59. In the USA, the incidence among men of the same age group is 21 per cent.

There is every reason to suppose that the disease begins to affect its victims early in life. One study found 15 per cent of a sample of US soldiers killed in the Korean war had damage to their coronary arteries.

Coronary heart disease is a true "disease of civilization" (*qv*), being almost unknown among primitive peoples, as is established in a number of well-documented studies.

The disease also seems to have been rare at the beginning of this century. Paul White, a famous heart physician, saw his first case of angina in 1921.

Features associated with our modern way of life that have been pinpointed as major causes of heart disease are overeating; high consumption of saturated fats, sucrose and other refined carbohydrates; smoking; and lack of exercise. (See also: *Diseases of civilization*©, *Junk food*©.)

Creys Malville

Site, 40km (25 miles) from Lyons, France, of the world's first commercial-scale fast reactor (qv). Called "Super-Phénix", the reactor is 51 per cent owned by Electricité de France (EDF), with other European countries (including the UK) having different shares of the remainder. Work began on the reactor in 1975. In July 1976, violent anti-nuclear demonstrations, brutally suppressed by anti-riot police, took place there. One death and many serious injuries occurred.

Construction proved difficult and costs tripled. It is now estimated that the Super-Phénix has cost between $2,500 million and $3,000 million – about two to three times more than France's light water reactors. France's atomic energy authority – the CEA – regards this escalation in costs as being of no significance, arguing that Super-Phénix is only a prototype and that future breeder reactors will be much cheaper. Electricity from Super-Phénix will be twice as expensive as that from France's conventional nuclear reactors. EDF is now in serious financial trouble, owing a total of $37,400 million by 1988. France had originally intended to build six fast reactor stations after Super-Phénix, but this plan was quickly dropped. There would, in any case, be a huge surplus of generating capacity in France by the end of the 1980s.

Another difficulty arose when France made it clear that it considered the plutonium bred in Super-Phénix as being available to its weapons programme. Objections were raised not only in France, but also in the other countries involved in the project. As a FBR, Super-Phénix is intended to "breed" its own fuel by transforming non-fissile uranium-238 into fissile plutonium-239. However, "breeding" depends critically on mastering the reprocessing (qv) of high-burn-up fuel and ensuring that the plutonium loss during reprocessing is kept very low, possibly as low as a few tenths of one per cent. This is ten times lower than achieved to date. Super-Phénix uses liquid sodium – which burns vigorously when in contact with air – as a coolant. In view of the massive amount of sodium it contains – some 5,000 tonnes – a fire would be very serious indeed. It has also been suggested that, unlike conventional reactors, FBRS can explode like an atom bomb.

The core of the Super-Phénix contains 5.5 tonnes of plutonium (qv). An accident on the same scale as Chernobyl would release between five per cent and 15 per cent of that plutonium into the atmosphere. With the cities of Geneva and Lyons just 50km (31 miles) away, the consequences would be too awful to contemplate.

In April 1987, Creys Malville shut down for 20 months after a serious leak of liquid sodium coolant in a tank used to store fuel rods. The plant was re-opened in January 1989, using a temporary replacement tank. The plant was closed again, however, in July 1990, following the discovery of corrosion in its cooling filters. For a combination of safety and economic reasons, it may never return to full operation. Its construction and operation probably rank as one of the most dangerous experiments ever conducted. (See also: *Nuclear accidents* Ⓝ.)

Cyclamates

A class of artificial sweeteners (qv) that has been the focus of a long-standing controversy. Cyclamates are three closely related compounds: cyclamic acid, calcium cyclamate and sodium cyclamate. These were discovered in 1937, but first introduced into the American market in the 1950s. Cyclamates are cheap to produce, but are not as sweet as saccharin (qv). They are, however, more stable than aspartame and can be incorporated into products that are to be cooked.

In 1968, evidence began to emerge indicating that cyclamates may not be entirely safe, and that they might have adverse effects on the liver, kidneys and chromosomes. A year later they were linked experimentally to the development of cancer in rats. The US government responded by banning cyclamates in October 1969, and the UK followed suit a month later. The use of cyclamates continues to be permitted, however, in almost all other European countries.

Efforts have continued, nonetheless, to try to get cyclamates reinstated in both the USA and the UK. In the mid-1980s, American experts were saying that cyclamates were probably not carcinogenic, or at worst only weakly so. But they could not dismiss the possibility that they might prompt the growth of cancers which had been initiated by other agents. Many of the recent problems concerning the safety of cyclamates are concerned with the effects of cyclohexylamine, which forms as cyclamates are metabolized. Cyclohexylamine has been shown to cause testicular atrophy in rats, and might therefore correspondingly damage human testicles.

The Joint Expert Committee on Food Additives of the World Health Organization and UN Food and Agriculture Organization has continued to give its approval for the use of cyclamates. In 1991, the British government's Committee on Toxicity announced that new evidence indicated that the problem of testicular damage was sufficiently serious to oblige them to set a level of acceptable daily consumption so low as effectively to render cyclamates unusable by the food industry, should the government decide to lift the cyclamate ban. The EC, however, has rejected this view. If the Commission's proposals are adopted, cyclamates would be permitted throughout the entire EC.

Daminazide
Dams
DDT
Debt-for-nature
swaps
Debt crisis
Decay products
Decommissioning
Deep ecology
Deforestation
Delaney Amendment
Demographic
transition
Desalinization
Desertification
Development
Dichlorvos
Dieldrin
Diethylstilbesterol
(DES)
Dilution and dispersal
Dioxins
Diseases of
civilization
Division of labour
Dounreay
Drift Nets
Drinking water
Drought-flood cycle

Daminazide
See: *Alar*.

Dams

By providing water for irrigation (*qv*) and plentiful supplies of electricity, large dams are popularly seen as playing an essential role in the battle against world hunger and poverty. Their construction has been actively promoted by the World Bank (*qv*) and other development agencies.

But, despite their claimed benefits, the record of large dams, particularly in the tropics, has been one of unmitigated ecological and social destruction.

Vast areas of land have been, and are expected to be, flooded as a result of dam projects. The reservoir of the Volta dam in Ghana, for example, flooded an area the size of Lebanon. Worldwide, by 1981 some 308,000sq km (119,000sq miles) had been flooded by dams – an area equivalent to the whole of Italy – and that figure is expected to increase by 38,000sq km (15,000sq miles) by 1990. Much of the land that is lost is fertile valley land or forest. The Balbina dam in Brazil alone flooded some 2,300sq km (890sq miles) of rainforest. Despite attempts at animal rescue programmes, the loss of wildlife and plants is inevitably widespread.

Millions of people have been uprooted to make way for the reservoirs of large dams. Seventy-eight thousand people were displaced by the Volta dam; 120,000 by the Aswan dam (*qv*) in Egypt; and 93,000 by the Damodar dam in India. If it goes ahead, China's massive Three Gorges dam (*qv*) would alone submerge ten cities and partially flood another eight.

Past resettlement (*qv*) programmes have been characterized by inadequate compensation, low-grade replacement land and inappropriate housing. For many – particularly those from isolated tribal cultures – the move proves disastrous. With their land, their sacred shrines, historic monuments, homes and villages are drowned beneath the reservoir – their whole way of life falls apart. Many simply drift towards the nearest city slums.

The reservoirs of dams, together with their associated irrigation schemes, provide ideal breeding grounds for the vectors of waterborne disease, in particular schistosomiasis (*qv*) and malaria (*qv*), the rates of which increase dramatically after the dam is built, even where the diseases were previously unknown. As a result of the Aswan dam, some villages near Lake Nasser have a 100 per cent infection rate for bilharzia. In Ghana, before the Volta dam was built, the rate was two per cent: it is now 80 per cent.

Downstream ecosystems are severely disrupted by dams, which trap silt and thus hold back valuable nutrients, with a consequent effect upon fisheries that can far outweigh the catches from any fishing programmes set up in a dam's reservoir. Before the Aswan dam was built, sardine catches in the eastern Mediterranean totalled some 18,000 tonnes a year; by 1969, the catch was down to 500 tonnes a year. Agriculture is also affected, since the floodplains downstream are also deprived of nutrients. In Egypt, the 100 million tonnes of highly fertile sediment previously deposited on farmland prior to the Aswan dam fell to just a few tonnes after its construction. To compensate for the loss, Egypt must now apply artificial fertilizer (*qv*) at a cost of more than $100 million a year.

Reduced silt deposition below dams also leads to coastal erosion: the homes of 10,000 people living in Keto on the Togo coast, below the Volta dam, fell into the sea as a result of erosion. Land downstream can also suffer from salt water intrusion, caused by the reduced flow of impounded rivers.

The sheer weight of the water impounded in the reservoirs of large dams has triggered earthquakes. Such earthquakes have occurred at a number of sites throughout the world, in China, India, Zimbabwe and Greece. In 1981, the area around the Aswan dam suffered an earthquake of magnitude 5.6 on the Richter scale. The Volta dam and the

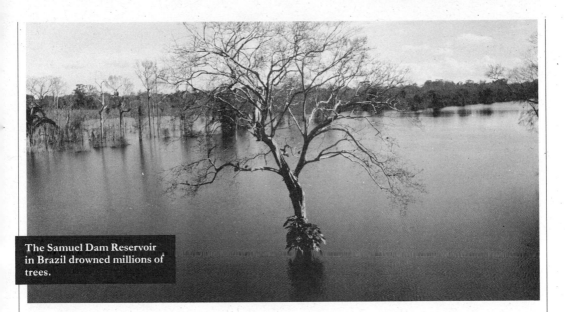

The Samuel Dam Reservoir in Brazil drowned millions of trees.

Bratsk dam have also experienced induced earthquakes, despite being in low-risk areas.

In addition, the irrigation and industrial projects which dams make possible bring further ecological and social destruction. Millions of acres of land now suffer from salinization (qv) as a result of perennial irrigation, while the industrial projects powered by the hydroelectricity (qv) from dams have caused massive pollution. In Brazil, for example, the biggest consumers of electricity are also the most polluting: aluminium plants, chrome and silicon works, and copper, lead and zinc foundries.

Lastly, the construction of dams frequently opens up areas that were previously remote to settlements. Thousands of hectares of tropical forest have been lost as a result of settlers using the access roads to dams (and the reservoirs themselves) to enter the forest. And while deforestation proceeds unchecked, so erosion increases and the soils of the watershed are washed into the local rivers, bringing the day when the dam's reservoir simply silts up inexorably closer and closer, eventually rendering the dam inoperable. Already, the debris in Balbina's reservoir regularly clogs the dam's turbines,

while, in China, the Laoying dam suffered such high rates of sedimentation (qv) that the dam's reservoir silted up before a single megawatt was produced.

Proponents of dams now acknowledge that considerable ecological and social damage has resulted from the construction of dams, but insist that the "mistakes" of the past have been learnt and will be corrected in the future. However, there are few grounds to accept such assurances. First, in most Third World countries, the agencies charged with environmental protection and with overseeing the resettlement of displaced peoples lack either the resources or the commitment to implement mitigating measures. Brazil is a case in point, a World Bank staff appraisal report commenting that the Brazilian electricity utilities pay "only rhetorical attention at higher managerial levels to sociological and environmental variables as reflected in some of the projects at present under construction." An animal rescue operation to save flora and fauna from the floodwaters of the Balbina dam, for example, quickly ran out of money and was described by one biologist as "a façade". Scarcely any of the 2,346sq km (905sq miles) of forest in the reservoir

area was cleared before flooding, this despite the experience of the Tucurui dam, where the drowning of uncleared forest led to massive eutrophication (qv) as the vegetation and trees rotted down beneath the floodwater, the resulting deoxygenation killing thousands of fish and poisoning the water supplies.

Secondly, it is extremely questionable whether any measures can ever reduce the full social and ecological impacts of large dams to an acceptable level, particularly in the tropics. No measures can ever undo the damage done to traditional cultures by resettlement. No animal rescue scheme can conceivably "mitigate" the loss of a belt of pristine tropical forest, where a single hectare may contain up to 400 trees, every other one a different species-diversity that can never be reconstituted, let alone be fully compensated for, by a reforestation programme. No measures can safeguard against the inevitable invasion of waterborne diseases. And no measures can forestall the impact of reduced silt loads on aquatic life downstream. (See also: *Development*③, *Environmental refugees*③Ⓛ, *Irrigation*Ⓐ③, *Mekong River Project, Resettlement* ③, *Salinization*Ⓐ, *Tehri Dam Waterborne diseases*③.)

DDT

Known technically as p,p'-dichlorodiphenyltrichloroethane, DDT was one of the most widely used pesticides (qv) in the world. First synthesized in the 19th century, DDT was introduced into US agriculture on a wide scale in the 1930s. Since then it has been used in many other fields throughout the world, notably against malaria.

DDT is highly persistent in the environment. The bioconcentration (qv) of DDT has led to the thinning of egg-shells in many bird species and the consequent failure to reproduce. The most famous examples are the osprey, the peregrine falcon and the bald-headed eagle, symbol of the USA. In 1945, Dr V.B.Wigglesworth of the British Agriculture Research Council, described DDT as "a blunderbuss discharging shot in a manner so haphazard that friend and foe alike are killed."

Research in the 1960s revealed DDT to be a potent carcinogen (qv). As a result, DDT was banned in the USA in 1971 – but only after an intense court battle with the major producers. It has also been banned in Germany, France and many other industrialized countries. In Britain, use of DDT was subject to a voluntary ban from 1974 to 1984, when it was finally withdrawn from the market. There is evidence, however, that it is still widely available on the black market.

Despite the ban on its use in most industrialized countries, exports to the Third World continue unabated – though Kenya has announced its intention to ban DDT altogether. It seems clear that many companies see the Third World as a dump for unused stocks of DDT. High levels of DDT have been found in the milk of many nursing mothers. (See also: *Cancer* ①⑫, *Circle of poison*③③, *Malaria*①③.)

Debt-for-nature swaps

Agreements under which Third World debts are effectively written off in exchange for commitments by the debtor country to undertake projects that protect the environment. As such, debt-for-nature deals are seen as a means of both relieving the Third World's debt burden and promoting conservation.

The first ever debt-for-nature swap occurred in 1987 when the US environmental group, Conservation International, bought $650,000 worth of Bolivia's debt from Citicorp Bank at a discounted price of $100,000. The debt was then "swapped" in exchange for the Bolivian government undertaking to set aside 9 million hectares (3,700,000 acres) of rainforest in an area adjacent to the existing Beni Biosphere Reserve in Amazonia. In addition, the Bolivian government agreed to set up a $250,000 trust in local currency to finance the administration of the new reserve, which has been granted Congressional Law Status, the highest legal protection afforded under Bolivian law. The land is still owned by the Bolivian government, or, where title deeds have been recognized, by the local Chimane Indians.

Several other debt swaps have now been carried out by conservation groups, notably the World Wide Fund for Nature. Participating countries include Costa Rica, Ecuador and the Philippines. Altogether some $95 million of debts have been "retired" through such projects.

However, if debt-for-nature deals are to make a significant impact on the problem of Third World Debt (qv), it is clear that they will have to be carried out at government level. Several initiatives have thus been proposed, aimed at securing an international agreement to relieve a sizeable proportion of the Third World's debt in exchange for protecting the environment. It has also been suggested that such debt relief should be accompanied by an annual sum paid by Northern countries to the Third World to safeguard such global assets as tropical rainforests. In June 1991, Brazil agreed in principle to debt-for-nature swaps worth up to $100 million per year.

Debt-for-nature deals are not without their critics. Many environmental groups argue that much of the Third World debt is "illegitimate", having been incurred by unrepresentative regimes for the benefit of a small elite. Such "immoral loans", it is argued, should be repudiated outright, rather than bargained away. It is also argued that debt-swaps which involve payments being made in local currency (as was the case in the Conservation Foundation's deal with Bolivia) are inflationary, since the debtor countries simply print more currency to meet the notes. Effectively, environmental groups are paying hard currency to banks and commercial institutions in order to persuade the governments of poor countries to protect their environments by transferring resources from other sectors of their economies. The money from the environmental groups, it is argued, might be more effectively employed in direct funding. Another objection is that if debt-swaps involve land traditionally used by tribal peoples, they may seriously prejudice the territorial claims of those groups seeking to establish their land rights. Finally, debt-swaps do not in themselves address the deficiencies of current development (qv) models, the fear being that they will effectively unleash a new wave of destruction by removing the constraints of debt. (See also: *Tropical rainforests.*)

Debt crisis See: *Third World debt.*

Decay products See: *Conversion products*①⑫, *Radioactivity*①⑫.

Decommissioning

Term used to describe the dismantling and disposal of old nuclear reactors. To date, experience of decommissioning is limited. In 1989, the 990-ton pressure vessel of the world's first pressurized water reactor (PWR) (qv) at Shippingport in the USA was buried in a waste dump virtually intact. However, this 72MW reactor presented far fewer technical problems than a full-scale power station. In Britain, work is continuing on dismantling the small prototype advanced gas-cooled reactor (AGR) (qv) at Sellafield (qv). It is intended to decommission all UK commercial reactors in three stages, the last of which may be delayed for 100 years and would involve cutting up the reactor pressure vessel by remote control, possibly under water. Britain's oldest Magnox (*qv*) station at Berkeley, in Gloucestershire, was closed for decommissioning in 1989: by the turn of the century decommissioning could have begun at eight further stations.

Decommissioning of commercial reactors will involve large volumes of radioactive wastes (see *Nuclear waste*) (but no high-level wastes) and considerable costs, officially estimated at $480 million for the Sizewell D PWR, or 20 per cent of its capital cost. However, the Washington-based Worldwatch Institute calculates that decommissioning will cost about $1 million a megawatt. This would work out at 40 per cent of the capital costs of a PWR.

The costs of decommissioning have not always been fully taken into account when estimating the total costs of operating reactors, nor sufficient funds set aside for financing decommissioning. In Britain, for example, the application of the government-determined discount rate gives a small present value to costs that are incurred far into the future. Thus most of the costs of decommissioning, like reprocessing (*qv*) and long-term fuel cycle costs, will have to be met by future generations. In 1989, it was revealed that the cost of decommissioning Britain's Magnox reactors alone could reach $5,400 million. The UK's Nuclear Electric has since announced a change of tack on decommissioning. Under its latest proposals, after removing the fuel, the station buildings would be left under a concrete shell for up to 130 years and then possibly turned into large artificial hills. The policy would save the company money but leave dozens of nuclear waste dumps dotted around the countryside. This approach contrasts strongly with the demands of regulatory bodies in other countries, notably the USA, where complete decommissioning within 60 years is required.

Deep ecology

A movement inspired by the Norwegian philosopher Arne Naess, who was the first to use the expression. His ideas have been further developed by Bill Devall, Georg Sessions, Warwick Fox and others.

The movement arose as a reaction both to the academic ecology taught in universities and the environmentalism of the ecological movement, neither of which questions the "dominant metaphysics" underlying our modern industrial society. Both attitudes have been classified as "shallow ecology".

Warwick Fox sees "deep" and "shallow" ecology as differing in three main respects. The first is that shallow ecology views humans as separate from their environment, and favours environmental preservation only because it is ultimately in the human interest. By contrast, deep ecology sees human beings as part of nature, indeed, in Fox's words, as "just one particular strand in the web of life" or "just one kind of knot in the biospheric net."

Secondly, deep ecology rejects the "mechanical materialism" that characterizes the industrial worldview and reflects outdated 19th-century notions of physics. Instead, deep ecology sees the world, as does the physicist David Bohm, as "unbroken wholeness" which denies the classical idea of the analysability of the world into separately and independently existing parts." Significantly, this "unified field" view of the new physics is also, as Fox notes, that of eastern mysticism.

Thirdly, shallow ecology accepts, at least by default, the dominant ideology of economic growth. Its adherents are therefore seen as willing, in Fox's words "to accept the reduction of all values to economic terms for the purposes of decision making." Deep ecologists, however, see economic considerations as firmly subordinate to ecological ones.

The movement undoubtedly represents a serious attempt to free environmental and ecological thinking from the fetters of the "dominant metaphysics" – that of

our industrial society – within which they are, indeed, still largely imprisoned. (See also: *Conservation*ⓕ, *Ecological movement*ⓛ, *Green politics*ⓛ, *Holism*ⓕ.)

Deforestation

Trees are essential to the ecological wellbeing of the Earth. They clean the air, conserve the soil, maintain its fertility, store water, provide a habitat for wildlife and play a vital role in regulating the climate. In addition, they provide a source of fodder for animals, and food fruits, fibres, firewood and timber.

Today, the world's forests – both temperate and tropical are under siege. In the industrial world, trees are increasingly falling victim to disease and the insidious effects of air pollution – most notably acid rain (*qv*). In the tropics, the threat is more direct – hundreds of thousands of square kilometres of forest being cut down, flooded or burned each year as forests are felled for timber, cleared for agriculture, or converted into reservoirs through the damming of rivers.

Since the turn of the century, the Third World has lost nearly half of its forests. The United Nations Food and Agriculture Organization estimates that the current rate of deforestation is 168,000sq km (105,000sq miles) of forest every year. During the 1980s, Brazil lost 2 per cent of its forests per year, India 4 per cent and Costa Rica 7.6 per cent.

Poverty, overpopulation and ignorance are commonly held to be the principal causes of deforestation. In support of that view, the UN Food and Agriculture Organization (FAO) (*qv*) points to the damage done by the 250 million peasant colonists who have moved into the forest in search of land. Describing their "slash-and-burn" (*qv*) methods of cultivation as "environmentally destructive" and "inefficient", FAO accuses these "encroaching cultivators" (*qv*) of being the prime agents of forest destruction, destroying 50,000sq km (19,000sq miles) of forest a year and degrading a further ten million.

The charge is grossly misleading. First, blaming encroaching cultivators for deforestation obscures the massive damage caused by plantation, ranching, road, and logging operations and dam projects. In peninsular Malaysia, where encroaching cultivators are few and far between, the logging industry has destroyed half the country's rainforests since 1960. In Ethiopia, massive plantations have stripped the Awash Valley of its forests, 60 per cent of the land now being under cotton with another 22 per cent devoted to sugar plantations. In central America, cattle ranching is responsible for the clearance of almost two-thirds of the forests. In Brazil, official government figures reveal that 60 per cent of forest destruction between 1966 and 1975 was caused by large-scale cattle ranching projects (38,650 sq km/15,000 sq miles) and road building (3,075 sq km/1,190 sq miles). Less than 17.6 per cent was lost to state colonization projects.

Secondly, the problem of encroaching cultivation is itself the direct result of policies intended to open up the forest to development. In Indonesia, more than 3,600,000 peasants have already been moved into the densely forested outer islands of the archipelago as part of the country's transmigration programme (qv). More than 33,000 sq km (12,700 sq miles) of rainforest are at risk from the project. In Amazonia (qv) thousands of colonists have been sent into the jungle. Every road built brings settlers who spread out into the forest, every dam brings new settlements on the shores of its reservoirs, every mining project attracts scores of migrant workers.

Thirdly, the issue of encroaching cultivation cannot be separated from the problem of landlessness in the Third World. At present, land holdings are concentrated in the hands of very few people – 93 per cent of arable lands in Latin America being held by a mere seven per cent of land owners. Much of that land is used for plantation agriculture or ranching – thus denying its use to

landless farmers. In the absence of land reforms, those farmers then have little choice but to invade the forests. Almost all those peasants who have invaded Rondonia in Amazonia have done so because their lands in the State of Rio Grande do Sul have been taken over by export-orientated plantations and ranches.

Undoubtedly encroaching cultivators do cause extensive forest destruction, but to blame them for the deforestation is quite unjustified.

In destroying their forests, the countries of the Third World are following a trail already blazed by the industrialized world. Prior to European settlement, North America had an estimated 3,200,000 sq km (1,235,000 sq miles) of forest. By 1930, less than 400,000 sq km (154,000 sq miles) were left – today, the figure is down to 220,000 sq km (85,000 sq miles).

But while the forests of the world's temperate areas can be stripped with relative impunity, the effects of deforestation in the tropics are environmentally disastrous.

Stripped of its forest cover, the land rapidly succumbs to erosion (qv), leading to the silting up of rivers and the loss of fertility. Eventually, if the land is not reforested (see *Reforestation*) it becomes victim to desertification (qv). Meanwhile, because the forests are no longer available to soak up rain and store it in the soil, a drought-flood cycle (qv) is initiated, with streams and rivers drying up during the hot, dry season only to become raging torrents during the wet. The loss of biological diversity as a result of deforestation is also a cause for increasing alarm.

The Washington-based World Resources Institute, together with the World Bank (qv), the United Nations Development Programme, and the UN Food and Agriculture Organization, have launched a Tropical Forest Action Plan (qv) to combat deforestation. But the plan has been rigorously rejected by Third World environment groups and indigenous rights groups, who argue that it fails to tackle the root causes of defore

station and that its accent on promoting commercial forestry would exacerbate the crisis. Indeed, many environmental groups in the Third World now argue that there is no solution to the problem of deforestation as long as Third World countries remain within the market economy. They urge "delinking" as the solution to the problem. (See also: *Acid Rain* Ⓟ, *Development*③, *Greenhouse effect*Ⓟ③, *Sedimentation*Ⓛ③, *Tropical forests*③, *Tropical Forestry Action Plan* ③.)

Delaney Amendment

The Delaney Amendment, enacted as a US federal law on September 6 1958, prohibits the intentional use of any carcinogenic (see *Carcinogen*) chemical as a food additive under any condition. This was based on the principle that, as was stated at Congressional hearings in 1960, "scientifically, there is no way to determine a safe level for a substance known to produce cancer in animals."

The amendment has come under concerted attack ever since its enactment. Most of the criticisms have been levelled by industrial groups, trade associations and their consultants. The argument has hinged mainly on the scientific methodology of testing for the toxicity of chemicals. The anti-Delaney lobby argue that it is possible to establish a threshold dose below which exposure to a chemical is safe. They also argue that chemicals can be made to appear carcinogenic by, for example, testing at higher doses, thus calling into question the value of carcinogenicity tests in general. However, it is quite clear that the scientific basis of the Delaney Amendment was, and remains, totally valid. To date, it is scientifically impossible to determine a safe level of exposure to carcinogenic chemicals, let alone predict any synergism (see *Synergy*) between a carcinogen and another chemical. This was the message of an ad hoc committee report submitted to the Surgeon General on April 22 1970.

Despite these attacks, the Delaney Amendment remains in

force today and is the main legal plank protecting the American citizen from food adulterated with carcinogenic chemicals. However, the US Food and Drug Administration is currently trying to change the amendment to permit the addition of carcinogenic food additives at levels described to be "devoid of significant risk." (See also: *Additives*Ⓛ, *Cancer*Ⓛ.)

Demographic transition

The theory that the rate of the population growth (though not overall numbers) slows down and eventually declines as material standards of living rise. It is based on population trends in Europe following the industrial revolution. Population levels that initially escalated later slowed down. Now several industrialized countries have reached, or are approaching, "zero" growth rates.

The same demographic transition, it is confidently asserted, will also now occur in the Third World as development proceeds, first through family planning (*qv*) and, secondly, by providing people with financial security that will supposedly reduce their desire to have so many children.

There are two flaws to the theory. First, it is conveniently forgotten that a growing population is not intolerable as such, only because of its impact on the natural environment. That impact, however, is not simply a function of the number of people in the world but also of their level of material consumption. To reduce the rate of population growth by increasing material consumption is thereby self defeating, since the impact on the environment is likely to increase.

Secondly, the theory claims that people have more children because they are financially insecure. But although the rate of population growth in the West has indeed fallen with rising affluence, this does not mean that it will necessarily do the same in the Third World. On the contrary, recent research in Brazil, Colombia and Mexico shows that where fertility rates have declined, the reduction not only occurred during periods of econo

mic depression, but among poor, rather than rich, communities. Indeed, to blame the population explosion (*qv*) on financial insecurity is to misinterpret the root cause of the problem. While economic development certainly reduces financial insecurity for a few, it increases social insecurity for the mass of people by breaking down traditional cultural patterns and thus destroying the traditional community and the extended family, by uprooting tribal peoples and peasants from their land to accommodate large export-oriented farms and other development projects, and by degrading the physical environment. The result is increasing social alienation and it is this alienation, not financial insecurity, that encourages people to have more rather than less children. Lester Brown, Director of the Worldwatch Institute, considers that though the demographic transition may have marked "the advance of all developed countries", in the Third World it "may be reversed for the first time in modern history." (See also: *Population*③, *Population explosion*③.)

Desalinization

The process by which drinking water is obtained from seawater or other sources of water containing high salt levels. The simplest process involves evaporating the water and condensing the vapour produced, the dissolved salts being left behind in the evaporation vessel. Large amounts of heat are required for this process and it is practised on a large scale only in the oil-rich desert countries where cheap energy is available. Desalinization programmes based on nuclear reactors have been suggested, but none is currently operating. A newer process, called reverse osmosis, has been developed in which a membrane separates the water from the dissolved salts. It, too, is expensive. The most promising means for desalinization under development is the solar-powered still.

In the USA, drainage water from large-scale irrigation schemes has raised the salinity of the Colorado

River to such levels that a massive desalinization plant has had to be built at Yuma on the US-Mexico border to reduce salinity levels before the river crosses into Mexico. Under an international treaty, the US guarantees to protect the quality of the Colorado's water. (See also: *Irrigation*Ⓐ, *Salinization*Ⓐ.)

Desertification

Final stage in a slow and insidious process of land degradation, which starts with the loss of vegetative cover and ends with the destruction of the soil's fertility and its transformation into barren desert. The most vulnerable soils are to be found in the dry tropics.

According to the Worldwatch Institute: "Every year, irreversible desertification claims an estimated 6 million hectares (14,800,000 acres) worldwide – a land area nearly twice the size of Belgium lost beyond practical hope of reclamation. An additional 20 million hectares (50 million acres) annually become so impoverished that they are unprofitable to farm or graze". The United Nations Environment Programme estimates that 30 per cent of the world's land surface is threatened with desertification – and that 75 per cent of this total (some 3,300 million hectares or 8,000 million acres) is already moderately degraded. Fully one-third of this land, reports Worldwatch, has "already lost more than 25 per cent of its productive potential". The livelihoods of one-fifth of humanity are at risk.

Nomadic pastoralism (*qv*) and traditional peasant agricultures are frequently, but quite unjustifiably, blamed as the principal "cause" of desertification. In fact, traditional farming systems place minimum pressure on the land. By contrast, modern mechanized farming and the introduction of vast livestock rearing projects have led to overgrazing and unsustainable agriculture. The problem has been compounded by the pushing of peasants onto more and more marginal lands.

Significantly, the 1977 UN Conference on Desertification concluded that nomadic pastoralism represented the only sustainable method of husbandry in the fragile lands bordering the Sahara.

Following the conference, UNEP was charged with implementing an action plan on desertification. The plan has yielded minimal results, most of its projects being directed at monitoring the extent of desertification rather than combating its spread. Political indifference has also dogged the project, with governments from both the Third World and the industrialized world refusing to provide more than a fraction of the funds required. (See also: *Cash crop*Ⓐ③, *Deforestation*ⒶⒸ③, *Erosion*ⒸⒸ③, *Nomadic Pastoralism*③, *Overgrazing*Ⓐ③, *Salinization*ⒶⒸ③.)

Development

It is generally believed that poverty and malnutrition in the Third World can be combated only by economic development – hence the subordination, during the last 40 years, of all other considerations to the achievement of this goal.

Economic development has certainly led to the emergence of a middle class consisting largely of government officials, but also of traders and manufacturers, some of whom enjoy considerable affluence. But that class represents only a fraction of the total population of the Third World. And specific policies designed to encourage economic development have caused increasingly serious social and ecological problems that have undoubtedly worsened the plight of most Third World people.

Even the institutions that have spearheaded development (such as the World Bank, the UN Food and Agriculture Organization and USAID) admit that their policies have been a failure and propose to replace them with more sensitive types of development that have been variously called "rural development", "appropriate development", "ecodevelopment", "alternative development", "integrated development", and "sustainable development". Unfortunately, none of these has been adequately defined, still less applied. Indeed, the accent is still on precisely the same sort of vast capital-intensive projects – such as large water development projects, livestock-rearing programmes, vast plantations, etc – that are known to have caused the current problems. These policies seem best to satisfy the short-term political and economic requirements of those who formulate them.

This becomes still clearer if we consider that the policies that go under the name of development are very similar to, indeed scarcely distinguishable from, those that were pursued under the aegis of the colonial system.

The prime object of colonialism was to obtain access to cheap raw materials, cheap labour and a captive market for Europe's manufactured goods. Cecil Rhodes expressed it clearly. "We must find new lands," he wrote, "from which we can easily obtain raw materials and at the same time exploit the cheap slave labour that is available from the natives of the colonies. The colonies would also provide a dumping ground for the surplus goods produced in our factories."

The economic development of the Third World achieves precisely the same goals. It consists in bringing Third World countries within the orbit of international trade by influencing them to eliminate subsistence agriculture and artisan modes of production catering for a largely local market and to replace them with capital-intensive plantations and factories geared to the international market.

If development has caused so many problems in the Third World it is for the following principal reasons.

1. Development inevitably causes a population explosion by destroying culturally in-built population-control strategies. It also leads to the inevitable displacement of tribal peoples and peasants from their traditional lands to accommodate various development projects, and to the destruction of their highly cohesive social groupings. The resulting social alienation encourages people to have more children for the security in old age with which such children may eventually provide them.

2. Development encourages the import of manufactured goods. This has the effect of putting local artisans out of business. Many of them are forced into urban slums.

In addition, all imported goods must eventually be paid for. Third World countries cannot do so from the sale of expensive high-technology devices as do most of the industrial countries of the West. They can do so only by selling the produce of their soil.

3. Historically this has entailed, first, the selling of their trees, if they have them. Indeed, development of such countries as Indonesia and Malaysia has been financed largely from the sale of tropical hardwoods, with disastrous ecological consequences. The deforestation (*qv*) involved has contributed significantly to the present escalation of malnutrition and famine.

Once the forests have gone, Third World countries must resort to selling cash crops, such as sugar, tea, coffee, jute, cotton, rubber and tobacco, as well as tropical fruits and vegetables. The large-scale mechanized cultivation of such crops on vulnerable tropical soils can only lead to erosion and desertification (*qv*). It also means vast livestock-rearing projects which are equally destructive to the soil.

In Third World countries, every square metre of land made available for producing export crops is a square metre of land made unavailable for feeding local people. And when local people are already undernourished, as is increasingly so throughout the Third World, the export of agricultural produce is only possible at the cost of increasing malnutrition (*qv*) and famine (*qv*).

Setting up vast enterprises geared to the export trade also means displacing those who previously derived their livelihood from the land. This has occurred on a massive scale, since in many countries as much as 50 per cent of the agricultural land is used for export crops. This gives rise to rural poverty and to vast slums to which the environmental refugees (qv) inevitably gravitate.

Tribal peoples and peasants are also displaced to accommodate the physical infrastructure of the growing conurbations and their industrial base. Still more agricultural land must therefore be diverted from feeding rural people, who are forced off the land and into the cities. The vast slums of the Third World can be seen as the necessary concomitants of economic development.

There is now increasing pressure on Third World countries to maximize foreign exchange earnings in order to pay interest on the massive debts they have contracted – partly, at least, to pay for uneconomic development projects such as large dams. As a result, the development process has been stepped up, with social and ecological considerations increasingly being subordinated to that overall goal.

Ironically, all this misery may well be in vain. The Third World cannot conceivably attain the sort of affluence that we know today in the industrial world. Neither its vulnerable and, indeed, fast deteriorating soils, nor the adverse climatic conditions of tropical areas, render feasible the agricultural surplus required to finance development. Nor are world economic conditions today anything like as favourable to economic development as they were when Western countries first developed. In the next decades, de-development rather than development may well be the rule.

Since the mid-1970s, when the disproportionate and increasing poverty of women and children was first recognized by researchers, the international development agencies have gradually taken up the catch-cry of "integrating women into development". The rationale is that if women could be made central to development programmes, the benefits supposedly accruing to men in the Third World would flow to women also. Rarely was the possibility raised that the "feminization of poverty" was a direct result of the development process

itself, despite overwhelming evidence of increased poverty among women in industrialized countries.

Drawing women further into the formal economy, which is the main thrust of the solutions offered, appears to have more benefits for international financiers and entrepreneurs than it does for women. Production of goods for an external market by women may provide a small amount of cash for purchasing other manufactured goods, but often at the cost of control over what women produce, for whom it is produced and at what price. In addition, the time available for family subsistence production and care is reduced. In some instances, the cash can provide some independence from a male-dominated culture. Too often, however, one form of control is replaced by another.

For these and other associated reasons, the very principle of development as a panacea to the problems of the Third World should be seriously questioned. (See also: *Aid*③, *Cash crops*③, *Dams*③, *Demographic transition*Ⓐ③, *Hamburger connection*Ⓐ③, *Population explosion*③, *Third World debt*③, *Tropical agriculture*Ⓐ③.)

Dichlorvos

An organophosphorus insecticide, also known as DDVP, used as a liquid in agriculture and in salmon fish-farming to control sea lice, but more familiarly as the active ingredient of slow-release fly strips for domestic use. In the USA such strips are marketed under the brand name "The No Pest Strip", and in Britain as Vapona.

Dichlorvos is a toxic material that affects the nervous system. As an organophosphate, very small quantities can badly affect sensitive people. It has been found to be carcinogenic in mice and this suggests that it may also cause cancer. American researchers suggest that women of child-bearing age should handle dichlorvos with caution, if at all. Its adverse effects on wildlife, particularly bees, game and birds,

are well documented. (See also: *Cancer*Ⓛ③, *Carcinogen*©③, *Insecticides*③, *Organophosphates*③, *Pesticides*Ⓛ③.)

Dieldrin

A highly toxic insecticide that has caused serious harm to wildlife in many parts of the world. It has been used in agriculture against a wide variety of insect pests, around the home to kill moths, and in the garden to destroy unwanted insects. Carpets are sometimes impregnated with dieldrin to protect them from moth attack, and it has been widely used as a timber treatment to protect wood against woodworm, death watch beetle and other insect pests.

Like other chlorinated hydrocarbons (qv) dieldrin is persistent in the environment and accumulates in food chains. Dieldrin pollution is known to have played a major role in the decline of the British otter, now extinct in England and Wales. The decline of the Sandwich tern population of the Dutch Wadden Sea – the number of breeding pairs fell from more than 40,000 in the 1940s to just 1,500 in 1964 – was also blamed on pollution by dieldrin and closely related compounds, endrin (qv) and telodrin.

Studies conducted in the USA as early as 1962 showed dieldrin to be carcinogenic (see *Carcinogen*) in mice. Seven years later, the newly-formed Environmental Protection Agency proposed that the use of dieldrin, together with aldrin, an insecticide that is converted to dieldrin in the environment, be severely restricted. Dieldrin and aldrin were banned for most uses in the USA in 1976.

In Europe, the regulation of dieldrin and aldrin has varied considerably from country to country. In Britain, the Pesticide Advisory Committee concluded that a ban was unnecessary, though it did recommend voluntary restrictions on use. The same data led the French Government to impose a ban in 1972. In Germany, on the other hand, the authorities decided that it was enough to restrict the use of the two insecticides, restrictions first being imposed in 1971 and then being strengthened in 1974 and 1979. In 1981 the European Community banned the marketing of aldrin and dieldrin in plant protection products. Even so, exports are still permitted. In 1985, clearance for the use of dieldrin in wood preservation was withdrawn in Britain. The sale of all products containing dieldrin was finally banned in 1989.

Collectively, dieldrin, aldrin, endrin and telodrin are known as the "drins".

In the Third World, where restrictions are less effective (and sometimes non-existent), dieldrin and the other drins are still widely used. In 1983 it was estimated that 99 per cent of the drins manufactured in the industrialized countries were exported, mostly to the Third World. That would have amounted to almost 5,000 tonnes. (See also: *Aldrin* ⓁⓅ, *Cancer*Ⓛ, *Circle of poison*Ⓟ, *Insecticides*Ⓟ, *Pesticides*Ⓟ.)

Diethylstilbesterol (DES)
Synthetic hormone, commonly known as DES, which until the mid-1970s was widely prescribed to pregnant women to prevent the occurrence of miscarriages.

First developed in 1938, DES was banned in the USA in 1971 after high rates of a rare vaginal cancer were found among a number of the daughters of those who had taken the drug during pregnancy. Sons born to women who had taken DES are reported to be more prone to infertility, while the women themselves suffer higher-than-normal cancer rates. In the USA alone, between four million and six million women and children were exposed to DES during pregnancy.

The reputation of DES as a drug that prevented miscarriage had little factual basis. According to Valerie Miké of the New York Hospital, Cornell Medical Center, "Of the six clinical trials carried out in the early 1950s with concurrent controls, not one found DES to be effective in preventing miscarriages."

Many hundreds of thousands of people have also been exposed to DES through its use as a growth promoter in livestock. Studies from Italy and Puerto Rico have incriminated DES residues in meat as a cause of premature sexual development of children.

In the USA, the use of DES in agriculture was finally banned in 1979, after a protracted legal and political battle dating back to the late 1950s. In Europe, the EC imposed a ban in 1981, though DES had been outlawed in many member states many years previously. The ban was vigorously opposed by Britain. (See also: *Cancer*Ⓛ, *Carcinogen*ⒻⓁ, *Hormones in meat* ⒶⓁⓅ.)

Dilution and dispersal
A philosophy that is fundamental to pollution control policies in most industrialized countries. Based on the assumption that, once in the environment, pollutants will be diluted and dispersed to harmless levels, it has been used to justify the dumping of wastes at sea, the discharge of wastes to rivers, and the emission of air pollutants via chimney stacks.

Given their vastness, it is easy to assume that the oceans or the atmosphere have an infinite capacity for assimilating pollutants. Time and again, however, pollutants that have been released on the assumption that dilution and dispersal will render them harmless have ended up bioconcentrated (see *Bioconcentration*) within specific species or, as with SO_2 emission, causing damage to ecosystems many thousands of miles away from the point of release – in the form of acid rain (*qv*).

Dioxins
A family of 75 closely related compounds, the most notorious of which is 2,3,7,8-tetrachloro-dibenzo-para-dioxin (or TCDD for short). TCDD has been described as "the most toxic man-made chemical ever produced". It first achieved notoriety as the chemical released during the Seveso (*qv*) accident and as a contaminant of Agent Orange (*qv*). TCDD pollution was also responsible for the evacuation of Times Beach and is now thought to pose a major threat to drinking water supplies in the Niagara Falls, New York, area.

The dioxins have never been manufactured deliberately, having no uses in their own right. Nonetheless, they occur as inevitable contaminants of a number of products and manufacturing processes involving chlorinated phenols. Such products include the phenoxy herbicide 2,4,5-T (*qv*) (which contains TCDD) and 2,4-D (*qv*) which is contaminated by octachlorodibenzo-paradioxin, though this is less toxic than TCDD.

In both France and the USA, buildings have been heavily contaminated by TCDD following fires involving the burning of electrical insulating equipment containing PCBs (*qv*). Dioxins – notably TCDD – have also been produced by the incomplete incineration of chlorinated wastes and domestic rubbish. Crematoria have also been found to release dioxins when plastics in coffins are burned. Recent work has suggested that the burning of gas from waste dumps may produce a dioxin hazard.

Dioxins are a major contaminant of the effluent from wood pulp mills and there has been growing concern over the presence of TCDD in bleached paper products from nappies to coffee filters. The dioxins result from the use of chlorinated compounds to bleach the paper. A typical pulp mill, with a daily production of 1,000 tonnes of bleached pulp, will discharge some 20 to 50 tonnes of chlorinated compounds a day, often causing severe damage to fishlife. Although the quantities of TCDD are small – typically 4 grammes a year – its extreme toxicity means that even this quantity constitutes an environmental and public health threat. After pulping, the dioxins are retained in the wood, samples of which have been found to contain up to 8 grammes of TCDD. As a result, bleached products universally contain small but significant amounts of TCDD: 5 parts per trillion (ppt) in tea bags, 11ppt in coffee filters, 90ppt in lavatory rolls, 90ppt in disposable nappies,

130ppt in tampons, and 400ppt in sanitary towels. A report by the Canadian Government's Food Research Division has concluded that, due to their packaging, food in carton containers could represent a significant source of dioxins to the human body burden. Several companies manufacturing nappies and tampons have now introduced a range of unbleached alternatives.

The health effects of the dioxins – particularly TCDD – are highly controversial. In 1984, the Carcinogen Assessment Group of the US Environmental Protection Agency (EPA) reviewed the published data on the health effects of TCDD and concluded that it was the "most potent animal carcinogen" it had ever evaluated. The agency estimated that TCDD was 50 times more carcinogenic (qv) than such well-established carcinogens as vinyl chloride.

Industry does not dispute that TCDD is carcinogenic in animal tests, but disputes that it is harmful to humans in low doses – insisting that its worst effect is a severe skin disease known as chloracne.

That view is contradicted by several major epidemiological studies, which show TCDD to be a cause of cancer, birth defects and other adverse health effects. According to the EPA, TCDD should be regarded as "probably carcinogenic in humans". Significantly, many experts now consider that there is no "safe" level of exposure to TCDD. (See also: Cancer①, Incineration℗.)

Diseases of civilization

Term currently used to denote a constellation of diseases whose incidence seems to increase with per capita economic growth. Included in this category are most forms of cancer (qv), coronary heart disease (qv), diabetes, tooth caries, peptic ulcer, appendicitis and diverticulitis (a disease of the bowel).

Though the incidence of these diseases seems to vary in different countries in direct proportion to per capita GNP, in the rich industrial countries it is generally highest among those on low incomes.

Many factors help to explain the association between the diseases of civilization and economic development. The principal factors would appear to be increased stress; increased exposure to chemicals and radiation (see *Radiation and health*); and the dramatic changes in diet that occur as society adopts a modern way of life, with natural, uncontaminated high-fibre wholefoods giving way to refined, processed foods that are often devitalized and contaminated with agricultural chemicals and food additives (qv).

The role played by diet and lifestyle as causes of the diseases of civilization has been stressed in numerous studies. One of the first to make the connection was a naval doctor, Surgeon Captain Cleave, who found that the diseases afflicting the industrialized world were largely absent among Africans living on traditional diets, but were present among Africans fed on a modern diet. Research carried out by D.P. Burkett (discoverer of Burkett's lymphoma), also in Africa, confirmed this thesis, as did that of Sir Robert McCarrison in India.

More recently, Dr. Albert Darmon of the Peabody Museum at Harvard University has established that the diseases of civilization are largely absent among Solomon Islanders, who still lead a traditional lifestyle.

Dr. Ian Prior of Victoria University in New Zealand has also shown this to be true of the inhabitants of Puka Puka, an isolated island of the Cook group, though the diseases of civilization were much more in evidence on the nearby island of Rarotonga, which has undergone considerable modernization.

Prior's highly documented 30-year study of the health of the Tokelau Islanders also reveals that the diseases of civilization are largely absent among islanders who remain on isolated atolls, but develop very rapidly among those who migrate to New Zealand, where they are exposed to a modern diet and a way of life with higher stress.

If the poor in the industrial countries have a higher incidence of the diseases of civilization than the better off, as has been shown to be true in repeated studies in the UK, then, as Dr. Richard Wilkinson of Sussex University points out, this can be largely attributed to the tendency of the poor to eat cheap, devitalized, processed foods and to their very low consumption of fresh fruit and vegetables. Though this thesis is becoming increasingly accepted, efforts to improve the diet of the poor in the industrial world have failed, largely because of commercial pressures.

In general, it would seem that the diseases of civilization are inextricably linked with our modern way of life and to combat them effectively would require socio-economic change. (See also: Cancer①, Junk food①, Development③.)

Division of labour

The rise of modern industrial society has dramatically changed traditional patterns of production and has instituted a division of labour based not only on class but also race and sex. With this division of labour has come a labour hierarchy, each level of which confers different employment conditions, wages, benefits, status, opportunity and environmental hazards.

At the international level, workers of industrialized countries are divided from workers of non-industrialized countries. Labour forces are "exported" and "imported" by industrialized countries according to the dictates of national economies. In 1980 it was estimated that there were at least 20 million migrant workers in the world and more than half of these were from developing countries. These workers generally do the dirtiest and most dangerous "unskilled" jobs for the lowest remuneration. As in the past, this division of labour has strong racist underpinnings.

Additionally, industries relocate to countries where wages are low and employment and safety regulations few. Fragmentation of production process and improved transport and communication facilities have allowed companies to site the labour-intensive sides of their industries in poor countries. Over 70 per cent of employees in the special export production zones that have been set up in many Third World countries are young women between the ages of 14 and 24. Women's wages in these factories are up to 50 per cent lower than men's wages for comparable work.

The sexual division of labour, which creates a division between the women and men within any other grouping, is exploited by managers and owners. In industrialized countries, the sexual division of labour has degenerated into a conceptual division between conscious, planned, productive tasks (men's work) and "natural", intuitive, unproductive and unskilled tasks (women's work). Hence the justification for the otherwise indefensible wage differences between predominantly women's occupations (such as nursing, childcare and housework) and men's occupations (such as engineering and mechanics). Conveniently forgotten are the long years of training women undergo to acquire "natural" skills, courtesy of their mothers and grandmothers. (See also: *Ecofeminism.*)

Dounreay
Located on the northern coast of Scotland, Dounreay has been the centre of British fast reactor (*qv*) development since 1954. The first experimental reactor started up in 1959 and operated until 1981, and the larger 250MW prototype fast reactor was ordered in 1966 and began operating in 1974. Development to commercial-sized reactors has been much more difficult than first envisioned, despite the large amounts of money spent. Indeed, the UK Atomic Energy Authority has estimated that another 20 to 25 years' work, and £1,300 ($2,080) million (exclusive of £2,000 ($3,200) million construction costs), will be needed before a commercial station is feasible.

Worried by mounting costs, the UK Government announced in 1988 that it was to cut funding for fast reactor research to one-tenth

of its previous levels. The era of fast reactor research at Dounreay will thus end with the decommissioning of the present prototype in 1994. However, the site has been singled out as a possible location for a nuclear waste dump, and after a public enquiry the government gave official clearance for a new reprocessing plant.

Drift nets
Of all the technological innovations that have revolutionized the fishing industry over the last few decades, none has had a more profound effect than the monofilament nylon net. Such nets are extremely light, invisible to fish, never rot and relatively cheap. The lightness of monofilament nets allows them to be of staggering size.

Since 1988, more than a thousand Japanese, Korean and Taiwanese boats have been scouring the Pacific Ocean with nets up to 60km (37 miles) long and 15m (50ft) deep. Such intensive fishing almost certainly decimates the stocks of the target fish – principally red squid and albacore tuna. In 1988 alone, boats in the South Pacific took between 20,000 and 40,000 tonnes of tuna, more than twice the recommended catch. But the toll is even heavier on the non-target creatures that blunder into the invisible nets. An estimated 1 million sea birds and 200,000 mammals – particularly dolphins and porpoises – drown in the nets each year. In total, an estimated 41 million sea creatures are killed.

Concerned about the health of their own fisheries, many countries have banned large-scale drift-netting in their waters, and the United Nations has proposed a moratorium on drift-netting from 1992. The Japanese responded by agreeing to suspend fishing in the 1990-91 season, and South Korea and Taiwan are cutting down their fleet. There have also been attempts to enforce a ban in Europe, but they have been blocked at different times by France, Spain and Britain, all concerned about the welfare of their own relatively small drift-

net fleets.

Purse-seining is another fishing method that has been assisted by the new nylon nets. It involves setting a net in a circle round a shoal of fish, and then drawing it together. The system is used in several fisheries, but it is the yellowfin tuna fishery that is particularly contentious. Yellowfin fishermen intentionally set their nets around schools of dolphin, because the tuna swim underneath the dolphins; inevitably large numbers of dolphins die when the nets are pulled in. In 1989, 100,000 dolphins were killed in this way, although the number fell considerably in 1990. (See also: *Fish stocks*©.)

Drinking water
The quality – and availability – of drinking water has become a major issue of environmental concern in both the industrialized world and the Third World. In the North, attention has focused primarily on the threat posed by chemical pollution, while in the South, bacterial contamination and the lack of water are the main issues.

Historically, the main threat to drinking water supplies has been bacterial contamination. In the Third World, particularly in urban areas, the discharge of raw sewage to waterways is the rule rather than the exception – and poses a major health hazard to the local population. In Thailand, less than two per cent of Bangkok's dwellings are connected to the city's sewers, while in Indonesia the sewage from two-thirds of the country's urban population is discharged without any form of treatment. It has been estimated that 75-95 per cent of all the waterborne diseases (*qv*) which affect urban dwellers results from poor sanitation.

In the North, more than a century of public health legislation, together with improved water treatment technology, have greatly reduced the threat of bacterial pollution. Nonetheless, as sewage treatment systems begin to age, pollution incidents have increased. In the Midlands and the north-west of England, some plants are so overloaded that they regularly discharge raw sewage into local rivers via their overflow pipes.

However, the main threat to water quality in industrialized countries undoubtedly stems from chemical pollution; discharges from industry, the run-off of agricultural chemicals, leakages from landfill (qv) sites, and accidental spillages of chemicals have all combined to render many drinking water sources increasingly unfit to drink. In Europe, more than 2,000 different chemical compounds are discharged daily by industry into the Rhine – and many other as yet unidentified chemicals have been detected in the river. The principal discharges include heavy metals, synthetic organic compounds, and radioactive waste. Every litre of drinking water recovered from the Rhine contains about 10 microgrammes of synthetic organic substances – some 90 per cent of which are thought to be harmful. Along many stretches, the river – on which 20 million people rely for their drinking water supplies – is little more than a chemical sewer. Indeed, the water is sometimes so polluted that local authorities have been forced to pipe in drinking water from alternative sources.

In Britain, millions of people are drinking water contaminated with chemical pollutants above international safety limits. The most publicized pollutants are lead (qv), nitrates (qv), aluminium (qv), pesticides and such micropollutants (qv) as trihalomethanes. A survey conducted by Friends of the Earth recently revealed that 298 sources in England breached EC standards. Simazine, a common weedkiller, was detected in 26 sources at up to nearly 13 times the EC standard. In 1989, Britain was taken to the European Court by the European Commission for failing to comply with the commission's drinking water standards for nitrate and lead. Prosecutions are also pending against several other European countries, including Germany.

In the USA, many eastern rivers are so polluted by industrial chemicals that they can no longer possibly serve as sources of drinking water, while the water of other less polluted rivers is treated at immense cost. More than 700 chemicals have been detected in US drinking water, 129 of which are considered dangerous by the US Environmental Protection Agency (EPA). Nonetheless, drinking water is regularly tested for only 14 of these contaminants.

Official figures almost certainly understate the true extent of drinking water contamination in the industrialized world. One reason is that only a minute percentage of the 2,000 or so chemical compounds regularly identified in water are monitored on a regular basis – and many compounds are not even subject to safety standards. The EC's directive on drinking water, for example, covers just 66 pollutants. Moreover, where safety standards have been set, they have frequently been criticized as inadequate. In the USA, for example, the US National Research Council has warned that the safety limit for trihalomethanes (currently 100 microgrammes per litre) is "unsupportable on the basis of risk values" and "should be reduced".

In the Third World, acute water shortages are a daily problem for millions of people. Although such shortages are often attributed solely to droughts, the problem of water scarcity cannot be blamed on climatic factors alone. Ecological degradation – in particular those practices which reduce the capacity of soils to absorb water and which thus reduce the flow of water to streams and rivers during the dry season – is also to blame. So, too, the abstraction of water for use on plantations and by industry deprives many local communities of water for drinking. In India, current plans for industrial and urban expansion (qv) are likely to lead to water requirements exceeding dependable supplies in all states by the turn of the century.

Nor are water shortages likely to be restricted to the Third World. The wasteful consumption of water in the industrialized world is already bringing water shortages in many parts of the south-western United States. In Arizona, for example, considerable areas of agricultural land have been taken out of production due to shortages of irrigation water. In Kansas, 75 per cent of exisiting irrigated cropland is predicted to be taken out of production due to lack of water by the year 2025. (See also: Cancer⊙, Groundwater ℗.)

Drought-flood cycle

In recent years, tropics have been subjected to increasingly severe droughts, alternating with equally devastating floods. Both phenomena have a common cause, environmental degradation, in particular deforestation.

Among the many ecological functions fulfilled by forest is the control of water regimes. Typically, in a well-forested watershed, 95 per cent of the annual rainfall is trapped in the soil by the elaborate sponge-like network of roots that underlies the forest floor. That water is then released slowly over the year, replenishing groundwaters and keeping streams and rivers flowing during the dry season. Recent research in Brazil reveals that forested soils absorb ten times more water than pasture. When the forest is removed, there is no longer any "sponge" to soak up the water: as a result, the rains simply rush down the denuded slopes, straight into the local streams and rivers, as little as five per cent of the rainwater being absorbed in what remains of the soil.

All too often, the consequence is massive flooding. In tropical countries, where monsoon rains are torrential, adequate forest is therefore critical to human welfare. Cherapunji in India, for example, receives 12,000mm of rain a year (London, by contrast, receives a mere 600mm), most of it falling within the few months of the annual monsoon. With the destruction of local oak forests, the bulk of Cherapunji's rainfall now cascades off the Meghalaya Plateau, unleashing floods downstream. As a result of deforestation in India's river catchments, the amount of land now classified as "flood prone" increased from 20 million hectares (50 million acres) in 1971 to 40 million hectares in 1980. By 1984, the figure had reached 60 million hectares. In the Ganges Valley alone, the annual cost of flood damage to crops and other property averages about $1,000 million.

In the densely populated regions of the tropics, flooding generally proves disastrous. According to the independent Commission on International Humanitarian Issues, the number of people affected by flooding trebled between 1960 and 1980, with more than 15 million people suffering flood damage in the late 1970s. All told between 1964 and 1982, floods killed 80,000 people and affected 221 million more. In 1988, Bangladesh had the worst floods in its history, rendering a quarter of its people homeless and placing two-thirds of the country under water. Pakistan saw a million people made homeless through flooding, while 780,000 people were affected in Thailand. In Malaysia, 70,000 people were forced to evacuate their homes.

The obverse of flooding is drought. By diminishing the ability of soils to retain water, deforestation undermines the ecological processes which allow rainfall to percolate into local aquifers, thus recharging local streams and rivers throughout the year. Consequently water sources dry up. The result is the so-called "drought-flood" cycle, with massive floods during the monsoon periods, alternating with devastating droughts during the dry season.

In the Indian state of Maharastra alone, deforestation is largely responsible for the drying up of water supplies in 23,000 villages, an increase of 6,000 villages during the period of the latest five-year plan. In Egypt, deforestation in the Ethiopian Highlands has been held to be responsible for the greatly reduced flow of the Nile, at present the major source of irrigation water, without which Egypt would be unable to feed its burgeoning population. (See also: *Development*③, *Deforestation*©③, *Famine*Ⓐ③.)

Ecofeminism
Ecological community
Ecological movement
Ecological succession
Ecology
Economics and
   ecology
Ecosystem
Electropollution
Emulsifiers
Encroaching
   cultivators
Endrin
Energy
Energy efficiency
E numbers
Environmental
   refugees
Erosion
Eucalyptus
Eutrophication
Export of pollution
Extinction
Exxon Valdez

Ecofeminism

Body of theory that has evolved from a feminist critique of modern industrial society and that seeks to expose male-orientated cultural assumptions that are used to legitimize ecological destruction. A central premise of ecofeminism is that the exploitation of women by men is closely paralleled by "Man's" assumed right to exploit nature. Ecofeminists argue that the one form of exploitation cannot be addressed in isolation from the other.

Ecofeminism, as with feminism, is interpreted differently by different women. For example, in the West Coast region of the USA, ecofeminism is orientated towards the rediscovery and revaluing of women's close association with nature. By contrast, in Europe, Australia and New Zealand, its approach is more firmly rooted in socialist traditions. However, the vast majority of "ecofeminists" – the numerous Third World women seeking to protect their environment by fighting modern development – might well consider such distinctions irrelevant.

Some of the approaches most central to ecofeminism include the deconstruction of patriarchal notions – such as the dualisms between body and mind, and between nature and culture – and the acceptance among many Western theorists of competition, hierarchy and dominance as part of human nature. In deconstructing such premises, ecofeminists are also attempting to reconstruct alternative concepts and relationships between men and women and between humans and nature.

Ecofeminist writers and activists have analysed and criticized a broad range of areas such as Marxist theory, mainstream economics, science and technology, environmental ethics and the history of science and industrialization. Importantly, they have also conducted successful international campaigns on pesticides, toxic wastes, genetic engineering, water and forest conservation, and nuclear weapons. Women constitute well over half the active membership of most environmental organizations.

Despite its solid intellectual foundations and its base of mass activism, ecofeminism has often been linked with, or subsumed under, other schools of thought – such as deep ecology (*qv*) – because it advocates a change in our perception of nature (or "social ecology") and because it opposes hierarchy and domination. Ecofeminism, however, gives a critique of society that is in many ways more fundamental than those of even the most radical schools of ecological thought.

Ecological community
See. *Ecosystem.*

Ecological movement
The ecological movement developed in the United States in the late 19th century. Ecologists distinguished themselves from conservationists and preservationists, with whom they nevertheless had much in common. Their response to the perceived ecological crisis of the times was a more fundamental one. It was our whole attitude to our relationship with the natural world that had to change. Humans were an integral part of nature, and if we destroyed nature then we destroyed ourselves too. It followed that our policies should subordinate humanity's apparent interests to those of nature.

Today, as in the 1890s, ecologists differ from conservationists and environmentalists in that they see the ecological crisis as a fundamentally social one. Setting up national parks and adopting stringent pollution control legislation, they argue, is not enough to solve the ecological crisis; more fundamental changes are required, changes in the way we view our basic relationship with the natural world, changes in the way our society is organized, in its basic social and economic goals. What is required is a new ecological world view – and a new ecological society geared to the maintenance of a stable or "steady state" relationship with the natural world. Such ideas underlie deep ecology (*qv*) and are reflected in the platform of green parties in different European countries. (See also: *Ecology, Green politics.*)

Ecological succession
An important principle of ecology is that ecosystems develop in a series of stages that must occur in the right order – a process referred to as "succession". This continues until a "climax" is reached – a situation from which there is then little change, as it is the most stable achievable in the circumstances.

The idea is an old one. However, in recent years, it has come under attack, the first critic being the biologist Professor Herbert Gleason in the 1920s, though his views were not, at the time, taken seriously. Later, with the development of the New Ecology after World War II, Gleason's views were resuscitated and expanded, and are now generally accepted among academic ecologists.

Modern ecologists have abandoned the old concept of succession for three reasons. First, it implied that an ecosystem was a sort of "superorganism" whose development took the form of a strategy, rather than being the result of random changes, and that this strategy was coordinated by the ecosystem itself. These concepts are irreconcilable with the tenets of modern science, which sees the world as atomized and random. It also implied that the goal of ecological development is the achievement of stability (defined as a state in which discontinuities are minimized) whereas science, in line with our modern industrial society, is committed to perpetual change in a single direction. In the natural world, such change can occur only by reversing the successional process and by maintaining artificially the ecosystem at its most productive pioneering stage. This is ecologically, at least, the least advanced stage in the process of succession – that most marked by discontinuities such as floods, droughts, epidemics, and population explosions among animals, plants and microorganisms.

The principle of ecological succession to a climax is thus contrary to modern notions of nature being in a state of continual flux. Succession implies stability: hence actions that interfere with succession encourage instability. From the ecological point of view, therefore, modern economic development, which inevitably disrupts the process of succession, cannot be identified with progress.

Many ecologists, recognizing, nevertheless, that ecological succession is a fact, have offered theories intended to reconcile ecological considerations and industrial growth. Detailing them is beyond the scope of this book, and the reader is referred to the specialist literature.

Ecology
The term "ecology" has been defined in different ways by different ecologists, according to their particular world view. Some have taken ecology to be "scientific natural history", others have seen it as the science of how living things relate to their natural environment or as "the science of communities".

Many early ecologists saw ecology as an approach rather than a discipline. Barrington Moore, the first President of the American Ecological Society, declared at a meeting of his society in 1919 that ecology was the science of synthesis, and such a science was clearly essential if we were to understand the functioning of the world as a whole rather than isolated bits of it.

Unfortunately, the full development of such a science was not allowed to occur. Ecology, of the type taught in our universities, soon lost its holistic (see *Holism*) character and became yet another reductionistic and highly specialized discipline.

However, the term was taken up in the late 1960s by environmentalists who sought to develop philosophical and, indeed, scientific foundations for their efforts to preserve what remained of nature from destructive economic development. Such basic ecological principles as that of the balance of nature (*qv*), the importance of diversity as a means of increasing stability, the holistic principle that the whole is more than the sum of its parts, and the principle of ecological succession (qv) to a climax have been taken up by the ecological movement (qv), while paradoxically they have been largely abandoned by academic ecologists. (See also: *Deep ecology* Ⓕ.)

Economics and ecology

Economists are having increasing difficulty in predicting economic developments, which can no longer be understood simply by perusing the value of "leading indicators". *Business Week* has gone so far as to state that "when all forecasts miss the mark, it suggests that the entire body of economic thinking – accumulated in the 200 years since Adam Smith laid the basis for modern theory with his inquiry into the Wealth of Nations – is inadequate to describe and analyze the problems of our times".

What has gone wrong? The answer seems to be that modern economics is studied in almost complete isolation. The economic process, however, does not occur within a closed system but within the world of living things, which it affects dramatically and which is, in turn, affected by it. As Lester Brown of the Worldwatch Institute writes: "Four biological systems – fisheries, forests, grasslands and croplands – form the foundation of the global economic system. In addition to supplying all our food, these four systems provide virtually all the raw materials for industry except minerals and petroleum-derived synthetics. The condition of the economy and of these biological systems cannot be separated".

In the last decades, the impact of our economic activities on fisheries, forests, grasslands and croplands has escalated, causing increasingly serious ecological degradation. In some cases, those "ecological costs" are now being translated into economic costs.

Current economic theory postulates that as ecosystems are degraded, so the demand for their produce increases – until it be-

comes economic to restore their proper functioning. The argument is flawed on a number of counts – not least because ecological degradation is rarely reversible, at least on a historic time-scale. However much people are willing to pay for the dodo, it can never be brought back, nor can the tropical forests we are systematically annihilating today, nor the arable land we are transforming into deserts – except on a purely symbolic scale.

For these and other reasons, a new economics is required, one that takes into account biological, ecological and indeed social factors. Such an economics would have practically nothing in common with the "closed-system" economics which are still allowed to guide present policies throughout much of the world.

Ecosystem

Term coined by the Oxford ecologist A.G. Tansley in 1934, though the concept is much older, to describe the basic functional unit in ecology. The ecosystem includes the "ecological community" – which is made up of closely interrelated living things – and its physical environment. These are inseparable and interact upon each other. (See also: *Ecological succession* Ⓕ, *Ecology* Ⓕ.)

Electropollution

Term coined to describe the health and environmental hazards of electromagnetic (EM) fields. Sources of electropollution include Visual Display Units (VDUs), power lines, electric lights and power units, radar systems, radio and microwave relay stations, and microwave ovens. Such sources generate electromagnetic fields of varying intensity.

Despite denials and obfuscation by electricity utilities and other vested interests, study after study has confirmed the health hazards posed by electropollution. Health disorders that have been linked to exposure to EM fields include childhood cancer, foetal abnormalities and spontaneous abortion, brain cancers and Down's syndrome. Minor ailments associated with exposure include de-

pression, headaches, sleep disturbance, short-term memory loss and skin complaints. Other less proven hazards include cot death and multiple sclerosis.

Scientific knowledge of the biological effects of EM fields is still scanty but a number of institutions have launched research programmes. In the EC, a Directive is due to come into force in 1993 requiring all EM emissions from VDUs to be "negligible", except at visible light frequencies. The VDU problem is urgent because there are some 100 million VDUs in use worldwide. Although the major manufacturers have already abandoned production of high-emitting screens, it will be some years before gas-plasma screen technology, which is not a source of electropollution, replaces the cathode ray tube in computer screens, and indeed television sets.

Emulsifiers

A large and diverse group of compounds that are added to food products to enable water to form emulsions with oils with which, otherwise, it would not form stable mixtures. They work by breaking up one component so that it can be dispersed in small droplets throughout the other.

Within the EC, emulsifiers are listed with E-numbers (qv) between E322 and E495, along with stabilizers (qv) and thickeners. These chemicals are generally controlled by permitted lists, and in most industrialized countries about 60 different compounds are allowed. Some of the most widely used emulsifiers are the lecithins (E322), polysorbate 60 (E435) and mono- and di-glycerides, known as the MDGs (E471), though emulsifiers are often used in complex combinations.

Emulsifiers are invaluable in the manufacture of products such as margarine, salad dressing, baked products, chocolate and ice cream, but they are also to be found in some meat products, confectionery, and dessert and whipping products. Lecithins are found in egg yolks, but are also extracted commercially from soya bean oil. While these naturally occurring emulsifiers were generally considered sufficient until the 1960s, subsequent technological developments in the food industry have depended on a complex range of synthetic compounds, such as the MDGs, which have emerged more recently from the laboratory.

There is less concern about the safety of emulsifiers than about most other classes of food additives. (See also: *Additives*Ⓛ, *Stabilizers*Ⓛ.)

Encroaching cultivators

Peasant colonists who move into forested areas in order to farm. Also misleadingly referred to as "shifting cultivators", they have been unfairly accused of being the prime cause of deforestation (*qv*), particularly in the tropics. In fact, most encroaching cultivators are themselves the victims of the development (*qv*) process. Many have been uprooted from their own lands to make way for plantations, dams, livestock-rearing schemes and other large-scale projects. If they are to survive, they have little option but to colonize the forests.

In general, encroaching cultivators clear land using slash-and-burn (*qv*) techniques, a method of agriculture that has been practised successfully for millennia by "swidden" cultivators. In inexperienced hands and when carried out at an individual, rather than on a communal, level, however, slash-and-burn farming can cause widespread destruction, particularly when fallow periods of sufficient length are not maintained on the cleared ground. (See also: *Swidden agriculture.*)

Endrin

A chlorinated hydrocarbon (*qv*) insecticide chemically similar to aldrin and dieldrin (*qv*). It is persistent in the environment and toxic to a wide variety of living organisms. It is highly toxic to humans but has not been used as widely as dieldrin, which it resembles closely in its environmental and toxic effects. (See also: *Biocides*Ⓟ, *Chlorinated Hydrocarbon*ⓇⓅ, *Dieldrin*Ⓟ, *Insecticides*Ⓟ, *Pesticides*Ⓟ.)

Energy

Literally, the measure of the ability to do work, existing as potential, or stored energy, or as kinetic energy, the energy of motion. Humans derive their bodily energy from the metabolization of carbohydrate foods, converting potential energy to kinetic energy.

For something like 95 per cent of our tenancy of this planet, humans only needed a little extra energy mainly in the form of firewood for camp fires and cooking.

With the Neolithic Revolution and the development of settled agriculture, energy consumption increased dramatically, mainly through the use of draught animals. With the development of industry, the energy of moving wind and water was harnessed and that of fossil fuels, mainly coal (*qv*), burned to convert chemical (potential) energy into heat. The great spurt in economic activity since World War II was based on a massive increase in the use of oil (*qv*) as an energy source. This tapered off in 1973 with the first oil shock. Since then most industrial countries have sought to reduce their dependence on oil by increasing their consumption of other fuels such as natural gas, coal, fissionable uranium (*qv*) and renewable sources of energy, such as wind and water, and by adopting various energy conservation strategies.

In 1973, the total amount of energy used worldwide amounted to the equivalent of nearly 6,500 million tonnes of oil. By the end of the 1980s, this had risen to the equivalent of over 8,500 million tonnes. In 1973, oil provided 41 per cent of energy used, natural gas 16 per cent, coal 25 per cent, renewable sources 17 per cent, and nuclear power 1 per cent. By 1987, oil provided only 32 per cent of total energy consumption, while natural gas provided 17 per cent, coal 26 per cent, renewable sources 20 per cent and nuclear 5 per cent.

Oil, of course, still remains the most important source of energy and, though it can be replaced for certain uses such as electricity generation, is difficult to replace as a liquid fuel for powering motor vehicles. Coal production, which increased between 1973 and 1984 by the equivalent of 10 million barrels of oil a day, is largely being used to fuel new coal-fired power stations. World coal reserves are enormous and the World Coal Study predicts that production will continue to increase at 4.5 per cent a year, which means that consumption of coal would triple between 1972 and the year 2000. Other energy studies have also accentuated the increased role coal is likely to play in world energy consumption in the coming years. Concern over pollution from coal-fired plants, however, may lead to a concerted effort to reduce coal consumption.

In the decade between 1973-84, the consumption of natural gas increased particularly rapidly – by 90 per cent for the world as a whole – except in the USA, where for various technical reasons it fell steadily during the seventies. World reserves of natural gas are considerable. Estimates have risen 34 per cent in the last ten years. Proven worldwide reserves were 3-4 quadrillion cubic feet in 1985, which is the equivalent of 590 million barrels of oil. They are just 15 per cent lower than oil reserves, but at the present rate of natural gas consumption, provide only half as much energy as oil. According to the World Bank, natural gas can be made available in many parts of the Third World for between $2 and $12 a barrel of oil equivalent, which is far lower than the cost of oil. The potential for increasing natural gas consumption is thus considerable.

Nuclear power was once considered to be the main replacement for oil in many countries. Vast investments were made in nuclear power and indeed nuclear power generation has increased worldwide more than five times since 1973. It is likely to continue increasing because of the many plants ordered but still unfinished. However, because of the high cost of construction, the unsolved problems of disposing of high-level waste, the still unknown problems associated with the decommissioning of old reactors and increasing public fears about safety, there is growing disenchantment with nuclear power in many countries. In the US, no new plants have been ordered since 1978 while 108 have been cancelled since 1974. The outlook for the nuclear industry is indeed grim. Christopher Flavin of the Worldwatch Institute in Washington DC does not consider that nuclear power is likely to provide more than six to eight per cent of world energy consumption by the year 2000.

Renewable sources of energy provide about six times as much energy worldwide as do nuclear power plants. Of these, hydro-power provides about a third and wood fuel and different waste materials provide most of the rest. The contribution of solar collectors (*qv*), wind generators, wave power (*qv*) and other alternative sources of energy is still very small though it is growing rapidly. On the other hand the use of wood fuel is growing slowly, at about 1-2 per cent per annum, largely as a result of the increasing shortage of firewood in Third World countries due to deforestation (*qv*). Many poor people in the Third World are increasingly forced to burn cow dung and other agricultural residues that should be returned to the soil if its fertility is to be maintained.

Perhaps the most important means of reducing our dependence on oil is energy conservation (*qv*). According to Flavin it has exceeded the contribution of all new sources combined and the potential for further increases remain high. Ecologically this is the most desirable approach to solving the world's energy problems. Indeed, to satisfy ecological requirements, energy use must be reduced rather than increased.

Several studies have argued that energy consumption provides a measure of our impact on ecological systems. They point to the ecological costs not only of producing energy but also of using it. Coal and uranium mining operations, for example, are generally destructive of the en-

vironment and detrimental to human health, with miners in both industries suffering high rates of lung disease due to exposure to dust and pollutants. Power generation is also highly polluting: emissions from oil- and coal-fired power stations are a major cause of acid rain (*qv*) and of the build-up of greenhouse gases; while nuclear power stations give rise to routine radioactive emissions (*qv*) and, when accidents occur, to larger releases of radioactive materials such as occurred at Chernobyl (*qv*) in April 1986.

In addition, many of the uses to which energy is put in a modern industrialized society are themselves destructive of the environment: industry, for example, is a major source of pollution, while energy-intensive agriculture is a prime cause of erosion and desertification, particularly in the vulnerable soils of the tropics.

Indeed, if our biosphere (*qv*) is to remain capable of supporting complex forms of life, there is a pressing need to reorganize society so as to reduce energy consumption rather than blindly seeking to increase it in order to accommodate our present destructive and non-sustainable activities. (See also: *Alternative energy*©Ⓔ, *Energy efficiency*©Ⓔ, *Fuelwood crisis*③.)

Energy efficiency

The application of measures designed to increase the efficiency with which fuel is used and so reduce the amount of fuel needed to sustain a particular level of production in an industrial or domestic enterprise.

Energy efficiency techniques fall into two categories: insulation (*qv*), and increased mechanical efficiency. Insulation reduces heat losses. Improving the efficiency with which machinery uses energy usually involves modification of the design.

After the dramatic increase in the price of oil in 1973, systematic efforts were made throughout the industrial world to increase energy efficiency, with impressive results. In the US, cars will now travel 29 per cent farther on a gallon of gasoline than they did in

1973. New cars in the US get about 26 miles to the gallon as against 17 mpg in the early 1970s – still a poor performance by European or Japanese standards. A prototype Volvo can now achieve 63 mpg in the city and 80 mpg on the highway, while a Toyota prototype can achieve 89 mpg in the city and 110 mpg on the highway. The engines of such cars make use of plastic and ceramics, which are also used in the bodies. However, new technologies such as direct injection diesel engines are also used.

Similar savings have been made in many other fields, both domestic and industrial. In the EC, the ratio of primary energy use to gross domestic product (GDP) fell by about eight per cent between 1973 and 1978, while prime energy use increased only by 0.42 per cent. Significantly, about 95 per cent of all EC economic growth was fuelled by energy conservation and only five per cent by expansion of energy generation. Denmark was able to reduce its total use of direct fuels by 20 per cent between 1979 and 1980. These improvements were prompted by the high price of oil in the 1970s. After 1983, the real price of energy fell, so there was less incentive to conserve it, and since the mid-1980s the rate of improvement has tended to diminish.

In the USA since 1973, the amount of energy needed to achieve a given level of gross national product (GNP) has dropped by more than 25 per cent.

Worldwide, some $300,000 million worth of energy has been saved since 1973 as a result of more efficient energy use. More is achievable. About 60 per cent of the energy available in the coal, gas, oil and uranium we use to generate electricity is wasted before it is even put to useful work. According to the International Energy Agency, energy use in the industrialized countries could be cut by 30 per cent by the year 2000 were the conservation measures that are now economically viable to be implemented fully.

In the USA, according to Amory Lovins of the Rocky Mountain

Institute, the potential for saving electricity through greater energy efficiency is "equivalent to 50 Chernobyl-sized reactors". By using throughout US industry the best electricity saving devices currently on the market, Lovins estimates that the US electricity bill could be cut by 75 per cent.

In Britain, it has been suggested that the demand for electricity could be reduced by 70 per cent if the most energy efficient lights, motors and appliances were to be used. A study by the Open University Energy Research Group has calculated that a nationwide energy efficiency programme could reduce peak demand by four gigawatts by the turn of the century – the equivalent output of four nuclear reactors – saving between $4,000 million and $7,000 million in oil and coal bills.

In the Third World, too, there is tremendous scope for cutting energy consumption. A study by Greg Kats, a consultant to the World Wide Fund for Nature, points out that, in Pakistan, "cost effective investments in efficiency in the industrial and commercial sectors would permit Pakistan to reduce projected required growth in electricity supply by 30 per cent by 2005. China, too, has become more efficient, achieving a reported 3.7 per cent per year decrease in energy use per unit of GNP since 1979".

Despite the cost-effectiveness of energy efficiency, however, there has been little enthusiasm for energy conservation programmes by governments internationally. Between 1972 and 1980, more than 90 per cent of the aid supplies to the Third World for energy programmes went to large-scale electricity generation projects. Less than one per cent was devoted to efficiency. In the late 1980s, reports commissioned by the World Bank estimated that 50 per cent of the future energy demands of Third World countries could be met by employing energy efficiency measures. Yet in 1988 and 1989, only two per cent of the Bank's loans were for projects that included such measures. In Britain, the budget of

the government's Energy Efficiency Office has been halved since 1986. In the USA, spending on efficiency programmes fell from $495 million in 1986 to $165 million in 1989.

In the face of global warming through the greenhouse effect, energy conservation is an international priority. According to the UK Association for the Conservation of Energy: "Concentrating solely on lighting in the commercial and industrial sectors, fridges and freezers in the domestic sector, and industrial motors, a 90 per cent uptake of "best available technology" would cut the UK's current electricity demand by nearly 12 per cent. This would lower CO_2 emissions in the electricity sector by more than 20 million tonnes, which is equivalent to 3.5 per cent of total UK CO_2 emissions." Better insulation of buildings could cut emissions by a further 32 million tonnes. The ACE concludes: "Pound for pound, energy conservation provides the quickest and cheapest means of reducing CO_2 emissions. One pound spent on saving electricity would reduce consumption by at least 30 kilowatts, cut 42kg of CO_2 and save the customer £1.90 ($3) per year in electricity bills. These are conservative figures". (See also: *Alternative technology*Ⓔ, *Energy*Ⓔ, *Oil*Ⓔ.)

E numbers
A system of identification for food additives that was introduced in the EC during the late 1970s, hence "E" for European. Taste additives (*qv*), the largest group of additives, do not have E numbers. The authority for ascribing an E number to an additive lies with the European Council of Ministers, but it acts on the advice of the European Commission and the Scientific Committee for Food.

Before the introduction of this system, European consumers often received no information on which chemicals were being used in the foods and drinks they were buying. For example, British labelling regulations used to require at most the use of expressions such as "permitted colouring" or "permitted preservative".

The initiative to develop the E numbering system was taken by the food industry in response to proposals to ban all of those food additives that were suspected of provoking symptoms of acute intolerance such as hyperactivity, asthma, eczema or migraine. Industry preferred to reveal their presence on labels, rather than having them banned altogether. The responsibility for protecting consumers has thus devolved from government onto the consumers themselves. (See also: *Additives*Ⓛ.)

Environmental refugees
Term applied to those who have been forced to leave their homes or their lands as a result of environmental degradation, natural disasters or development projects. They are often also referred to as "development refugees".

Accurate figures are hard to obtain but a large proportion of the 2,000 to 3,000 people made homeless every day may be presumed to be environmental refugees. There are estimated to be 10 million refugees worldwide, and in some areas, women and children make up 80 per cent of the numbers. The causes of their plight vary, but the most obvious are the construction of large dams (*qv*), plantation projects, livestock-rearing schemes, and desertification and soil salinization, often caused by such development schemes.

Industrial accidents that require the evacuation of local inhabitants are also a cause of environmental refugees. More than 220,000 people fled Bhopal (*qv*) in the wake of the 1984 accident at Union Carbide's pesticide (*qv*) plant. In the industrialized world, notable examples of accidents which have led to evacuations include: Love Canal (*qv*), Seveso (*qv*), Three Mile Island (*qv*) and Chernobyl (*qv*).

Erosion
The removal of soil due to the action of the wind and rain. Under natural conditions, erosion is an extremely slow process, but as a result of deforestation (*qv*), overgrazing (*qv*) and inappropri-

African soil erosion caused by deforested soil that can no longer absorb water run-off.

ate agricultural practices, the Earth's topsoil is now being eroded at an alarming rate.

Erosion is today a worldwide phenomenon, but is particularly serious in the dry tropics where the soils are very vulnerable.

- In India, where 800,000sq km (300,000sq miles) of land are affected, 6,000 million tonnes of topsoil are lost annually.
- On the steeper slopes of the Highlands of Ethiopia, annual topsoil losses amount to some 269 tonnes per hectare – 1,600 million tonnes a year.
- In the USSR, the annual loss is 2,500 million tonnes, with 2,320,000sq km (895,000sq miles) – ten per cent of the agricultural land – being affected.
- In Australia, six tonnes of topsoil are eroded for every tonne of produce grown – and in some regions, the figure is 300 tonnes.
- In Britain, which has long denied having soil erosion problems, a 1987 survey reveals that nearly 37 per cent of agricultural land in England and Wales – nearly 20,000sq km (7,700sq miles) – is subject to a "higher than acceptable degree" of erosion. In the European Community as a whole, some 140,000sq km (54,000sq miles) are at risk.
- In the USA, one-third of cropland is seriously affected by erosion. Despite expenditure of more than $15,000 million on soil con-

servation since the mid-1930s, topsoil losses are 25 per cent greater than in the dustbowl years of the 1930s. By 1981, the US was losing 4,000 million tonnes a year, enough soil to fill a train of freight cars long enough to circle the Earth 24 times.

According to the US Department of Agriculture (USDA), 430,000sq km (166,000sq miles) of land now suffer from unacceptable levels of erosion. Much of that land may soon have to be retired from agricultural use. Production in the corn belt could decline by 15-30 per cent over the next 50 years due to erosion. In Illinois alone, average grain yields fell by two per cent between 1979-84.

In general, the annual loss of production due to soil erosion in the USA is put at one per cent. According to Dr. David Pimental of Cornell University, however, the problem has been grossly underestimated, since researchers have only taken account of the depth of soil lost and have ignored the loss of both nutrients and organic matter in the eroded soil. For example, Kansas is estimated to have lost half its soil-borne nitrogen in the last 30 years. Many soil specialists also argue that the USDA has overestimated the rate at which soil is replenished, leading to overoptimistic "tolerance levels" being set

for erosion in many areas.

Belatedly, a few governments worldwide are now beginning to implement soil conservation measures, albeit on a small scale. Remedial measures include: reforestation (qv), terracing, reduced tillage, and the reintroduction of rotation with grass leys.

It seems clear, however, that no long-term solution to soil erosion is possible under an economic system that continues to encourage over-production, deforestation, and overgrazing regardless of the long-term consequences. (See also: *Deforestation* ©③, *Global 2000* ©, *Overgrazing* Ⓐ③, *Sedimentation* ©③.)

Eucalyptus
Australia is the least forested of all continents, with the exception of Antarctica. At the time of European settlement in 1788 only nine per cent of the land area was forested. Less than half this area was left in 1987.

Eucalyptus species dominate the Australian forests and to a large extent determine the distinctive character and feel of the continent. In ecological terms eucalypt forests share many characteristics, that in combination, and often singly, make them unique. For example, eucalypt forests prosper on extremely poor soils, are outstandingly adapted to frequent fire, are genetically flexible, tolerate an extraordinary range of ecological conditions and support a unique array of arboreal fauna.

Eucalypt forests are being clearfelled and converted into tree farms to be cut every 40-80 years by forestry operations. A radically impoverished habitat results, with soil nutrient levels falling and major ecological imbalances occurring. The re-growth is not suitable for many birds and arboreal marsupials for at least 150 years, which means that many of these animals could be driven to extinction.

The major catalyst for the onslaught against the eucalypt forests is an industry known as "woodchipping". Ancient eucalypt forests are clearfelled and much of the timber is converted to small wooden chips, which are then used to make paper pulp. Most of the woodchips are exported to Japan, with the industry having grown from 770,000 tonnes a year in 1971 to levels in 1987 of five million tonnes a year. More than a square kilometre of eucalypt forest is clearfelled every day to feed the woodchip industry.

Environmentalists in Australia are vigorously opposing the current woodchip schemes, as well as plans to expand the industry, and in July 1987 turned woodchipping into a major Federal election issue. In a nationwide "Vote for the Forests" campaign the environmental movement was critical in returning the Australian Labor Party to power.

Outside of Australia, there is increasing concern over the use of eucalyptus as a timber crop and in reforestation projects. Planted in arid areas of the Third World, often displacing land used by local villagers to grow food crops, eucalyptus has proved an ecological disaster. Its thirst for water inhibits the growth of ground cover, depriving farmers of valuable fodder, and preventing the replenishment of groundwater. Eucalyptus also depletes the soil of nutrients, returning far less in leaf litter than it absorbs through its roots. Indeed, such is the depth of resentment against the imposi-

tion of eucalyptus plantations – usually to feed paper mills – that villagers in many Third World countries have resorted to uprooting eucalyptus saplings. (See also: *Deforestation③, Reforestation©*.)

Eutrophication

The process by which a lake or stream becomes richer and richer in plant nutrients until, eventually, plants overgrow and their decomposing remains cause the deoxygenation of the water, which becomes foul-smelling and virtually lifeless.

Nitrate fertilizers draining from fields cause serious eutrophication in some areas, as do nutrients from animal wastes. These, like human sewage, also have a high biochemical oxygen demand (see BOD) which exacerbates their effect on the waterway. In some badly affected areas – such as Britain's Norfolk Broads – the key nutrient is phosphate (*qv*), which is used in detergents as a water softener and enters the waterway via sewage. The North Sea (*qv*) is now also subject to algae blooms, which many scientists blame on the dumping of sewage at sea.

Eutrophication can be prevented by treating sewage to remove nitrate and, in some cases, phosphate. Banning the use of phosphate in detergents would help, but there is strong resistance to this from manufacturers. Restrictions on the use of nitrate fertilizers may be necessary and it is important that slurry and other animal wastes are not allowed to enter streams or lakes. (See also: *Algal blooms ℗, Artificial fertilizers Ⓐ℗, Nitrate Ⓐ℗, Biochemical oxygen demand Ⓕ℗*.)

Export of pollution

As pollution controls are tightened in the industrialized world, many companies are moving their most polluting industries to the Third World, where pollution controls are either less strict or non-existent; included are the asbestos (*qv*) industry, the steel industry, and the vinyl chloride, pesticide (*qv*), chromate and chloralkali industries. Many are tempted to the Third World by "freedom to pollute" agreements.

The relocated factories operate at far lower standards than would be permitted in their home countries – both in terms of discharges to the environment and worker safety. Dr. Barry Castleman, a US environmental consultant specializing in the export of hazardous industries, reports cases of workers not being informed of the dangers of their work, of defective machinery, of safety codes which are mandatory in the US not being implemented by US subsidiaries, and of high levels of pollution. The Bhopal (*qv*) disaster resulted from just such double standards.

In addition to exporting hazardous industries, Western companies have also taken advantage of lax safety standards in the Third World to export banned or hazardous produce and goods. Such products include banned pesticides and unwanted drugs. In the wake of Chernobyl (*qv*), several European companies exported food contaminated with levels of radiation above the 600 becquerels per kilo permitted in the EC. Milk, lamb and game contaminated with 1,000 becquerels per kilo were exported by Britain but were returned as unfit by the health authorities in Iran, Kuwait, Egypt, Israel, the Philippines, Hong Kong and Singapore. Britain's Ministry of Agriculture insisted the food was safe – though it would never have been permitted to enter Britain. In Germany, the government banned similar exports.

In 1988 the voyage of the orphan waste ship *Karin B* (*qv*) highlighted the growing export of toxic waste to the Third World from both Europe and the USA. West Africa, Haiti, the Dominican Republic and Mexico have become favoured dumping grounds. Following the *Karin B* scandal, Italy banned the export of hazardous wastes to the Third World. The Netherlands have instituted a similar ban. A Dutch proposal to introduce an EC-wide ban on hazardous waste exports to the Third World was blocked by Britain in 1988. However, at the 4th Lome Convention in 1990, the export of toxic and radioactive wastes from the EC to 68 African,

Caribbean and Pacific nations was banned, except to those states with "adequate technical capacity" to dispose of them.

In 1986, the Organization of African Unity requested the United Nations to draft an international treaty to control the export of hazardous wastes. A treaty was signed at the Basel Convention in March 1989, but still has to be ratified by many industrialized nations. The EC is at present considering a draft proposal to translate the convention's recommendations into Community law. The treaty relies on "prior notification" as the main means of policing the waste trade, but does not define what constitutes a hazardous waste, although some 40 classes of waste are listed. The formula is likely to lead to legal argument but little firm action. There is also no definition of what constitutes the adequate disposal facilities required of importing nations. Although shipments have to be agreed by the authorities in the importing nations, the governments of the exporting countries have no role to play in negotiating the deal, which is left solely to the companies involved. Many fear that bribery will see to it that cargoes receive the necessary documentation. There is also a fear that a clause allowing the export of waste for "recycling" will be exploited to the detriment of the environment. As *New Scientist* notes: "Such dispensations have often led to 'sham recycling'". To avoid the expensive handling required for hazardous material, waste is exported ostensibly for re-use. It often ends up in facilities which cannot in practice recycle it. *New Scientist* sees little hope that the treaty will clean up the trade in waste: "With such weak controls, many poor nations will feel under great pressure to earn foreign currency by allowing their territory to become the dumping ground for other nations' rubbish." (See also: *Circle of poison*Ⓟ.)

Extinction

Since life first began on Earth, numerous species of animals and plants have fallen prey to extinc-

tion, either because they were unable to survive or because they evolved into other forms of life. Today, species are being lost at such a rate that scientists warn that we are heading for the kind of mass extinction that occurred at the end of the Cretaceous Period, some 65 million years ago. But whereas previous mass extinctions have been largely the result of climatic and geophysical factors, today's extinctions are almost exclusively man-made (see illustration).

As wildlife habitats are destroyed, so their indigenous species disappear with them. The loss of the world's tropical forests (*qv*) alone could account for the extinction of a third of the world's species: other critical habitats under threat include coral reefs (*qv*) and wetlands (*qv*). In addition, wildlife must contend with pesticide (*qv*) pollution, hazardous wastes (*qv*), acid rain (*qv*), the degradation of farmland, coastal development and hunting.

Species are now being lost at an unprecedented rate – some 400 times faster than at any other period during recent geological time – and the range of species affected is far wider than ever before. As the US biologist Edward O. Wilson, Professor of Science at Harvard University, points out: "In at least one respect, this human-made hecatomb is worse than any time in the geological past. In earlier mass extinctions ... most of the plant diversity survived: now, for the first time, it is being mostly destroyed."

The long-term outcome of today's extinctions cannot be predicted with precision: but the loss of species cannot continue with impunity forever. Sooner or later, the Earth's life-support systems will simply be overwhelmed. To avoid such a disaster will take more than the setting up of national parks or better land-use: it will require a fundamental reappraisal of our whole way of life, with priority being given to ecological imperatives rather than the pursuit of economic gain. (See also: *Economics and ecology*Ⓕ, *Genetic diversity*Ⓒ, *Genetic resources*Ⓒ.)

Exxon Valdez

Prince William Sound, off the south coast of Alaska, is an area of great natural beauty and is one of the world's largest herring spawning grounds. In March 1989, the super-tanker *Exxon Valdez* ran aground releasing 240,000 barrels of crude oil into the sea. Emergency clean-up equipment did not arrive for 10 hours, and there were insufficient numbers of oil-skimming vessels and not enough boom-laying equipment to contain the slick. When the wind rose, the oil was blown onto the nearby rocky shores.

The damage to wildlife was immense. When US government figures were released two years later, it emerged that about 350,000 seabirds had died. Populations of many marine animals, from killer whales to clams and snails had plummeted, and a high rate of abnormal defects were observed in fish that spawned in the area. The devastation had been aggravated by the use of pressurized hot water sprays to wash down the polluted shoreline. These had had the effect of sterilizing the beaches, killing barnacles, mussels, eelgrass and rockweed. Beaches that had not been sprayed at all often recovered more quickly than those that had been treated – although the speediest recovery was observed where fertilizer had been sprayed on the shore to encourage oil-eating bacteria.

The costs of cleaning the affected area were considerable. Exxon spent nearly $2,000 million on the clean-up exercise and a further $180 million in damages to fishermen and other inhabitants. The company was also charged $1,000 million damages by the Alaskan courts and fined $125 million.

The spillage cast doubts on the wisdom of expanding the Alaskan oil fields, and for a time the proposal to start drilling in the Arctic National Wildlife Refuge was put on hold. But the Gulf War (*qv*) caused the USA, concerned at its dependence on oil from the Middle East, to look once more to the Alaska fields for its future supplies. (See also: *Alaska*Ⓒ.)

Family planning
Famine
FAO
Fast reactor
Feedlots
Fenitrothion
Fertilizers
Fish stocks
Fission
Flavourings
Fluoridation
Fluorides
Food additives
Food aid
Food and Agriculture
  Organization
  (FAO)
Food dyes
Food irradiation
Food storage
Formaldehyde
Fuelwood crisis
Fusion

Family planning

The official term for birth control, which has unacceptably authoritarian connotations. Its use implies that it is for a family to decide whether to limit its size, and that the role of government is restricted to providing families with the means of so doing.

In practice, many governments today actively seek to persuade families to limit their numbers, either through advertising campaigns extolling the virtues of modern contraception, or, as in India during the 1970s, by more sinister methods, including compulsory sterilization.

The emphasis placed on family planning programmes as a means of reducing population growth has been criticized on many grounds. One is that some modern methods of contraception can have serious health effects for women.

Another is that family planning programmes are exorbitantly expensive. Indeed, the World Bank estimates that to achieve "a rapid fertility decline" in Sub-Saharan Africa would mean increasing the funds spent on family planning 20-fold by the end of the century.

A third criticism is the increasing control of the state over women and their bodies through coercive "family planning" programmes. Women have become the objects of control where the modern instruments of contraception are firmly in the hands of the pharmaceutical and medical industries, supported by international and national population agencies.

Women in the industrialized world are not exempt from this and may also be faced with pressure to undergo the experimental and invasive techniques of the New Reproductive Technologies (NRTs) to deal with problems of infertility.

Another serious criticism is that family planning programmes fail to tackle the root cause of population growth (*qv*) in the Third World. They stand or fall on their success in persuading people to use contraceptives. But ignorance of contraception is not a major problem in the Third World, where traditional contraceptives are widely available.

Rather the problem could well lie in an unwillingness to limit the size of families, with people in many parts of the Third World actively seeking as many children as possible, in part to compensate for the social alienation caused by the development (*qv*) process. Additionally, undermining of the status of women in Third World societies may lead to resistance on the part of women to submit to further control in the guise of "choice" about birth. Under such circumstances, the distribution of free contraceptives and advice on contraception has little impact.

Family-planning programmes, however, have a role to play as part of an integrated population control campaign. (See also: *Population*③, *Demographic transition*③, *Genetic Engineering*.)

Famine

For the first time in human history we are witnessing famine on a continental scale, with two-thirds of African countries affected. Within a few years, famine is likely to spread to other major areas of the globe – and will eventually become both a global and a chronic phenomenon.

Four factors are officially seen as causes: unfavourable climatic conditions, in particular the terrible drought (*qv*) that has affected many Third World countries over the last decades; the population explosion (*qv*) which is such that there is no longer enough food to go round; archaic, low-yielding traditional agriculture (*qv*); and poverty, as a result of which people do not have the money to buy food.

The first is seen as "an act of God" against which we can do nothing. The solution to the other three problems, however, is seen to lie in economic development (*qv*). This, it is assumed, will assure that Third World people can afford to modernize their agriculture, buy their food, and acquire the financial security that, in the industrial world, has made it unnecessary for people to have a large number of children to look after them in their old age.

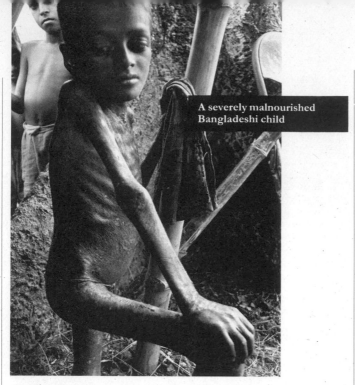

A severely malnourished Bangladeshi child

Each of these arguments can be seriously contested. To begin with, many climatologists now dispute that the drought is "an act of God", arguing instead that it is the result of the terrible deforestation (*qv*) of the last 40 years. This has reduced rainfall in certain areas and has led to the degradation of the soil, which severely reduces its water-retaining capacity, so much that drought occurs even in areas where rainfall is constant.

Secondly, the population explosion (*qv*) is itself the inevitable result of development, which has destroyed culturally determined population control strategies, while creating the insecurity that leads people to have more children.

The evidence also suggests that while traditional agriculture (*qv*) is superbly adapted to local social, ecological and climatic conditions, modern mechanized farming has contributed to malnutrition and famine. In particular, mechanization has made vast numbers of small farmers redundant, depriving them of their land and turning them into landless labourers or slum dwellers, who are vulnerable to famine. In addition, modern agriculture has had a very damaging impact on fragile tropical soils.

A feature of traditional agriculture is that it is geared to subsistence rather than to production for a distant market. According to Karl Polanyi, the economic historian and author of *The Great Transformation*, the development of the market system has been the main cause in the increase in famines throughout history.

Polanyi showed that the great famines of India during the British Raj were mainly due to the operation of market forces. There had always been crop failures, but these did not necessarily lead to famine, as farmers would conserve sufficient stocks, either in their homes or at a village level. With the development of the centralized market economy, however, peasants, as in most of the Third World today, had to sell their grain to city merchants, usually at a price fixed by the government well below that obtainable on the open market. The result was far greater vulnerability to crop failures. When these occurred, peasants, forced to sell their grain rather than eat it, now had to buy it back at an inflated price which, needless to say, they were not able to do. Hence the extraordinary spectacle of famine in the countryside but not in the cities.

At the same time, the market system, by its very nature, caused radical social changes. The communitarian society that provided people with great security, slowly disintegrated, as vast plantations took over from small farming communities, as peasants moved to the cities in search of jobs, and as the state took over an increasing number of functions that were previously fulfilled at a communal level. This meant that when there was a crop failure, peasants no longer had sufficient reserves to tide them over; instead they had to buy the food they needed.

Polanyi's analysis applies only too well to the current African famine. In the Sudan, for instance, the recent famine was largely the result of a massive increase in the production of cash crops, in particular cotton, which rose from 518,000 million bales in 1982-83 to 1,200,000 bales in 1983-84. Inevitably, production of sorghum, the staple food for local consumption, fell from 3,350,000 tonnes to 1,980,000 tonnes. Moreover, the price of sorghum increased dramatically as a result of food speculation – the inevitable concomitant of famine in a market economy. Stocks, instead of being distributed to the starving, were hoarded by merchants and resold at a vast profit, so much so that the price of a bag of sorghum rose 28-fold. How, in such conditions, could famine be avoided?

Famine is therefore best seen as the result of a constellation of closely associated changes brought about by economic development – changes that adversely affect the land's capacity to feed people, the number of people it must feed, and the way the food is distributed. (See also: *Cash crops*Ⓐ③, *Demographic transition*③, *Desertification*Ⓒ③, *Drought-flood cycle*③, *Erosion*Ⓒ, *Green Revolution*Ⓐ③.)

FAO
See *Food and Agriculture Organization*.

Fast reactor
Nuclear reactor so termed because it uses fast neutrons to

bring about the chain reaction. A prime purpose of the fast breeder is to generate more plutonium than is actually consumed in the chain reaction. In time, there should be sufficient surplus plutonium to start up a new fast reactor and give rise to a whole succession of second-generation plants – hence the popular appellation "fast breeder reactor."

The period taken to obtain enough fuel for a new fast reactor is known as the doubling time. If the reactor is to make any impact on power requirements, it is essential that the doubling time be as short as possible, a couple of decades at most. To achieve a reasonable doubling time, the spent fuel from fast reactors must be reprocessed – and the sooner after removal from the core the better. However, spent fuel from fast reactors is much more radioactive than that from conventional reactors and reprocessing can present both technical and safety problems. The chief dangers lie in the build-up of plutonium deposits in the reprocessing plant and in the risk of a sudden criticality accident irradiating any operators nearby.

The operation of fast reactors is intrinsically risky. Liquid sodium (or a mixture of sodium and potassium) is the usual choice of coolant, and sodium voids – caused when the sodium overheats, leading to a sharp rise in reactivity – present a major problem, particularly in the larger fast reactors. In that respect, they suffer from the same basic defect as the RBMK reactor at Chernobyl (qv). Should the reactor's fuel become distorted through overheating, then its reactivity will also increase, thus compounding the problem of sodium voiding. In theory, fast reactors can explode with the force of a small nuclear explosion, particularly should one lump of molten fuel be forced violently against another. Another hazard is presented by the spent fuel, which must be transported to the reprocessing plant in special flasks cooled by liquid sodium.

A number of serious accidents have already occurred in fast reactors, one a partial core meltdown in the Enrico Fermi plant close to Detroit in 1966 that threatened the entire city. In 1955 the first-ever fast reactor – the EBR-I reactor – suffered a core meltdown and came less than a second away from exploding. To date most fast reactors have had problems in their steam-generating systems, Russia's 350MW Shevtchenko fast reactor by the Caspian Sea developing a serious hydrogen fire in the secondary circuit. Fast reactors are today fitted with hydrogen-flaring systems.

Several countries have been developing experimental fast reactors, including Japan, the Soviet Union and the UK. The largest and most advanced in the world is the 1,240MW Super-Phénix plant at Creys Malville (qv) in France. However, a combination of safety problems and the relatively plentiful international supply of mined uranium (obviating the need to "breed" new fuel) has led to severe setbacks for the technology.

In 1988, the British government announced that it would phase out funding for a fast reactor at Dounreay (qv) in Scotland. In 1991, the German government withdrew financial support from the SNR-300 reactor at Kalkar, which had cost $4.4 billion to build and had never been allowed to start operating. The French government is also on the verge of cancelling its commitment to the Super-Phénix following a series of technical problems. These various moves by governments signal the virtual collapse of European collaboration on fast breeder development. (See also *Dounreay*Ⓝ, *Nuclear accidents*Ⓝ, *Reprocessing*Ⓝ.)

Feedlots

A system of livestock husbandry, used almost exclusively in the USA for beef production, in which animals are confined in large pens and their food is brought to them. The system is profitable in that it produces large amounts of beef at economic prices, but it is open to a number of objections.

Where cattle graze in the open, the animals are fed on, and help fertilize with their manure, land that is often unsuitable for any other agricultural use. In feedlots the feed brought to then. must be specially grown. It often consists of grain, augmented with high-protein foods such as soybean or fishmeal – foods that could be eaten directly by humans.

In effect, the cattle are competing with people for food. A third of the world's fish catch, for example, is used for feeding Western livestock. Since much of the feed used in feedlots is derived from developing countries, those who ultimately suffer are the already undernourished peoples of the Third World.

Cattle are ruminants, and a high-protein diet may be harmful to them. In addition, it may induce biochemical changes that alter the composition of the meat. The concentration in a small area of large numbers of cattle also creates an ever-present risk of epidemic disease, and yields as a by-product vast quantities of manure, whose disposal often creates serious problems and may cause pollution, especially of watercourses. (See also: *Hormones in meat*ⒶⓁ.)

Fenitrothion

An organophosphate (qv) used as a general insecticide in agriculture and to control malaria mosquitoes. It is also used to control parasites on animals.

It is not the most toxic chemical in the organophosphorus group, but it is regarded by the World Health Organization as being at "the limit of acceptable toxicity for conventional indoor application" when used for malaria control. (See also: *Pesticides*ⒶⓅ.)

Fertilizers

See: *Artificial fertilizers*, *Organic farming*.

Fish stocks

Fisheries supply 23 per cent of the world's protein and a livelihood for millions of people. However, world fish stocks are now threatened by a number of forces, notably overfishing, pollution, wetland (qv) reclamation schemes, barrages and dams (*qv*).

The modernization of fishing fleets has led to the decimation of fish stocks in many parts of the world. Faced with the need to repay loans, trawler owners have sought to maximize catches, regardless of the long-term consequences. In the North Atlantic, the herring has been fished to the verge of extinction, while stocks of the Atlantic cod, haddock and capelin have been severely depleted. In the South Atlantic, pilchard catches have seriously declined, while in the Pacific, the anchovie, salmon, halibut, King Crab and Pacific Ocean Perch have all been overfished.

According to a 1983 survey by the UN Food and Agriculture Organization (FAO) (*qv*), 11 major oceanic fisheries are now overfished to the point of collapse, the annual loss of potential catches amounting to some 11 million tonnes. It is not only old established fisheries which have been affected: as the Worldwatch Institute notes, "even newly developed fisheries in the more southern latitudes have quickly been fished to the point of collapse." In the decade between 1976 and 1986, the continents of Europe and Africa, and 37 individual countries, saw a decline in their fish catches.

Pollution too has destroyed many fisheries. In Britain, the Humber estuary used to support a thriving fishing industry: now it is dead, the victim of industrial pollution from the factories, mills and chemical plants that line the Humber.

In the US, fish stocks in the Chesapeake Bay have been all but destroyed by pollution: oyster catches fell by 50 per cent between 1962 and 1984; and catches of striped bass by 90 per cent in the decade from 1973-1983. The cost of restoring fisheries in the Bay is expected to reach more than $1,000 million. Though a clean-up programme was launched in 1983, little has yet come of it. According to the World Resources Institute, "More than 2,641 facilities hold permits to discharge into the bay or the tidal portion of its major tributaries. The total discharge from Mary-

land and Virginia amounts to 15 trillion litres of wastewater per year – about one-fifth the amount of water in the bay at any given time."

Unless action is taken soon to ease the pressure on fish stocks, the prospects for world fisheries are not good. Though aquaculture (*qv*) is being promoted as an alternative to ocean fishing, its potential has been overstated and its produce is often not available to the poorer sections of society. (See also: *Aquaculture*Ⓐ③, *Dams*③, *Ocean dumping*Ⓟ, *Wetlands*Ⓒ.)

Fission

Process by which atoms are split. A rare isotope of uranium (*qv*), U-235, is the only fissile substance that occurs in usable quantities in nature. It makes up 0.7 per cent of the natural metal, the rest of which is non-fissile U-238. Other fissile isotopes are plutonium (*qv*) 239 and 241, and uranium-233, most of which have been manufactured in nuclear reactors.

On being hit by a neutron, the fissile nucleus splits at random into two nuclei and brings about the release of two or three neutrons, generating considerable quantities of heat in the process.

The aim in operating a nuclear reactor is to achieve a constant rate of fissioning. One way of achieving this is to employ a moderator in the reactor that will cause the neutrons to slow down from their very fast ejection speeds so that they are more likely to be absorbed by a fissile atom. In Britain's gas-cooled reactors, the moderator consists of blocks of graphite. In light water reactors, water is used. In the Canadian Candu (*qv*) reactor, heavy water is used.

In addition, the nuclear material used to fuel a reactor can be manufactured from uranium that has been "enriched" in uranium-235, thus enhancing the likelihood of fission. Uranium enrichment (*qv*) also means that the reactor can be more compact and, therefore, supposedly cheaper to build. Usually enrichments of between two and four per cent are used in reactors with moderators.

When fuel is enriched above 15 per cent, it is possible to dispense with the moderator. The neutrons maintain high speeds – some 16,000km per second (10,000 miles per second). The advantage of such fast breeder reactors (*qv*) is that some of the fast neutrons are more likely to be absorbed by uranium-238, which then transforms into fissile plutonium. (See also: *Fast reactor*Ⓝ.)

Flavourings

See: *Taste additives*.

Fluoridation

Technique of adding fluorides (*qv*) to public water supplies, with the intention of reducing tooth decay.

Fluoridation transformed a liability of the aluminium industry (bulk sodium fluoride) into a commercial product. Some fluoridation is done with hydrofluosilicic acid, a waste from manufacture of superphosphate fertilizer.

Tooth decay turns out to have declined to about one-third since the 1950s in the wealthy countries that gather dental statistics. This welcome trend is not understood; possible causes may include improved diet and brushing, widespread antibiotics secreted in saliva, and, recently, fluoride in toothpaste, a concentrated direct application that may well be effective. But thorough surveys have corrected the earlier claim that natural fluoride in water is correlated with relative freedom from tooth decay. Trials claimed to demonstrate benefit from fluoridation have been severely criticized for lack of controls, and other major defects.

In some still controversial studies, fluoridation has, on the other hand, been rather closely correlated with cancer. Various other types of harm have been suspected; the one established beyond dispute is dental fluorosis – diffuse white mottling of the teeth, a form of damage commonly observed among children drinking water fluoridated to 1ppm. The margin, if any, is uncomfortably slim between 1ppm and levels known to cause serious damage to bones (skeletal fluorosis). In addition, there is the possibility of adverse synergistic reactions between the fluoride added to water and the thousands of other chemicals to which modern industrial systems expose us.

Fluorides
Simple inorganic compounds of the element fluorine. Soluble fluorides, and in particular the acidic gas hydrogen fluoride, are extremely toxic. Hydrofluoric acid – a solution of hydrogen fluoride in water – will eat its way through most materials, including glass, and causes horrific burns to human tissue. The repeated ingestion of small quantities of fluorides leads to the condition known as fluorosis. This is a crippling disease in which excess calcium is deposited in the bones and ligaments, the bones becoming dense but brittle. Mottled teeth are an early symptom.

Fluorides are emitted by two main industrial processes. The smelting of aluminium and the manufacturing of bricks, in which fluorine compounds naturally present in the clay are released as the bricks are baked. (See also: *Fluoridation*.)

Food additives
See: *Additives*.

Food aid
Food aid to poor countries has accounted for about 10 per cent of all official development assistance in recent years, and has been worth about $2,500 million per year. About half of this comes from the USA, with the EC providing about 30 per cent. Only a small proportion of the aid is given free of charge. For example, 80 per cent of food aid from the USA is sold to the recipient country at slightly less than market value or is exchanged for raw materials. The food is available because of the overproduction caused by the subsidies given to agriculture in the industrialized world. As the former head of Britain's Overseas Development Agency remarked, food aid is "frankly more a means of disposing of agricultural surpluses, than of helping the poor."

Food aid may be given for three different purposes: to provide emergency relief, to complement specific development projects, or as part of a programme to bolster an ailing economy.

Emergency food aid, although it receives a high media profile, in fact constitutes only 5 per cent of the total. In cases of natural disaster, the rapid delivery of relatively small quantities of basic foodstuffs can save numerous lives. All too often, however, the provisions arrive too late, in the wrong place, are of the wrong kind or reach the wrong people. Twenty-five per cent of food aid goes towards specific projects – often in the form of "food for work." Its usefulness depends partly upon the appropriateness of the project. For example, if peasants abandon their holdings to work on a road or irrigation scheme, this ultimately benefits only wealthy farmers or town dwellers, and then great harm may have been done to the region's agricultural self-sufficiency.

The bulk of food aid, some 70 per cent, is supplied on the undertaking that it will be sold on the market to boost the economy of an ailing country. This is the most effective means of dumping surpluses from wealthy countries, and the aid is often tied to the export of certain raw materials or sold only slightly below market price. In some countries, not necessarily the poorest, such aid has become an integral part of the economy. For instance, the sale of food aid on the market provides the Bangladesh government with up to 40 per cent of its total budget.

Quite apart from the obvious danger of depending on a source of income that might suddenly dry up if economic circumstances change, reliance on food aid has other harmful effects. Much of the food tends to fall into the hands of those who need it least. In the 1970s in Bangladesh, 27 per cent of rations went to the police, the military and the civil service, and 30 per cent to middle-class city dwellers. These recipients developed a taste for imported foodstuffs that could not be produced locally, thus lowering the price for local farm produce, and further impoverishing the peasantry.

Many of the problems associated with food aid are now being recognized at all levels. It is to be hoped that more attention will be given to the roots of the hunger crisis, such as international debt, and declining prices for agricultural produce; and that future food aid will be carefully assessed to ensure that it does not destabilize or undermine local economies. (See also: *Aid③*.)

Food and Agriculture Organization (FAO)
The principal international organization for the development of agriculture, fisheries and forests. Its original role was confined to determining food policy and designing appropriate projects, but it has increasingly taken part in the implementation of its policies.

The FAO's activities have also expanded in another direction. Whereas its advisers in Third World countries used to be members of the United Nations Development Programme (UNDP) missions to those countries, and were largely paid by that agency, today the FAO has its own representatives in the field.

FAO policies may be criticized on several grounds. To begin with, it insists on the mechanization of agriculture, which is difficult to justify in Third World countries where farms are small, the soil is delicate, and unemployment is massive. The organization also insists on a maximum use of chemicals. This is equally difficult to justify on many grounds, among them that yields comparable to those achieved with the use of chemicals can be obtained with organic methods, and that chemicals are largely used for export crops, which means that their use is irrelevant to what should be the overriding goal of feeding the starving masses of the World.

The FAO also insists on massively increasing the amount of land under perennial irrigation, a policy again difficult to justify in view of the disastrous experience, over the last 40 years, with the large dams (*qv*) and other water development projects needed to provide this type of irrigation.

A further criticism is that the organization plays an important role in encouraging pesticide-intensive post-harvest technology (see *Post-harvest losses*), rather than encourage methods of cultivation and the use of crop varieties that are less vulnerable to pests during storage. And, finally, it has helped petro-chemical companies acquire a large share of the world's distribution of seeds by helping to legalize the patenting of seeds and in general by adopting policies that must lead to the extinction of vast numbers of valuable traditional varieties.

Critics charge that the FAO has lost sight of its original intention to help those countries whose populations are increasingly malnourished, and threatened with starvation, and has instead adopted policies that seem to favour the agro-chemical industry. (See also: *Dams*③, *Desertification*③, *Erosion*Ⓐ③, *Green Revolution*③, *Land reform*Ⓐ③, *Salinization*Ⓐ③, *Waterborne diseases*③.)

Food dyes
Food dyes are the most conspicuous group of additives (*qv*) and also the most controversial.

There are arguments about both their necessity and their safety. Dyes can, however, be valuable to food manufacturers especially where their use does not have to be fully declared. Consumers tend to associate a bright colour with freshness, wholesomeness and tastiness.

Laboratory experiments have shown that if a range of drinks is presented with identical flavours, most consumers will report that the more darkly coloured they are, the stronger they appear to taste. Moreover, banana-flavoured drinks dyed red will be reported as having a strawberry flavour.

The safety of dyes is highly controversial, especially, but not exclusively, as regards the coal-tar dyes (*qv*). Dyes have been linked to symptoms of acute intolerance such as hyperactivity, asthma, eczema and migraine.

In the USA, 28 dyes are positively listed, while in the UK the list consists of 48 distinctive compounds. In 1986 the UK food and drink industry spent about $4,800,000 to buy approximately 700 tonnes of synthetic dyes, and about $3,200,000 buying some 16,000 tonnes of other dyes, mostly caramels. The market for dyes in the USA amounts to about $55 million a year.

One British researcher has estimated that by the age of 12 an average child will have consumed 225g (half a pound) of food dyes. (See also: *Cancer*Ⓛ.)

Food irradiation
The use of ionizing radiation to extend the "shelf life" of food. Proponents of food irradiation claim that it kills insect pests and the bacteria responsible for food poisoning. In addition, food irradiation is held to inhibit the sprouting of vegetables, such as potatoes, and delay the ripening of fruit.

With many chemical fumigants now suspected of causing cancer, food irradiation is now being promoted as a major weapon in the fight against world hunger. In particular, it has been hailed as the solution to the massive "post-harvest" losses (*qv*) of food incurred in the Third World due to rotting during storage. Food that had been irradiated, it is argued, would not even need refrigeration to remain "fresh."

Modern commercial food irradiation plants use cobalt-60, a powerful source of gamma radiation (*qv*) derived from Canadian nuclear reactors. Its gamma-rays are so penetrating that they require two metres of concrete to shield operating staff adequately. Significant leaks of cobalt-60 at food irradiation depots have already occurred.

Caesium-137, a major waste product of reprocessed nuclear fuels, is now being promoted as an alternative source of nuclear material for food irradiation, leading many critics to argue that the nuclear industry is hoping to use food irradiation technology as a "socially acceptable" means of getting rid of its nuclear waste (*qv*). Recently, the US Department of Energy has offered to lease caesium-137 to food irradiation companies for ten cents a curie, one-tenth of the price of cobalt.

Food irradiation is carried out in specially-constructed plants. The treated food is typically exposed to between 30,000-1,000,000 rads. By comparison, a chest X-ray delivers less than one-tenth of a rad. A commercial plant may hold the radioactive equivalent of one tonne of radium – more medium-lived radioactivity than was released at Chernobyl.

Tests on rats have shown that irradiated food causes cancer, mutations and perhaps chromosomal disorders. Under some conditions, food irradiation has also been found to cause the production of aflatoxin (*qv*), a highly carcinogenic mould. Given that aflatoxins are a major cause of post-harvest losses in Third World countries, the role that food irradiation might play in cutting such losses is open to doubt.

Where partly rotted food has been irradiated, most of the putrefying bacteria are killed but the toxins remain. Abuse of food irradiation to disguise rotten food has already occurred illegally in Britain and will continue.

At present, the use of food irradiation is limited, though the practice is permitted for most foods in the USA. In Britain, food irradiation was banned in 1967, but in July 1989 the government announced it would lift the ban, despite the opposition of consumer and health groups. In March 1987, the European Parliament refused to clear the sale of irradiated food in EC countries and called for a ban on the imports of irradiated food to the EC. Irradiated food is already permitted in Belgium, Italy, France, the Netherlands, Denmark and Spain. The European Commission would like to extend the use of irradiation to cover a wider range of foods than at present permitted. (See also: *Industrial Biotest Laboratories*Ⓛ, *Nuclear waste* ⓃⓅ, *Post harvest losses*Ⓐ③, *Radioactivity*Ⓝ.)

Food storage
See Post harvest losses.

Formaldehyde
A toxic gas used in many industrial applications, either in gaseous form or in a solution that is sometimes known as formalin. It is an ingredient of resins and glues, such as those used in the manufacture of building board, and is a major component of some foams used to insulate cavity walls. Formalin is also used as a disinfectant and soil sterilant.

The irritant effects of formaldehyde on the eyes, lungs and, in high concentrations, the skin are well known. More recently, concern has been expressed about its carcinogenic potential. Experimental evidence in the USA suggests that it may cause lung cancer.

Concern about human health has led the US authorities to ban the use of cavity wall insulation foams based on formaldehyde and to consider restricting its other uses. Germany is also considering tighter restrictions, but Britain's Health and Safety Executive insists that no human cancers have been formally attributed to formaldehyde. (See also: *Cancer*ⓁⓅ, *Carcinogen*ⒻⓁⓅ.)

Fuelwood crisis
Forests have long provided humanity with wood for cooking and heating, and today some 2,000 million people still rely on firewood for their fuel.

In many areas, demand has now outstripped supply. At present, 1,500 million people lack adequate supplies of fuelwood: by the turn of the century, that figure is expected to have reached 2,300 million, with 350 million facing acute shortages. In almost all rural societies that use firewood for fuel, it is women who are responsible for collecting and using it. Searching for firewood is taking more and more time as forests are depleted. In parts of the Himalayas, the gathering of wood and fodder can take a whole day, compared with two hours a day just a generation ago. In some regions of Africa, the time taken has increased four-fold and some women spend from midday to nightfall every day collecting enough firewood to cook the evening meal. Scarcity of firewood leads to fewer cooked meals and an increase in malnutrition and the spread of infectious diseases. Additionally, younger girls are now employed in the search, who thereby miss out on schooling.

As fuelwood supplies become exhausted, animal dung is frequently used as a substitute, thus depriving the land of nutrients and, ultimately, the farmer of food. In mountainous regions, such as the Himalayas, the declining fertility of the soil has led to steeper and steeper slopes being cultivated in order to make up for falling yields, thus exacerbating the problems of erosion (*qv*) and deforestation (*qv*).

The roots of the fuelwood crisis are complex. Population (*qv*) pressure is undoubtedly a major factor, but equally important are the degradation of woodlands as a result of commercial forestry and the clearing of forests for plantations, cattle, and other projects.

In terms of volume, firewood accounts for 54 per cent of the wood consumed worldwide every year – some 1,200 million tonnes.

Encouraged by the World Bank (*qv*), several governments have started "social forestry" (*qv*) programmes, ostensibly to provide villagers with firewood trees. Unfortunately, the bulk of the trees have almost universally gone for commercial uses, such as rayon production and paper milling.

However, successful reforestation (*qv*) schemes have been implemented by local groups, acting at the village level, and often working without outside funding. Such groups include the Chipko movement (*qv*) in India and the Green Belt movement in Kenya, both initiated by local women.

Local groups have also helped promote the use of biogas machines (which generate cooking gas by composting dung and organic waste) and better designed stoves, with vastly improved thermal efficiencies. Such technologies have helped reduce the pressure on local woodlots but their overall impact has proved marginal. Indeed, the only real solution to the fuelwood crisis lies in putting an end to further deforestation and in implementing massive village reforestation plans, using non-commercial species. (See also: *Energy*Ⓔ.)

Fusion
In fusion, light elements such as hydrogen are made to coalesce into heavier elements under extreme conditions of temperature and pressure. Such fusion processes lie behind the enormous releases of energy from stars like the sun. On Earth fusion has been achieved only in thermonuclear bombs in which the initial extreme conditions are brought about through the explosion of an atomic fission bomb.

Since the 1950s, scientists working on internationally funded projects such as JET – the European Torus Project – at Culham in Oxfordshire, have tried, so far in vain, to construct a machine that would produce a net surplus of energy from fusion, in a sustainable fashion.

Currently $1,000 million a year are being spent worldwide on fusion research. Fusion has considerable lure as an energy source. If the deuterium – a heavy hydrogen isotope – found in just one cubic metre of seawater were fused, it would release the energy equivalent to the burning of 2,000 barrels of crude oil, but at the moment the difficulties of building a viable, economic reactor seem insuperable.

A fusion reactor will have simultaneously to operate with temperatures that are both the hottest and coldest achieved on Earth. The fusion reaction will need to take place in temperatures probably higher than 270 million degrees Fahrenheit (150 million degrees Centigrade), while the giant magnets that keep the plasma away from the reactor walls will have to be superconducting and cooled by liquid helium or some other superconducting substance at temperatures approaching absolute zero.

To compound the problem, most of the energy released during the fusion process will be in the form of fast-moving neutrons that are between 15 and 30 times more energetic than those released in nuclear fission reactions. The fusion neutrons will bombard the walls of the reactor vessel, heating it up – thus offering the opportunity to raise steam and generate electricity – but also knocking each atom of the wall out of its lattice position at least 30 times every year; hardly a recipe for structural longevity.

Meanwhile, the tritium to be used as fuel in the fusion reactor is, in combination with deuterium, at least 100 times more reactive than deuterium alone. The tritium will be bred from a lithium blanket interposed between the reactor wall and the superconducting magnets. However, lithium is highly reactive, burning violently when in contact with either air or water. Claims that fusion reactors are a cleaner source of energy than conventional reactors have now been exploded. In 1987, Britain's National Radiological Protection Board (NRPB) calculated that a single reactor would generate an estimated 100 tonnes of radioactive debris – much of it high-level waste. This is considerably more on a megawatt to megawatt basis than an equivalent conventional reactor. A commercial pressurized water reactor PWR (*qv*), for example, generates some 40 tonnes of waste a year. The NRPB calculates that a fusion programme sufficient to power Britain would generate 100,000 tonnes of radioactive waste a year, much of which would require deep disposal for at least 100 years.

Most depressing of all for fusion enthusiasts, the power density of a large fusion reactor will at best probably be one-tenth that obtained in a light water fission reactor, such as the PWR (*qv*). Therefore the fusion reactor will be considerably larger, and in many respects considerably more expensive to operate, than a fission reactor. Moreover, judging from the extant problems in getting fusion reactors to work at all, the chances of producing a commercial reliable machine appear to be slim. (See also: *Fission*Ⓝ.)

Gaia
Gamma-HCH
Gamma radiation
GATT (General
    Agreement on
    Tariffs and
    Trade)
Genetic diversity
Genetic engineering
Genetic resources
Geothermal energy
Ghost acres
Global Environmental
    Facility
Global warming
Global 2000
Gorleben
Grande Carajas
Gray
Great Barrier Reef
Great Lakes
Green consumerism
Greenhouse effect
Greenhouse gases
Greenpeace
Green politics
Green Revolution
Groundwater
Growth promoters
Gulf War

Gaia

Theory put forward by the atmospheric scientist James Lovelock to explain the ability of the biosphere (*qv*), or world of living things, to create the environment that most favours its own stability, and to maintain that stability in the face of change. Lovelock argues that the biosphere acts as a single living system, which he calls "Gaia," after the Greek goddess of the earth.

Although he calls his theory "The Gaia Hypothesis," Lovelock invokes no goddess. He proposes that life on Earth is not only regulated by its environment but that it regulates the environment itself, gradually transforming it, over aeons of time, into the optimal conditions for life. The Gaia hypothesis therefore implies that life is bountiful and rich not because it has luckily found a suitable planet to survive on, but because life itself has used the special resources of the planet to *create* an environment capable of harbouring living organisms.

Lovelock says that living organisms act as the Earth's sensors – the interplay between different species and types of organisms adjusts the planet's global metabolism in response to change. Thus one organism's effluent is another's food, until the point where a complete cycle is formed and a balance is established. At times, the balance is disturbed; catastrophies do indeed occur; yet such has been the power of life and its grasp on Earth that the equilibrium is soon restored. Evolution is therefore a response by Gaia to re-establish balance, new species arising to fill the gaps left by the demise of the old order of organisms.

According to Lovelock: "The history of the Earth's climate is a compelling example in favour of Gaia's existence. We know from the record of sedimentary rocks for the past 3,500 million years that the climate has never been, even for a short period, wholly unfavourable for life. Because of the unbroken record of life, we also know that the oceans can never have frozen or boiled."

The sun's output of heat is 30

per cent greater than when life began nearly 4,000 million years ago. The primitive atmosphere was favourable to the origin and evolution of life, yet that same atmosphere today would make the earth largely uninhabitable. Indeed, the original atmosphere was rich in greenhouse gases (qv), such as carbon dioxide and ammonia, which allowed radiant energy to pass through from the sun to the Earth's surface, but absorbed the Earth's infra-red radiation. Given the sun's rising energy, is it pure coincidence that today's atmosphere has only 0.03 per cent carbon dioxide and only trace amounts of methane and ammonia?

The Gaia hypothesis points to many other such subtle adjustments at work, from the proportion of the Earth's surface covered by polar ice, which alters the amount of solar heat reflected, to the activities of coral reef-building bacteria. Lovelock posits a special role for the coral reefs (qv) in forming shallow lagoons which allow salt to be deposited by evaporation, thus maintaining ocean salinity at a level suitable for life.

Inherent to the Gaia hypothesis is the notion that the flow of essential nutrients through the system is promoted and regulated through the activity of living organisms. Gases are thus circulated through the atmosphere and various nutrient substances, such as sulphur or nitrogen, are oxidized and washed down with the rain to become again part of the terrestrial and marine ecology. The entire Gaian system has many features in common with the physiology of warm-blooded animals, the atmosphere acting as global lungs, and the water system, including rivers and the oceans, acting like the blood in the circulatory system. All the living components of the system are like cells and tissues, each fulfilling some role in the regulatory process. With animal physiology in mind, Lovelock has called this process "Geophysiology," echoing the notion, first stated by the geologist James Hutton in the late 1870s, that the

Earth was a superorganism and that its proper study would be physiology.

The nitrogen cycle is a classic example of nutrient interchange between terrestrial and aquatic organisms and the atmosphere. Nitrogen is an essential component of amino acids, proteins and nucleosides, and the capture of nitrogen from the air is carried out by bacteria such as *Rhizobium* which live symbiotically in association with leguminous plants. According to estimates in 1976, terrestrial nitrogen-fixers capture some 139 million tonnes each year, and aquatic organisms up to 120 million tonnes. The fixed nitrogen is in the form of highly soluble nitrate, which is taken up by plants and converted into useful organic compounds, such as proteins. When the plant dies, bacteria and fungi decompose proteins and other nitrogen-containing protoplasmic compounds into amino acids and then to ammonia, which either escapes into the atmosphere, where it undergoes oxidation to the gaseous oxides of nitrogen, or is converted again by bacteria into first nitrites and then nitrates. If those nitrates are not taken up by plants, then they may be reduced to nitrogen by denitrifying bacteria.

Without the intervention of human beings, the cycle was in balance, nitrogen fixation being counterbalanced by denitrification. The use of artificial fertilizers (qv), however, adds at least 55 million tonnes to the terrestrial balance and combustion in power stations and motor vehicles another 24 million tonnes. Those additions, combined with other man-made perturbations to Gaian cycles, are beginning to cause fundamental changes – most of them deleterious – to a broad range of ecosystems. Clearly, the Gaian balances that have been established over aeons of evolution are delicately maintained.

But there are limits to Gaia's capacity to act as a self-regulating organism. As Lovelock points out: "Gaia theory sees the Earth as a responsive living organism that will at first tend to resist adverse

environmental change and maintain homeostasis. But if stressed beyond the limits of whatever happens to be the current regulatory apparatus, it will jump to a new stable environment, where many of the current range of species will be eliminated."

As such, the Gaia hypothesis has important implications for the way we live. Our modern way of life is rapidly undermining the very mechanisms that have enabled Gaia to maintain her homeostasis. In that respect, Lovelock warns: "It is in humanity's interest to live well with the Earth. If we do not, Gaia will live on but with a new biosphere that may not include humans."

Gamma-HCH
See: *HCH*.

Gamma radiation
Discrete quantities of energy in the range of about 0.01 to 3.3 million electron volts that are without mass or charge and which move at the speed of light.

Gamma rays are extremely penetrating, being able to pass through steel and, depending on thickness, through concrete. They pass easily through the body, leaving some energy behind in the form of ions that, as with other types of radiation, cause changes and damage to the cellular structure. In general, cells are better able to cope with the damage caused by gamma radiation compared with other types of radiation, such as alpha particles, but there is always the possibility that faulty repair will lead to an aberrant line of cells. (See also: *Alpha radiation*①Ⓝ, *Beta radiation*①Ⓝ, *Radiation and health*①Ⓝ, *Radioactivity*Ⓝ.)

GATT (General Agreement on Tariffs and Trade)
The GATT was set up in 1948 to complement the International Monetary Fund (qv) and the World Bank (qv), its main purpose being to foster free trade and to reduce tariffs, quotas and other forms of protectionism. Until recently it has done so in a piecemeal way, frequently giving approval to blatantly protection-

ist measures. But as monetarist doctrine became more dominant in the 1980s, GATT's aims have become more ambitious. The present Uruguay Round of negotiations, which began in 1986 and involves 101 countries, set out to renegotiate the basic rules and principles governing international trade, and to sweep away almost all national barriers to a global free market.

Whereas GATT was until recently concerned principally with manufactured goods, it has now extended its brief to almost every sphere of economic activity, including services and investments. Under the proposed Trade-Related Investment Measures (TRIMS), governments would be powerless to control the activities of foreign banks, law firms, hotels or advertising agencies that had set up in competition to local businesses. For example, they would no longer be able to require foreign companies to use a percentage of local materials, nor to prevent them from taking profits out of the country, nor to reserve certain markets for vulnerable local businesses. Although ostensibly a reciprocal arrangement, it takes little imagination to appreciate that poorer Third World countries would soon be overrun by wealthy and aggressive Western and Japanese companies. Moreover, labour is not regarded by GATT as coming within the sphere of the service economy. While the TRIMS proposals would allow the unrestricted movement of capital investment into the Third World from industrialized nations, there are no parallel measures to ease restrictions upon the immigration of labour from South to North.

The Uruguay Round has also undertaken to ensure that all countries conform to standard laws concerning patents, copyrights and trademarks. These Trade-Related Intellectual Property Rights, as they are known, are already administered by bodies such as the World International Property Organization. But there is pressure to bring them under the jurisdiction of GATT, because it alone would have the

power to enforce retaliatory sanctions upon countries that did not comply. At present only one per cent of patents worldwide are owned by Third World companies or individuals. Of the 200,000 patents granted by Third World countries, 80 per cent are owned by foreign companies, not for the purpose of developing a local manufacturing base, but simply to stifle competition against goods imported by that company from abroad. The rigid enforcement of patent laws will encourage this procedure, and ensure that manufacturing industries remain firmly in the hands of transnational corporations. It is effectively a form of protectionism.

The Americans and the Japanese wish to take TRIMS even further by extending the regulations to cover life forms. Seeds, animal hybrids and any other genetic material subject to manipulation by humans would be deemed to be owned by the manipulator. This would include even strains taken from domestic species that had been developed over the centuries by generations of farmers, who never dreamed of receiving royalties for their work. Since the bulk of available genetic material is found in the tropics, Third World countries would find themselves denied access by agricultural and pharmaceutical companies to their own flora and fauna.

The impetus for this sudden drive to impose a globally managed "free market" upon every sphere of human activity is the spectre of the 1930s slump. Global recession, it is feared, might encourage creeping protectionism, trade wars, and the total collapse of international commerce. Unfortunately this concern comes at a time when the world's environment, too, is fighting for survival. Many of the hard won gains made in the last few years to protect our environment have involved some form of trade restriction, and they are now in jeopardy. For example, the restrictions upon the exportation of whole logs from countries such as Indonesia and the Philippines could fall foul of the GATT prescriptions for free trade. Ama-

zingly, throughout the entire negotiations of the Uruguay Round, the question of environmental protection was not even discussed. An environmental working group was set up within GATT in 1971, but in the intervening 20 years it has never actually met.

The main obstacles to the successful conclusion of the Uruguay Round have come from the countries of the EC that do not want to see a reduction in the nearly $50,000 million per year given in subsidies to European farmers. There are now frantic manoeuvres to engineer a compromise, the most promising being the plan proposed by Swedish farms minister Mats Hellstrom, which proposes 30 per cent cuts over 5 years.

Conventional wisdom holds that a reduction in support for agriculture in the North would prevent the accumulation of the vast surpluses of produce that are currently dumped on Third World countries, undermining their own agricultural economies. But it is unlikely that agricultural production in the North would decline significantly under a compromise such as the Hellstrom plan. Meanwhile, poorer countries would be obliged to reduce progressively the meagre price support systems and import restrictions that protect their agricultural producers. As the Jamaican delegation to the GATT talks observed: "There is a world of difference between subsidies used in the North to underpin overproduction and distort world markets, and subsidies designed to encourage self-reliance, protect rural employment, and encourage ecological sustainability in the South."

Genetic diversity

The Earth possesses a staggering diversity of plant, animal and insect species, each equipped with a different genetic make-up. To date, biologists have classified 1,700,000 species, but recent research suggests that the final total could top 40 million, insects alone accounting for 30 million species. Estimates of the number of flowering plants range from 275,000 to 400,000 – a figure which is increased still further if different varieties and strains are taken into account.

Such genetic diversity is vital to the maintenance of ecological stability, enabling the different species to meet different challenges and to fulfil different functions within the biosphere (*qv*). It also provides the redundancy of species that ensures that the loss of a single species is unlikely to threaten the survival of the ecosystem as a whole.

The reduction of diversity greatly increases the vulnerability of an ecosystem. Nowhere is this more evident than in the monocultures (*qv*), favoured by modern farmers, which are vulnerable to pests and disease.

Today, the genetic diversity of the biosphere is being rapidly eroded, 1,000 species becoming extinct every year – more than two a day. By the end of the century, that figure could have risen to 10,000, one species being lost every hour. An estimated 25,000 plants are now threatened with extinction (*qv*) and, at the current rate of destruction, 60,000 plant species may be lost by 2050. Worst hit are small islands: of the original 3,000 plant species in Hawaii, 270 are now extinct.

The implications of such mass extinctions are serious. Though nature has considerable resilience – ensured in part by the sheer number of species on Earth – there is a limit to how far that resilience can be stretched. (See also: *Genetic resources*©.)

Genetic engineering
In 1973, Stanley Cohen of Stanford University and Herbert Boyer of the University of California announced that they had performed the world's first successful experiment in "recombinant DNA" – or "genetic engineering" as it is more popularly known.

In 1974, the US biologist Paul Berg, one of the fathers of recombinant DNA research, called for a moratorium on the genetic engineering of cancer-causing viruses or toxin-producing genes that might infect humans.

Though the moratorium was supported by many eminent biologists, it did little to halt the onward march of the "biotechnologists". In 1980, the pro-engineering lobby in America won a considerable legal victory when the US Supreme Court ruled that companies had the right to "patent" novel forms of life. Three months after that ruling, Genotech, one of America's first biotechnology corporations, went public: in the first 20 minutes of trading, its shares rose in value by 54 points.

Advocates of biotechnology are starry-eyed about the benefits that genetic engineering will supposedly bring humanity.

In agriculture, it is suggested that recombinant DNA will give non-leguminous plants the capacity to fix nitrogen from the air, thus expanding output.

In the mining industry, there is talk of developing microorganisms that will mine ores and thus replace miners. One company has engineered a bacterium that produces an enzyme which eats away the salts in copper ores, "leaving behind an almost pure form of copper."

In medicine, it has been predicted that "by the year 2000 virtually all the major human diseases will regularly succumb to treatment by disease-specific artificial proteins produced by specialized hybrid microorganisms".

More ominously, it has been suggested that recombinant DNA be used to screen humans for genes associated with "anti-social behaviour" – the XYY karyotype, for example, which is frequently found in aggressive males.

But what of the dangers? Though the evolutionary success of bacteria is due to their natural ability to recombine DNA, only a minute number of the millions of possible new strains have survived. Rigorous natural controls have ensured that strains threatening to disrupt the balance of nature have died out. However, in the crude ecosystems developed by modern agronomists – the monocultures (*qv*) of the prairies, for example – nature's control system has been greatly simplified. The fear is that humans

have disrupted the natural balance to such an extent that some new opportunistic pathogen – released into the environment either accidentally or on purpose – will play havoc with the biosphere.

Such an accident is inevitable, according to critics of genetic engineering. They point out that absolute containment is impossible; that laboratory leaks frequently occur without being detected until it is too late, and that human fallibility alone will ensure that one day, sooner or later, a genetically engineered organism will escape into the environment. "Once it has escaped, there will be no way to recapture it," argues Professor Robert Sinsheimer, Chairman of the Biology Division at the California Institute of Technology. "And so we have the great potential for a major calamity."

The scale of that calamity will depend on the type of organism released and on its ability to survive outside the laboratory.

Accidental releases are not, however, the only threat to the environment. Genetic engineering operates not at the level of the organism, but at the level of the cell. It is therefore possible for genetic material from one strain or species – or genetic material that has been synthetically produced – to be transferred to unrelated species. Even if this is done with the best of intentions, for instance to impart resistance to a certain pest, it can cause major problems. Just as the widespread use of chemical pesticides has led to many species of insect developing resistance to one or more of these pesticides, so the use of transgenic methods of pest control is likely to lead to the development of pests with a resistance to the natural biological toxins used in genetically engineered plants. Laboratory research already suggests that pests are capable of rapidly developing resistance to such plants.

Once pests have developed this kind of resistance, crop varieties that now have good resistance to certain pests will no longer be immune from attack by these new strains of pest. By encouraging the development of new pest strains, genetic engineering could undermine not only production systems that rely on genetically engineered plants and chemical pesticides, but also those systems that rely on more traditional varieties of plant and techniques of pest control – such as organic systems.

Now that biotechnology has come of age, the battle over its applications is intensifying. In April 1986, Jeremy Rifkin, a major US critic of genetic engineering, took the US Department of Agriculture to court to prevent the release of two genetically engineered microbes into the environment. One was a pig vaccine against pseudo-rabies, the other an ice-resistant bacterium that prevents frost damage to crops.

After an extensive legal battle, two strains of ice-resistant bacteria were eventually released in the USA on April 24 and 29 1987. Britain has also licensed the release of genetically engineered bacteria in test trials.

The technology of in-vitro fertilization (IVF) is closely connected with the potential for human genetic manipulations. For example, only a relatively small modification of current medical procedures would be involved to experiment with injecting genetic material into an egg during laboratory fertilization. To date, however, no such experiments have been reported, and in many countries they are illegal.

However, Monsanto, the US chemical giant, has transplanted a human gene into a petunia plant in order to secrete a female reproductive hormone for use in pharmaceuticals. And, as Linda Bullard reports, gene technology opens up new possibilities in the field of biological weaponry, such as the development of new and more virulent pathogens. Indeed, in the USA in the early 1980s, there was a 10-fold increase in the amount spent by the military on biological weapons and genetic engineering research.

Genetic resources
The genetic variability within wild species has long been ex-
ploited through selective breeding by humans to create new hybrid strains of domesticated plants and animals and to refine existing ones. As such, the genetic variability of the natural world constitutes a major resource, wild plants and animals providing a huge potential for new crops, medicines, fibres and foods.

The rainforests, for example, have already supplied humanity with a host of products – from rubber to numerous drugs including quinine. Recent surveys reveal that the Indians of Amazonia (qv) use more than 1,000 plants of medicinal or nutritional value. Drugs developed from the rosy periwinkle, a rainforest plant, have already saved many children from leukemia. Maize contributes to aspirin, penicillin, plastics, paper manufacture and tyres.

According to the International Union for the Conservation of Nature (IUCN), 40 per cent of the prescription drugs that were on sale in 1976 contained a drug of natural origin.

Wild strains of domesticated plants have also saved some crops from being completely destroyed by pests. In the 1860s, for example, Europe's grape vine was saved from total destruction by phylloxera, an insect pest, only by grafting European vines onto the native American vine, which is phylloxera-tolerant. The practice still continues today.

Unfortunately, the world's genetic resources are rapidly being destroyed. With every acre of rainforest that we cut down, for example, we lose numerous species. "If present levels of deforestation continue," notes E.O. Wilson of Harvard University, "the stage will be set within a century for the inevitable loss of about 12 per cent of the 700 bird species in the Amazon Basin and 15 per cent of the plant species in South and Central America."

Quite apart from their ecological impact, today's mass extinctions of species represent a stupendous waste of resources which, if allowed to survive, could be tapped for the benefit of humanity. (See also: Extinction ©, Genetic diversity © Ⓕ.)

Geothermal energy
The obtaining of useful heat by exploiting anomalies in the rate at which rocks become warmer with increasing depth in the Earth's crust (the geothermal gradient).

Hot water can be tapped by drilling boreholes directly into it, much in the manner of drilling for petroleum or natural gas. Installations for this purpose exist in many parts of the world where such hot water can be found. Extracting heat from dry rock involves drilling several boreholes into it, fracturing the rock with down-hole explosions, then pumping cold water under pressure down one hole. The water fills the fractures and cavities made in the rock, is heated, and emerges from the other boreholes.

Depending on the temperature, the water can be used for district heating, but more usually it is used to pre-heat water for electrical steam-generation.

Geothermal energy can make only a minor contribution to the satisfaction of our energy requirements as there are very few suitable sites. The leading research sites in hot dry rock geothermal technologies are at Los Alamos in the USA and in Cornwall, England. Test drilling in Cornwall has been linked to an increase in earthquakes. (See also: Alternative technology Ⓔ, Energy Ⓔ, Soft energy paths Ⓔ.)

Ghost acres
Most of the rich nations of the industrialized world depend for their prosperity on importing food from abroad; that is, they depend on exploiting "ghost acres" abroad to grow their agricultural inputs and food. More than a million sq km (386,000sq miles) of arable land in the Third World are exploited in this way.

Georg Borgstrom, the US agronomist who coined the term "ghost acres," also uses the concepts of "fish acreage" (a measure of the land that would have to be tilled to provide the animal protein provided by imported fish) and "trade acreage," which refers to the net amount of agricultural produce being imported or exported for food and feed.

Borgstrom cites Germany, the United Kingdom, Japan, the Netherlands and Italy as countries that are all heavily dependent on ghost acres abroad to feed themselves. The United Kingdom, for example, "farms" two ghost acres for every acre of land under the plough in Britain itself. The Netherlands depends on about 40 million ghost acres, which is roughly eight times that country's own acreage of farming land.

The USA also exploits vast tracts of ghost acres, importing, for example, 782 million kg (1,725 million lb) of beef in 1977, much of it reared on ranches hacked out of South America's rainforests.

Without access to ghost acres abroad, many industrialized countries would be hard-pressed to feed their population without radical changes to their diet and to their agricultural practices. The extent to which a country relies on ghost acreage is thus a measure of its vulnerability. (See also: *Cash crops*③, *Malnutrition*①③.)

Global Environmental Facility (GEF)

In November 1990, the Global Environmental Facility (GEF), an international "Green Fund," was set up under the auspices of the World Bank to provide finance, in the form of grants and low-interest loans, for environmental protection in developing countries. So far $1,500 million have been pledged by a number of countries, Britain promising $40 million. The fund will be administered jointly by the World Bank and the UN Environment and Development Programmes (UNEP and UNDP).

The GEF will finance projects in four areas: protection of the ozone layer, prevention of marine pollution, conserving biodiversity, and the prevention of global warming. To qualify, projects must be based in a country with an annual per capita income of less than $4,000 in 1989, and they must also be shown to be beneficial to the global community. Grants will be given mainly to government-backed projects.

Although welcomed as a step in the right direction, the GEF has been greeted with suspicion in some quarters. The World Bank has, by its own admission, a poor record on environmental matters, and there are fears that the fund may be a hastily concocted public relations exercise. At issue is not so much the low level of funding – equal to 1.5 per cent of the Bank's annual budget – because the GEF is still a pilot scheme. Critics are more concerned that the existence of a separate environmental fund will tempt World Bank project planners, under pressure to produce realistic investment returns, to continue ignoring the environmental impact of their projects on the grounds that such matters will be dealt with by the GEF.

The Bank argues that results can only be assessed within a three-year time span, by linking GEF initiatives to already existing schemes. Thus a model has already been established for the Fund to serve as a remedial agency – a green afterthought. For example, the GEF will provide $25 million for the protection of wildlife habitats in Cameroon. But the World Bank-sponsored Tropical Forest Action Plan (*qv*) already has a strategy of extending logging into the virgin forests in the south of the country.

Some of the GEF schemes do appear to be breaking new ground. For example, there is an experimental project to develop solar power in the Philippines. But such initiatives can be viewed only as a token attempt to combat global warming while the Bank continues to direct less than one per cent of its new loans into energy efficiency programmes. Until there is a radical shift in the World Bank's core policy, the GEF may serve mainly as a "fig leaf" for loans that are environmentally unsound.

Global warming

See: *Greenhouse effect*.

Global 2000

In 1977, President Jimmy Carter commissioned a study of global environmental trends to determine what would be the main features of life on our planet by the year 2000. This study was directed by an independent consultant, Dr. Gerald O. Barney, with the cooperation of relevant US government departments.

Barney's report published under the title of "The Global 2000 Report to the President" was published in 1980. The general conclusion was that "if present trends continue, the world in 2000 will be more crowded, more polluted, less stable ecologically, and more vulnerable to disruption than the world we live in now. Serious stresses involving population, resources, and environment are clearly visible ahead. Despite greater material output, the world's people will be poorer in many ways than they are today.

"For hundreds of millions of the desperately poor, the outlook for food and other necessities of life will be no better. For many it will be worse. Barring revolutionary advances in technology, life for most people on Earth will be more precarious in 2000 than it is now – unless the nations of the world act decisively to alter current trends . . ."

Barney called upon the US government to undertake immediate measures to counteract these devastating trends. A complementary report was written by the Council on Environmental Quality and the Department of Trade, entitled "Global Future, Time to Act." It made various recommendations, mainly for setting up various institutions to monitor the course of environmental destruction.

The report was an immediate success. It sold a million copies in the USA, and spawned such groups as the Global Tomorrow Coalition which, three years later, had some five million members. It also exerted considerable influence on the thinking of some members of the US establishment, such as Senator Edmond S. Muskie, the then Secretary of State, and Mr Robert McNamara, then President of the World Bank.

The Carter administration did not survive long enough to implement the report's recommendations, and the Reagan administration not only ignored the report but set about systematically to dismantle what environmental legislation had been passed during the Carter era.

Various efforts have been made to discredit the Global 2000 Report. These have included the publication in 1984 of a report entitled "The Resourceful Earth," largely inspired by the late Herman Kahn of the Hudson Institute and Professor Julian Simon, a mail-order specialist. Its conclusions are the diametric opposite of the Global 2000 Report. In words that parody those used by Barney, the authors conclude: "If present trends continue, the world in 2000 will be less crowded (though more populated), less polluted, more stable ecologically, and less vulnerable to resource supply disruption than the world we live in now. Stresses involving population, resources and environment will be less in the future than now . . . The world's people will be richer in most ways than they are today . . . The outlook for food and other necessities of life will be better . . . life for most people on earth will be less precarious economically than it is now."

Events since 1984 do little to enhance the credibility of Kahn and Simon's conclusions.

Gorleben
See: *Wakersdorf*.

Grande Carajas
Brazil's giant Grande Carajas project is intended to open up the north-east of the country to industry and industrialized agriculture. One-sixth of the whole of Brazilian Amazonia will be affected.

The centrepiece of the project is the Serra dos Carajas open-cast iron ore mine, which is backed by a $600 million loan from the EC. The railroad and port that will service the mine are to be funded by the World Bank.

Other projects include a bauxite mine capable of producing eight million tonnes of bauxite a year, and an aluminium smelter that will produce 800,000 tonnes of aluminium and 20,000 tons of aluminium oxide a year for sale to

Japan. More than 6,000sq km (2,300sq miles) of forest will be cleared each year to provide charcoal for the smelter.

In addition, some 55,000sq km (21,000sq miles) will be cleared to make way for export-oriented plantations and biomass fuel farms. A further 30,000sq km (11,500sq miles) will be given over to ranches. The project as a whole will affect 23 tribal groups.

The project is likely to lead to severe water and air pollution problems. Many companies have been enticed into it through the promise of "less stringent" pollution controls. Companies are also being offered a ten-year tax holiday. (See also: *Amazonia*③, *Dams*③, *Hamburger connection*Ⓐ, *Tribal societies*③, *Tropical rainforests*③.)

Gray
The unit of radioactive dose, equivalent to 1 joule per kilogram. The gray is replacing the rad: 1 gray equals 100 rads.

Great Barrier Reef
The Great Barrier Reef is a spectacular mosaic of coral, plant and animal life of immense complexity, which was inscribed on the World Heritage list in 1981. It extends for 2,000km (1,240 miles) along the north-east coast of Australia, the largest reef ecosystem in the world. Comprising about 2,600 separate reefs, shoals and coral formations, and covering an area of 348,700sq km (134,600sq miles) it stretches from Fraser Island to the Torres Strait near the coast of Papua New Guinea.

The living reef, built up from tiny coral polyps over millions of years, is the richest ecosystem on earth. About 400 different coral types form the reef structure, home to a variety of plant life, thousands of marine invertebrates, 1,500 fish species and 240 species of sea birds. The Great Barrier Reef also includes major feeding grounds for the endangered dugong and the nesting grounds for many turtles.

Reefs are extremely vulnerable to changes in their environment. They require warm, shallow, clear waters to grow. In particular, they

cannot tolerate pollution, which can cloud the waters, reducing light and changing the water temperature, choke the pores of marine animals and coral, or simply poison reef organisms.

During the late 1960s, public concern for the future of the reef began to grow and focused on proposals for oil drilling and mineral exploitation of the reef. A long battle by a young Australian environmental movement ensued as the beauty and biological significance of the Great Barrier Reef was brought to the attention of the Australian people. In 1975, the Great Barrier Reef Marine Park Act was passed, excluding mining from all sections of the reef, and a joint Federal-State government authority was established to manage the region. By 1987, 95 per cent of the reef lay within the marine park.

Current management involves zoning the reef to allow access by various user groups, for commercial fishing, shell collecting, tourist operations, recreational and scientific uses. Unfortunately, the authority has not eliminated all threats to the reef environment. A survey by the Australian Institute for Marine Science has revealed that 35 per cent of the reef has been invaded by crown-of-thorns starfish, which eat the coral. Overfishing of the natural predators of the starfish is a possible cause of this latest threat to the reef, but it is likely that pollution from tourism and new housing developments is also to blame. (See also: *Coral reefs* Ⓒ.)

Great Lakes
Known as "North America's inland seas," the five Great Lakes – Superior, Michigan, Huron, Erie and Ontario – contain 18 per cent of the world's liquid fresh water, supplying drinking water to 21 million people and a habitat for many fish.

Strict pollution controls have helped to rid the lakes of conventional sources of pollution, such as sewage, which causes eutrophication (*qv*) and which threatened to turn the lower Great Lakes – notably Lake Erie – into "dead lakes." However, there is growing concern about levels of toxic chemicals in the lakes, chemicals which have already led to a US ban on the sale of several species of fish. Acid rain (*qv*) damage to the streams that feed the lakes is also a problem.

In 1985, the eight US states and two Canadian provinces that border the five Great Lakes signed the Great Lakes Charter, in which they agreed to consult each other on any plans to divert water from the lakes. The charter was followed a year later by the Toxic Substances Control Agreement, which aims at reducing toxic discharges into the lakes "to the maximum extent possible." Under the agreement, discharges from the Niagara River into Lake Superior, for example, are to be cut by 50 per cent by 1995. A bilateral agreement between Michigan and Ontario binds both states to eliminating toxic compounds from areas bordering their lakes. Oil drilling in all the lakes is banned under the Toxic Substances Control Agreement. (See also: *Love Canal*Ⓟ.)

Green consumerism

Movement to encourage consumers to use "the power of the purse" to persuade companies, through market pressure, to produce more "environment-friendly" consumer goods. The movement in the UK received a considerable boost with the publication in 1988 of *The Green Consumer Guide*, by John Elkington and Julia Hailes, which rapidly became a bestseller.

The guide urges consumers to avoid products which are likely to:

• endanger the health of the consumer or of others;

• cause significant damage to the environment during manufacture, use or disposal;

• consume a disproportionate amount of energy during manufacture, use or disposal;

• cause unnecessary waste, either because of over-packaging or because of an unduly short useful life;

• use materials derived from threatened species or from threatened environments;

• involve the unnecessary use – or cruelty to – animals, whether this be for toxicity testing or for other purposes;

• adversely affect other countries, particularly in the Third World."

As a result of pressure from green consumers many companies are attempting to change their image. Unfortunately their enthusiasm has led them to make false or exaggerated claims. For example, one car maker claimed that its vehicles were ozone-friendly because they ran on unleaded petrol, even though lead has no effect upon the ozone layer. Frequently one item in a range of products is improved, while others remain unchanged; or one worthy aspect of a product is advertised while other harmful effects upon the environment are ignored.

The extent to which consumer power has effected genuine change has so far been limited. Many consumers lack the time, money and information to alter their habits. The proportion of "green" products on the supermarket shelves is still tiny. Yet opinion polls have shown that the public does want action. The use of a government's fiscal and regulatory powers is potentially a simpler and quicker way to change what is produced and retailed than waiting for a slow and unsteady shift in spending patterns.

But beyond the move to "environmentally friendly" products, there lie deeper issues. Green consumerism seeks to reassure the public that by making only marginal changes to our lifestyles, increase in personal consumption can continue indefinitely – as if we could save the Earth by converting cars to unleaded petrol. But at the root of much ecological destruction lies the sheer volume of consumption in Northern industrialized countries, and green consumerism is consumerism nonetheless. It still equates happiness with the acquisition of commodities.

Genuinely green consumers would attempt to cut their levels of consumption, heading their shopping lists with the question "do I really need to buy all of these items?" Refusal is the first "R" in a range of options open to the prospective buyer: reduction, reuse, repair and in the last resort recycling. Unfortunately this order of priorities is rarely considered.

Greenhouse effect

The greenhouse effect caused by rising levels of greenhouse gases (*qv*) is the most serious environmental problem facing the planet. There is some disagreement whether or not the rise in global temperature of 0.5 degree centigrade in the last century is due to global warming caused by human activities or is a natural climatic fluctuation. However, it is almost unanimously agreed among climatologists that immediate action to curb global warming is needed.

Together with the hole in the ozone layer (*qv*), the greenhouse effect has finally awakened the international community to the environmental crisis. In 1988, during the middle of the worst US drought for 50 years, NASA scientist James Hansen created headlines around the world when he declared: "It is time to stop waffling . . . and say that the evidence is pretty strong that the greenhouse effect is here." A few weeks later an international conference of scientists and policy makers held in Toronto concluded that the greenhouse effect constituted an "uncontrolled, globally pervasive experiment whose ultimate consequences could be second only to a global nuclear war." In March 1989, British Prime Minister Margaret Thatcher stated that "major changes in the chemistry of the earth's atmosphere are taking place, with potentially calamitous effects for mankind." The language of the "emotional" and "doom-mongering" environmentalist had become the language of the politician and diplomat.

If greenhouse gas emissions continue increasing at present rates, climate models suggest that global temperature will rise 1.5 to 4.5°C (2.7 to 8°F) by 2050 and that sea levels will rise by from 25 to 110cm over the next century, mainly due to thermal expansion and the melting of glaciers and Antarctic ice. If counter measures are not taken, global warming will not, of course, stop in 2050 but is likely to continue. The large uncertainties are used by researchers to argue for more funds for research, and by politicians as an excuse for inaction while waiting for the results of further research. The mechanisms of global warming are, however, well enough understood to make action imperative and urgent.

The predicted climatic consequences of global warming include: the drying out of the midwest grainbelt and the wheatfields of the steppes; the flooding of coastal agricultural lands (around a third of all cropland is estimated to be at risk from flooding or salt water intrusion from a sea level rise of one metre); and the consequent inability of a rising world population to feed itself. Hundreds of millions of people are at direct risk from flooding, especially in the densely populated river deltas of Egypt and Bangladesh.

Those who are forced to become "environmental refugees" will find little welcome in neighbouring countries struggling to cope with the effects of climatic change. Diminishing food and freshwater resources will fuel increasing civil unrest and international conflict. Species extinctions will accelerate greatly as changes in ecosystems outpace the ability of animals and plants to adapt, especially as so many species are now confined to parks or reserves surrounded by towns, roads or agricultural "deserts."

The importance of acting now is underlined by the many possible feedback mechanisms which may fuel a "runaway greenhouse effect." The melting of the arctic permafrost, for example, will release billions of tonnes of methane into the atmosphere. A reduction in the size of the ice caps will reduce the earth's albedo or reflectivity, therefore allowing it to absorb yet more heat (the arctic ice cap thinned by 30 per cent between 1976 and 1989). As soils dry out they will release

large amounts of carbon and as the habitat range of tree species is reduced the important role which they play in absorbing carbon dioxide will be diminished. The interaction of the greenhouse effect with other problems such as increased ultraviolet light due to depletion of the ozone layer (*qv*), soil erosion (*qv*), and acid rain will obviously worsen the consequences of global warming by lessening the ability of the biosphere to adapt to change.

Yet another frightening scenario is the possibility of a "climatic flip." The atmosphere may not react to increasing pollutants in a linear and (at least partly) predictable manner but may reach a threshold point above which there would be a global change to an entirely new and unpredictable climate. This theory is consistent with the Gaia hypothesis (*qv*) put forward by James Lovelock.

Responding to climate change will mean drastic and, for some, painful action. Massive changes in economic and social priorities will have to occur. Stabilizing atmospheric concentrations of carbon dioxide will require emissions to be reduced by 60 to 80 per cent. Even if CFC emissions cease completely by 2000, atmospheric concentrations will still be higher at the end of the next century than they were in 1985 due to their long residence times.

Recognizing the threat, however, is a far cry from actually doing something about it. Governments have been quick to adopt a rhetoric of concern for the global climate, but meanwhile have exacerbated the problem by continuing the policies that lead to increases in greenhouse gas emissions. For example, only a few weeks after Margaret Thatcher had chaired a seminar of scientists, politicians and policy-makers on the greenhouse effect, the British government unveiled a £12,000 million road-building programme that would encourage an increase in greenhouse gas-producing traffic. Britain's output of carbon dioxide rose 1.6 per cent in 1990, largely because of an increase of 1.8 per cent in fossil fuel consumption.

Some of the EC countries have

taken a lead in proposing national targets for reductions in carbon dioxide emissions, which they urge other nations to emulate. Germany is aiming for a 30 per cent reduction by 2005, Italy 20 per cent by the same year, and France 50 per cent by 2030. Other countries, including Britain, aim only to stabilize emissions by 2005. In September 1991, the European Commissioners, anxious to establish a common policy, proposed an energy tax of $10 per barrel of oil, or its equivalent, for all EC nations.

So far, attempts to establish a global strategy have been fraught with disagreement. A series of world climate conferences, involving 137 countries, is due to culminate in the formulation of a legally binding policy at the United Nations Conference on Environment and Development in Brazil in 1992. But progress has been consistently blocked by a number of powerful countries who maintain that imposing carbon dioxide targets is an interference with national sovereignty. Chief among them is the USA, which is responsible for 23 per cent of the world's carbon emissions. The USA refuses to accept that global warming is probably taking place, or even to employ the expression "global warming," and is calling for more research before action is taken. At the second World Climate Conference in November 1990, the USA was criticized as "the only wealthy country not to make tangible promises."

The impossibility of dealing with the enormity of the greenhouse problem with conventional political and economic policies was admitted by US Environmental Protection Agency chief William Reilly in June 1989. Reilly acknowledged that "under our most optimistic control scenario, we could reduce global warming in the year 2025 by only onefourth" and even that would require massive economic and industrial restructuring which "the world . . . is not yet ready for." A realistic strategy to deal with the emergency will have to encompass huge increases in energy efficiency (*qv*) and the use of renewable energy sources, an end to deforestation and a massive programme of reforestation, a change to organic farming practices and a reduction of demand and productive output on a global scale. The latter measure is inconceivable to most industrialists and politicians outside of the Green (*qv*) parties.

Contrary to the claims of the British and other governments, a global expansion of nuclear power is not an option in the battle to curb climate change. It would bring in its wake environmental, social, economic and security problems which may rival those associated with global warming and it has been shown that even under optimistic cost projections, one US dollar spent on energy conservation is up to seven times more effective in reducing CO_2 emissions that one dollar spent on nuclear power. Replacing current fossil fuel electricity generating capacity worldwide with nuclear power would require the impossible goal of commissioning one nuclear plant every few days over several decades. The construction of nuclear plant on such a massive scale would itself entail the emission of large quantities of carbon dioxide. Indeed a recent study for Friends of the Earth concluded that, taking into account the energy needed for uranium mining and processing, "the eventual use of low-grade uranium resources by an expanded nuclear power system will result in the release of as much carbon dioxide from the nuclear fuel cycle as from a conventional fossil fuel-fired power station."

The greenhouse gases which have already been released already commit us to a global temperature rise of 0.5 to 1°C (0.9 to 1.8°F). If we are to have any chance of preventing further rises we must, in the words of the British Green Party, develop policies based on "harmony with the planet, local production for local need, minimal use of energy and material, recycling and repair, decentralization of power, freedom of information and the regeneration of a healthy sustainable environment. Continuing to worship the lie of economic growth is killing the planet by degrees."

Greenhouse gases

The main greenhouse gases are carbon dioxide (CO_2) (*qv*), chlorofluorocarbons (CFCs) (*qv*), methane (CH_4), nitrous oxide (N_2O) and tropospheric ozone (*qv*). These gases allow solar radiation to pass through them but trap the long-wave infra-red radiation reflected back from the earth's surface, therefore warming the lower atmosphere – the so-called greenhouse effect (*qv*).

Carbon dioxide, emitted mainly by the burning of fossil fuels and the destruction of forests, accounts for around half of the expected warming. Levels of carbon dioxide in the atmosphere have already increased by 25 per cent from pre-industrial levels and without drastic action to reduce emissions, levels will double by the second half of the next century.

Methane is responsible for nearly 20 per cent of global warming and its concentration in the atmosphere, which has already doubled from pre-industrial times, is increasing at around one per cent per year. The many sources of methane include rice paddies, flatulence in cattle, the burning of organic material, landfills, coal mining and natural gas distribution systems.

CFCs are molecule for molecule the most potent greenhouse gases. Although their concentrations are currently small they are increasing rapidly and if effective worldwide action to curb the release of CFCs is not taken, by the year 2030 they could account for a third of the total greenhouse effect.

The relative contribution of the various sources of nitrous oxide is very much an unknown. A large proportion of these emissions come from nitrogen fertilizer applications and other intensive agricultural practices as well as from the burning of organic material and the manufacture of nylon. Nitrous oxide is also implicated in the depletion of the ozone layer (*qv*). It accounts for around six per cent of the greenhouse effect and its concentration is increasing in the atmosphere at around 0.5 per cent per year. It is the most stable of the greenhouse gases with an atmospheric residence time of 170 years.

Tropospheric or low-level ozone is responsible for around 12 per cent of the greenhouse effect and although its distribution is more localized than the other gases, it is assumed to be increasing globally at a quarter of a per cent per year.

Green politics

The first Green party was founded in New Zealand in 1972. Though the Values Party, as it was called, never gained any seats in national elections, it did work out a detailed programme that became the first statement of Green politics.

The programme explicitly stated the need for a steady-state population and economy, decentralization of government, human-centred technology, soft energy (*qv*) systems, and such values as co-operation, nurturing and peacemaking.

In early 1973, a green party called "People," inspired by *The Ecologist*'s Blueprint for Survival, was set up in the United Kingdom. In 1987, its name was changed to the Green Party. In 1989, the Party won 15 per cent of the British vote in the European elections, but because of Britain's electoral system won no seats in the Parliament.

On the Continent, however, the Greens have been more successful. In 1983, the West German Green Party won five per cent of the national vote in the General Election, which, thanks to proportional representation, gave it 27 seats in the Bundestag. Contrary to the predictions of Christian Democrats and Social Democrats, the Greens managed to increase their representation to 42 seats in 1987.

The success of the German Greens lay partly in their being a coalition of groups spanning the political spectrum from right to far left; their success, however, has waned somewhat recently.

Their ideas of ecology, social responsibility, grass roots democracy and non-violence, which hold this diverse coalition together, attract a growing number of young voters born after 1945, and they have also become the political voice of the anti-nuclear movement.

In Belgium, the Greens gained national representation two years before the Germans, and enjoyed the success of becoming the first Greens to participate in governing when they went into coalition with the Social Democrats after municipal elections in Liège. In Italy, too, Greens have been elected to Parliament, winning 15 seats in the 1987 general election. Sweden has two Green Party members in parliament. In the US, a Green party has been formed, and has held its first convention in San Francisco. (See also: *Conservation*©, *Deep ecology*Ⓕ, *Ecological movement*Ⓕ.)

Green revolution

The growth of world hunger, and the spectre of still worse hunger to come, led the United Nations Food and Agriculture Organization (FAO) (*qv*) to organize its first World Food Congress in 1963 and to set up its Freedom from Hunger Campaign. On the assumption that world population would grow by 2.6 per cent a year, and that incomes would also grow, FAO argued that if hunger was to be overcome, an annual increase in food supply of 3.9 per cent was required as compared to the 2.7 per cent increase of the years 1956-66. This meant in effect increasing world food production by 140 per cent by 1985.

To achieve this, FAO launched its "Green Revolution," known formally as the Indicative World Plan for Agricultural Development. The Green Revolution involved the introduction of high-yielding cereal varieties or HYVS (*qv*) developed by the International Rice Research Institute (IRRI) in the Philippines and a similar institute in Mexico. The hybrid cereals were short-stemmed to avoid lodging (being blown over by the wind), and quick-maturing, making it possible to grow three crops

on the same land every year. Their yields were impressive.

Most people were persuaded that the Green Revolution would provide the solution to the world food problem and, significantly, Norbert Borlaug, generally regarded as the father of the Green Revolution, was awarded a Nobel prize. The plan, however, was and still is criticized on a number of counts.

The first criticism is that the Green Revolution affects only cereals, which are easily stockable and saleable on the world market, no interest being shown in vegetables, fruit or any of the staple crops grown in different parts of the Third World for local consumption. This alone suggests that the Green Revolution cannot overcome the problem of hunger.

In addition, the food quality of the hybrids is lower than that of traditional varieties, their taste rarely being appreciated by rural people. They are also difficult to stock because of their high moisture content, which not only makes them vulnerable to moulds, such as aflatoxins (*qv*), but reduces their keeping qualities – a serious problem since, according to the FAO, something like 30 per cent of the food produced in the Third World is destroyed by pests during storage.

Furthermore, high yields are obtained only in highly favourable soils and climatic conditions. On the marginal soils, where most Third World people live, the results have been far less impressive.

Worse still, the hybrids provide high yields only when used in conjunction with heavy applications of fertilizer. In India, the Green Revolution has increased wheat yields by 50 per cent and rice yields by 25 per cent. However, this has required a more than twenty-fold increase in fertilizer use (from 212,000 tonnes in 1960-61 to 4,264,300 tonnes in 1982-83). The abandonment of the traditional crop varieties in favour of the high-yielding hybrids has also led to a terrible loss of genetic diversity (*qv*) and a corresponding increase in vulnerability to pest infestations.

Moreover, the hybrids have also proved vulnerable to pests and diseases, which has meant a massive increase in the use of pesticides (*qv*). A 1981 survey undertaken in the Philippines reveals that expenditure on insecticides increased from two pesos to 90 pesos per hectare between 1966 and 1979 – an increase of 4,500 per cent. The use of pesticides has had serious consequences, including the destruction of fish stocks (*qv*), with severe nutritional implications for Third World peoples who depend on fish as a major source of animal protein.

In addition, high-yielding varieties require irrigation water, which has helped justify massive dam-building programmes with terrible ecological consequences such as salinization (*qv*) and an increase in waterborne diseases (*qv*).

Finally, the cost of the chemical inputs and irrigation water have proved to be beyond the means of small farmers, many of whom have fallen into terrible debt, while others – the majority – have simply been put out of business to become landless labourers and slum dwellers.

The costs of fertilizer, pesticides and irrigation water has also caused an escalation of the Third World debt, making it imperative that the food produced be exported. As a result, despite higher yields, less food is available to feed local people. This in itself makes a nonsense of the claim that the Green Revolution has provided a means of feeding the rural masses of the Third World. (See also: *Cash crops*, *Development*③, *High-yielding varieties*Ⓐ ③.)

Groundwater

The technical name for water stored within the pores of soil and rock formations.

Worldwide, groundwater supplies are being depleted at an alarming rate, mainly for agricultural purposes. In addition, many groundwater sources are being polluted by the dumping of hazardous wastes and by the slow seepage of agricultural chemicals through the soil.

In many arid areas of the world, groundwaters are being depleted at an unsustainable rate. In the southern Indian state of Tamil Nadu, water tables fell by 25-30m (80-100ft) between 1975 and 1985, while production in many areas of the Punjab and Haryana – the breadbasket states of northern India – is at risk due to the mass use of tubewells. The problem is compounded by excessive deforestation (*qv*) which has reduced the rate of groundwater recharge. In the High Plains of the USA, the area under irrigation has dropped dramatically as a result of excessive "mining" of the vast Ogallala aquifer.

One consequence of groundwater depletion is that aquifers begin to compact, causing the land above them to subside. The classic case is the city of Venice, which has sunk by 25cm (10 inches), resulting in widespread flooding during spring tides.

The pollution of groundwater is now a major problem in industrialized countries – and, increasingly, in the Third World. One-fifth of California's major drinking water wells have pollution levels above the safety limits set by the state, carcinogenic chlorinated solvents being the most common pollutants.

Hazardous waste dumps are the most common source of groundwater pollution in the US, but agricultural chemicals also pose a major threat. Half of the so-called "Superfund" (*qv*) sites in the US are now known to be leaking.

In Britain, a 1985 report from the Department of the Environment revealed that ten per cent of Britain's potable aquifers could be contaminated with concentrations of chlorinated solvents above the World Health Organization's "safe" limits. Sixteen aquifers in Scotland alone were found to contain tetrachloroethylene – five of them at levels five times higher than the WHO limit of 10ppb.

Two years later, in 1987, the British Geological Survey published the results of a desk study on the threat posed to groundwaters by agrochemicals and industrial wastes. It warned that "the

number of reported incidents of potable groundwater supplies being polluted by industrial solvents has increased significantly". The four most widely used solvents in Britain – tetrachloroethylene, trichlorethylene, methylene chloride and methyl chloroform – are all known to cause cancer in laboratory animals. Because chlorinated solvents have a low solubility in water, they are more liable to penetrate rapidly and widely into aquifers. Should this happen, says the report, the result "would be an environmental disaster."

The BSG survey was followed in 1989 by a DOE report, which acknowledged that groundwater pollution by organics (pesticides, solvents and other compounds) "is not known with certainty but appears to be widespread and poses a significant threat to groundwater quality." Describing landfill as "a major threat to groundwater quality," the DOE noted that "all water authorities report groundwater pollution problems with landfill sites to a varying degree and in many cases it is regarded as the most significant threat."

Toxic agrochemicals are also a major source of groundwater pollution. Each year, American farmers spray or spread some 260,000 tonnes of pesticides and 42 million tonnes of fertilizers. Twenty-three states now report finding groundwaters contaminated with a wide range of agrochemicals. The most common contaminants are nitrate (*qv*) and the carcinogenic nematocides EDB, DBCP and aldicarb (*qv*).

In Britain, nitrate pollution is already a major problem in such agricultural areas as East Anglia, the East Midlands, Lincolnshire, and Essex.

Experts are agreed that worse is yet to come. Because water moves so slowly through the ground, many of the chemicals sprayed or dumped on the land two or more decades ago have yet to reach underlying groundwaters.

Once polluted, groundwaters are difficult (in some cases impossible) to cleanse. There are no microorganisms to break down

the pollutants, and groundwater moves too slowly to permit any significant dilution and dispersal of contaminants. In Britain, an aquifer near Norwich that was polluted with whale oil in 1815 still contained significant toxic residues when wells were dug in 1950. (See also: *Aldicarb*Ⓐ Ⓟ, *Deforestation*③, *Hazardous waste*, *Landfill*, *Nitrate*Ⓐ Ⓟ, *Ogallala aquifer*Ⓐ, *Superfund*Ⓟ.)

Growth promoters

The main use to which hormones (*qv*) are put in the livestock industry is as growth promoters. For a long time Diethylstilbesterol (DES) (*qv*), a synthetic oestrogen, was in wide use. It permitted a weight gain of 15-19 per cent and increased feeding efficiency by ten per cent in steers.

It was banned in 1979 when it was found to cause clear cell adenocarcinoma, a rare form of cancer of the vagina, in some daughters of women exposed to it. However, it continued to be widely used illegally.

The incentive to use these growth promoters is considerable. According to Dr. Garry Duhl of Kansas State University, for a cost of $2 they make it possible to increase the weight of an animal by 18kg (40lb), which means a $10 (1983 prices) return for each dollar invested.

Lutalyse has been known to cause abortions and changes in the menstrual cycle. Melengesterol acetate (MGA), a synthetic progesterone manufactured by a division of the Upjohn Corporation, is, like other progesterones, a suspected co carcinogen; that is to say, it can become carcinogenic when used in conjunction with another substance that alone is not a carcinogen (*qv*).

In 1982, there was found to be a considerably increased incidence of premature thelarche (breast development) in Puerto Rico. Some of the children affected also showed other signs of precocious sexual development. Little girls of no more than three or four, for instance, developed pubic hair and even menstruated. In most of these children increased oestrogen levels were found. This

Kuwaiti oil wells fired by retreating Iraqi troops blacken the sky.

problem was ascribed to the use of oestradiol in locally produced pork and chicken. Significantly, many of the affected children also developed ovarian cysts. This fits in with the result of a study undertaken by the Commonwealth Health Department, which showed a higher incidence of cancer in precisely those areas in Puerto Rico where most of the children with thelarche and precocious puberty came from.

We know something of the effects of oestrogens from the experience of young women taking the birth control pill, which leads to an increased incidence of thromboembolism and is suspected of causing melanoma, a skin cancer that can often be fatal. High levels of oestradiol have also been held responsible for heart attacks.

In the UK, the use of growth promoters such as Zeranol and trenbolen acetate, or Finaplix, has been encouraged by the Agricultural Development and Advisory Service (ADAS) of the Ministry of Agriculture, Fisheries and Food (MAFF). However, in October 1985 the European Parliament banned the use of zenarol (Ralgro) and Finaplix and the three so-called natural hormones testosterone, progesterone and 17-beta-oestradiol, which are in reality synthetic compounds identical to the sex hormones common to many mammals.

In 1988, the EC ban came into force in Britain, despite a last-ditch attempt by the British government to have it overturned. Nonetheless, there is strong evidence of a thriving black market in banned growth promoters throughout the EC.

Gulf War

The 1991 Gulf War, precipitated by the Iraqi invasion of Kuwait, has put the ecological effects of war firmly on the environmental agenda. As Iraqi troops fled Kuwait, the awesome spectacle of 730 burning oil wells (most deliberately set on fire) was broadcast on television screens around the world, and it became clear that the environmental impact of war could no longer be overlooked.

In March 1991, at the end of the war, the number of wells burning in Kuwait was equivalent to the entire number of oil well blowouts in previous world history. Some 5 million barrels of oil were burnt every day – roughly three times the amount normally exported daily by Kuwait before the war. A cloud of smoke and soot, 900km (570 miles) long, 600km (390 miles) wide and 1km (0.6 mile) high shrouded the region.

The area affected to some degree by the smoke has been vast. Black rain and snow have been reported falling in Bulgaria, Turkey, Russia, Iran, Afghanistan and India. Abnormal concentrations of soot in the atmosphere were observed as far away as Wyoming and Hawaii in the USA, and Japan. Both Greenpeace and *Scientific American* accused the US Environmental Protection Agency of withholding information, to maintain the fiction of "a smart, clean war."

The effect of the oil-well fires on Kuwait and its surrounding area has been disastrous. The 5,000 tonnes of soot released every day by the fires has blackened the landscape and poisoned the atmosphere. Livestock have died from eating contaminated grass, and crop yields in the next two years are expected to plummet. The number of patients suffering from asthma and other respiratory diseases has risen dramatically. Two independent studies have predicted an increase of ten per cent in Kuwait's death rate from lung cancer and other illnesses.

By November 1991, all of the well fires had been put out. But even when its fire is extinguished, a damaged oil well may still be pumping thousands of barrels of oil into the surrounding area. Round Kuwait city there are now huge oil lakes, which threaten the wildlife and release volatile hydrocarbons into the atmosphere. Some of this oil may be seeping into the drinking water, as may various heavy metals given off by the fires, such as nickel and vanadium.

During the course of the conflict, vast amounts of oil were released into the waters of the Gulf. There was great damage to seabirds and sea mammals, such as the dugong. This may be followed by a decline in fish and shrimp stocks if their breeding grounds are affected.

By no means all the damage has been caused by oil. The surrounding desert was churned up by the movements of thousands of military vehicles and pummelled by the Allies' bombs. An Egyptian geologist expects a doubling in the intensity of sandstorms, causing dunes to encroach on roads and farms. Similar damage will have occurred in Iraq, although its extent is not clear to the outside world. Nor is it known whether the bombing of Iraqi nuclear installations has released significant amounts of radioactivity.

Halons
Hamburger
    connection
Hanford
Hazardous waste
Heart disease
Heat pump
Heavy metals
Hedgerows
Herbicides
Hexachlorocyclo-
    hexane (HCH)
High level waste
High yielding varieties
    (HYVs)
Hinkley Point
Holism
Hormones in meat
Hydro-electricity

Halons

Halons, used extensively in fire protection systems, contain bromine, which damages the ozone layer (qv) in much the same way as chlorine from CFCs (qv). Although halon levels in the atmosphere are much lower than CFC levels, they are increasing at a faster rate. The Montreal Protocol, which (as originally negotiated) aims to halve CFC production by 1999, only seeks to freeze halon production at 1986 levels by 1992.

Hamburger connection

Since 1960, thousands of square kilometres of tropical forest in Central America have been cleared to make way for cattle ranches. In Latin America as a whole, according to Dr. Norman Myers, author of *The Primary Resource*, "the cattle raiser is accounting for at least 20,000sq km (8,000sq miles) of forest a year." If current rates of clearance continue, most of the remaining forests in Central America – some 200,000sq km (80,000sq miles) – will have been destroyed by the mid-1990s.

In the Brazilian Amazon, the introduction of cattle is a secondary feature of a more profound process of land settlement, and yields only marginal returns. Fresh meat cannot be exported to the USA because of regulations concerning foot and mouth disease, and nearly all of it is consumed locally. But most of the beef raised on the cattle ranches of Central America is exported, 85-90 per cent of exports going to North America. Because the meat is too lean for American tastes, it is primarily used to make hamburgers for sale by such fast-food chains as Roy Rogers, Bob's Big Boy, Jack-in-the-Box and Hot Shoppes. McDonald's deny using beef from Central America – a claim which it is impossible to disprove since, once it has entered the USA, much of the beef enters the domestic market where it is indistinguishable from home-raised beef. In 1987, after a boycott organized by the Rainforest Action Network, Burger King announced that it would no longer use Central American beef to make its hamburgers. In Britain, the beef for hamburgers comes from the domestic market or from Europe. However, beef from Brazil is imported to make corned beef.

Cheap beef imports from Central America have reduced the price of hamburgers in North America by five cents a pound. However, the cattle trade has done little to help the poor of the cattle-exporting countries, few of whom can afford to eat beef. In Costa Rica, per-capita beef consumption fell by more than 40 per cent between 1960 and 1979, while production rose three-and-a-half times. "By 1978, the average Costa Rican was eating only 28lbs (13kg) of beef a year," comments Catherine Caufield, in her book *In the Rainforest*, "The average American pet cat ate more."

The ecological destruction caused by ranching programmes is long term and sometimes irreversible. To date, more than 5,000 million trees have been cut down in Central America alone.

Once deprived of its tree cover, the land is quickly depleted of nutrients and invaded by toxic weeds. In a few years, it is so degraded that it must be abandoned – a fate that has befallen nearly all the cattle ranches established in Amazonia before 1978. The ranchers have not been deterred: they have simply moved.

For billions of birds that migrate each year from North America to over-winter in Central America, the loss of their forest habitats is proving calamitous. More than 150 species are affected, including warblers, peewees, vireos and kingbirds. Scientists at the Smithsonian Institution in Washington warn that the numbers of migrating species are declining by between one and four per cent a year.

Recent research suggests that the adverse climate effects of tropical forest clearance are likely to be exacerbated by ranching projects. As unlikely as it may sound, cattle add appreciable amounts of methane to the atmosphere through belching. Like CO_2, methane is a greenhouse gas (*qv*) and will therefore contribute to the general warming up of the

Earth's surface. (See also: *Amazonia*③, *Cash crops*③, *Deforestation*③, *Development*③, *Tropical forests*③, *World Bank*③.)

Hanford

Major nuclear complex in Washington State. There are now nine plutonium reactors, plus reprocessing plants and a large number of storage tanks for high-level waste at Hanford, which at present covers some 1,490sq km (575sq miles).

Since the early 1970s, the Hanford site has become notorious for the failures of its high-level nuclear waste storage tanks, some of which are made of ordinary carbon steel, rather than stainless steel. One leak in 1973 released 118,000 US gallons (450,000 litres) of high-level waste. Billions of litres of radioactive waste and toxic chemicals have also been dumped straight into the ground. Later they were stored in ponds and seepage basins, the operators relying on the size of the reservation to prevent them from reaching the outside environment. However, in 1988, one spring flowing from the Hanford area into the River Columbia was found to contain a level of 352 becquerels of strontium-90 per litre. This is 1,000 times the allowable limit for drinking water set by the US Environmental Protection Agency. (See also: *Low level radiation*Ⓝ, *Nuclear accident*Ⓝ, *Nuclear waste*Ⓝ.)

Hazardous waste

The improper disposal of hazardous wastes is proving an increasing problem throughout both the industrialized world and the Third World. Worldwide, some 325-375 million tonnes of hazardous waste were generated in 1984, 90 per cent arising in the industrialized world. In the USA, some 260 million tonnes are generated each year – the equivalent of one tonne for each US citizen. In 1984, the ten nations which then made up the EC generated an estimated 160 million tonnes of industrial waste a year, of which 30 million tonnes were classified as "toxic and dangerous." Conservative estimates put

the amount of hazardous waste generated in England and Wales at some four million tonnes. Unless disposed of with great care, hazardous wastes pose a severe threat to public health and the environment. In particular, the use of landfill (*qv*) has led to the pollution of surface and groundwaters, to the contamination of land, and to the mass exposure of whole communities to the dangerous effects of highly toxic chemicals.

Numerous "problem" sites have now been unearthed, the most infamous being Love Canal (*qv*) in New York State. All told, the USA has an estimated 50,000 hazardous waste landfills, 20,000 of which are thought to pose a potential threat to human health. In addition, there are some 170,000 industrial impoundments – used to dump liquid wastes – and 7,000 deep wells into which hazardous wastes have been injected under pressure. According to the EPA, 2,000 sites require immediate clean-up under federal "Superfund" (*qv*) legislation. The Office of Technology Assessment estimates that clean-up costs could total $100,000 million. That figure, most of which will have to be borne by industry, is greater than the combined 1987 profits of the *Fortune 500* largest companies in the USA. For insurance companies, too, hazardous wastes look set to become "the most serious economic problem of the 1990s."

In Europe, the problem of old waste sites is also acute. Germany has closed 6,000 dump sites after identifying them as potential hazards, 800 being deemed a threat to public water supplies. The clean-up bill is estimated at $10,000 million.

In the Netherlands, a national survey of old sites was initiated after a housing estate at Lekkerkerk had to be evacuated due to a leaking dump. Within six months, 4,000 illegal dumps had been found. Clean-up costs are put at $1,500,000.

No one knows how many polluting dumps exist in the United Kingdom. The British government has yet to undertake a survey. Nonetheless, an independent survey puts the figure at 600 sites – including potentially dangerous domestic landfills. In 1989, the House of Commons Environment Committee strongly criticized the government's record on hazardous waste, charging it with failing to implement existing legislation (some of it 15 years old) and of allowing local authorities to evade their responsibilities. Britain's waste disposal system has been called "shambolic" and "ramshackle" by the government's own pollution inspectorate.

If properly treated, most of today's wastes can be rendered harmless before disposal, primarily through high-temperature incineration (qv). However, the long-term solution to the problem of hazardous wastes lies as much in reducing the production of wastes, not least through recycling (qv), as in the use of more sophisticated disposal technology. (See also: *Groundwater*Ⓟ, *Incineration*Ⓟ, *Ocean dumping*Ⓟ, *Ocean incineration*Ⓟ, *Rocky Mountain Arsenal* Ⓟ, *Recycling*Ⓟ, *Waste reduction*Ⓟ.)

Heart disease
See: *Coronary heart disease.*

Heat pump
A device that abstracts heat from a cold area, cooling it further, and releasing it in a warmer area. (See also: *Energy conservation*Ⓔ, *Soft energy paths*Ⓔ.)

Heavy metals
A group of elements with a wide range of chemical properties and biological effects. Some of them, such as manganese, copper and zinc, are essential trace elements in the diet and their absence can lead to serious illness. Others, such as mercury, lead and cadmium, have no biological function and their presence in all but very small quantities can cause poisoning.

Human activities such as mining, smelting, waste dumping, burning rubbish and the addition of lead to gasoline have greatly increased the amounts of heavy metals circulating in the environ-

ment, and much harm has been caused as a result.

In 1988, it was estimated that, worldwide, some 7 million tonnes of heavy metals were dumped into the environment every year. Some 75 per cent of the metals were discharged to land, the major sources being ash from coal combustion and the dumping of rubbish on land.

Because they are elements, heavy metals cannot be destroyed: they can only be converted from one chemical compound to another. They tend to build up in soils, watercourses and living organisms. Some plants can accumulate high levels of heavy metals from the soil in which they grow, while animals can build up dangerous levels through eating contaminated food. Marine animals – such as shellfish – are particularly efficient at concentrating heavy metals from the water and sediments in which they live.

Heavy metal wastes are difficult to dispose of safely. If burned, they cause air pollution and if dumped at sea – a process banned (except in trace quantities) in the North Sea (qv) and North Atlantic as far as the more toxic heavy metals are concerned – they can accumulate in the environment. Dumping on land can lead to pollution as heavy metals in leachate (qv) may contaminate groundwater or rivers. Some heavy metals can be recycled, but as they often appear as complex mixtures this is often difficult. Some countries – notably Sweden – are restricting the use of certain heavy metals to prevent their appearing as wastes and subsequently causing pollution. (See also: *Cadmium*, *Hazardous wastes*Ⓟ, *Leachate*Ⓟ, *Lead*, *Mercury*, *North Sea*Ⓟ).

Hedgerows
Since 1945, thousands of kilometres of hedgerows have been lost in Britain alone. The process is encouraged by government grants and justified by civil servants and farmers alike as a move towards more "efficient" farming. Hedges, it is argued, take up potentially productive

land – 280sq m for each 90m of hedge (3,000 square feet for each 100 yards) – and make ploughing more difficult: their removal thus saves both time and energy.

Numerous studies have shown the value of hedges in providing shelter to both livestock and crops. If a hedge is semipermeable, then wind speeds can be reduced by as much as 80 per cent for distances up to five times its height. Where such protection is present, the gain in production can be between two and four times greater than the loss incurred by keeping the land beneath the hedge out of production.

Hedgerows also act as vital shields against erosion, either by wind or rain, because runoff is significantly reduced, and storms appear to be less severe in hedgerow country.

But perhaps the most overlooked benefit of hedgerows lies in the habitat they provide for wildlife. Though they harbour some insects and fungi that can harm crops (the bean aphid and wheat rust are two examples), the greater part of their population are the natural allies of the farmer – from the bumble bee, which plays such a vital role in pollinating flowering crops, to birds of prey and insect predators, which keep farm pests in check. Once the habitat for these natural enemies of farm pests have been destroyed the only course open is chemical treatment (see *Insecticides* and *Herbicides*).

If domesticated livestock is included as part of the hedgerow ecosystem, then the case in favour of hedgerows is still more overwhelming. The removal of hedges has been associated with a rise in bovine tuberculosis, grassland tetany, and bruscellosis. Hedgerows not only help break the cycle of parasite diseases but, in hot countries, they reduce cattle mortality from sunstroke. (See also: *Conservation*Ⓒ, *Erosion*ⒶⒸ.)

Herbicides
Chemicals used to kill weeds and other undesirable plants. There are many different types, varying in their mode of action, the plants against which they are used and

their persistence in soil. Modern Western agriculture, with its large fields and intensive applications of fertilizer, requires a substantial input of herbicides to keep down weeds, which would otherwise thrive, and few fields remain unsprayed.

Some herbicides – sulphuric acid, for example – destroy only the plant tissue they actually touch. These are known as contact herbicides and contrast with the translocated herbicides, such as glyphosate, which are absorbed by the leaves and carried within the plant to other parts, thereby killing the whole weed. Another class of weedkiller is the hormone type of which the phenoxy herbicides (qv) are the most important. These mimic the effect of plant hormones and cause the weed to overgrow and die.

Most of the herbicides in general use are not persistent in the environment, though some are deliberately used because they do persist. An example is simazine, used on paths and tennis courts, which leaves residues in soil for two years or more. The conversion product of one fairly persistent herbicide, aminotriazole, is thought to be carcinogenic.

Herbicides are not usually acutely toxic to humans or other mammals, the main exceptions being paraquat (qv), dinoseb and DNOC, all of which are poisonous.

Some species are more susceptible to herbicide poisoning than others. Fish are very sensitive. The widespread use of herbicides has also led to reductions in the numbers of insects in fields in many parts of the world, thereby restricting the food supplies of insectivorous birds.

Modern herbicides are extremely powerful and some are volatile. Serious damage has been caused when warm weather has evaporated sprayed herbicide from one field and allowed it to drift onto crops growing on adjacent farms.

Agriculture is currently highly dependent on the use of herbicides, but weeds in some areas are becoming more resistant to their effects. More research into alternative methods of weed control is becoming an urgent prior-ity. (See also: *Biocides*①⑫, *Paraquat*①⑫, *Phenoxy herbicides*①⑫.)

Hexachlorocyclohexane (HCH)

An organochlorine insecticide used for a wide variety of agricultural and public health purposes as well as for preserving wood. It exists in several chemical forms, known as isomers, and is used as a mixture of those isomers. Products containing more than 99 per cent of the gamma isomer are known as lindane. HCH was formerly known as benzene hexachloride (BHC), but this name has been dropped as it is chemically inaccurate.

Like other chlorinated hydrocarbons (qv) HCH persists in the environment and can accumulate in food webs. It is especially toxic to fish and bees. Birds of prey have also been seriously harmed by lindane and HCH, as have bats when rafters have been sprayed to protect them against insect attack.

The toxicity of HCH depends to some extent on the isomers present. The mixture has been shown to cause cancer in laboratory animals and has been linked to anaemia in humans. Liver and kidney damage have been reported in people exposed to HCH over a long period.

Lindane is generally more dangerous than mixtures of HCH. It has also been linked with leukaemia and is embryotoxic, causing spontaneous abortion. It also damages the nervous system.

Because of their environmental and health effects, the use of lindane and HCH is banned or severely restricted in Scandinavia, the USA, New Zealand, the USSR, France, Germany and many other countries – though they are aggressively marketed for use in the Third World. In the UK, however, despite EC restrictions, products containing lindane or HCH can still be bought freely by gardeners and farmers.

In 1989, a major pollution alert was triggered when a container containing five tonnes of lindane was washed overboard from a freighter and lost in the English Channel. Greenpeace warned that if the lindane were to escape from the container, it would cause an ecological disaster, posing a serious threat to anyone eating fish caught from the Channel and devastating marine life. (See also: *Chlorinated hydrocarbons*⑫.)

High level waste
See *Nuclear waste*.

High yielding varieties (HYVs)
Modern hybrid strains of cereals that can produce higher-than-normal yields. They were mainly developed by the International Rice Research Institute (IRRI) in the Philippines, and provide the basis of the Green Revolution (qv).

The first successful HYV was a rice variety, IR8, developed in 1966. It was a cross between the Indian tall rice plant and a Taiwanese dwarf variety. It produced a high yield, but needed a great deal of fertilizer. This has been a feature of all HYVs. In addition, it could support such heavy fertilization without lodging (flattening), which traditional varieties could not do.

HYVs also generally require irrigation (qv), which goes a long way toward explaining the proliferation of large-scale irrigation schemes throughout the Third World. A further feature of HYVs is that they are more susceptible to disease. This is fully admitted by Dr. M.A. Swaminathan, one of the fathers of the Green Revolution, and a director of the IRRI. He notes how the IR8 rice proved particularly vulnerable to bacterial blight (BB) both in 1968 and to rice tungro virus (RTV) in 1970 and 1971 in the Philippines. It was largely because of its great vulnerability to such diseases that it was replaced by IR20 in 1971. Though IR20 was resistant to BB and RTV, it proved vulnerable to the brown plant hopper (BPH) and the grassy stunt virus (GSV), which in 1973 devastated vast areas planted with that variety. In 1973, the IRRI was thus forced to develop another variety, IR26, which had built-in resistance to BPH. For two years it was used throughout the Philippines, but in 1966 it proved vulnerable to a new type of BPH, so it too had to be replaced with a new variety, called IR36. This has done well since. However, it is now being threatened by yet another biotype of BPH as well as by two totally new diseases.

The experience in India has proved similar. A taskforce of eminent rice breeders notes how the introduction of HYVS has brought about "a marked change in the status of insect pests like gall midge, brown plant hopper, leaf folder, whore maggot etc." Most of the HYVS released so far are susceptible to major pests with a crop loss of 30-100 per cent.

There is now a growing trend to breed for resistance to possible pests rather than for increased yields only. However, breeders are unlikely to develop a variety that displays resistance to more than a few specific pests. The only strategy for achieving real security is by planting a large number of different varieties that between them ensure against pest losses. Traditional agriculturists had already achieved this. Unfortunately, the vast stock of valuable plant genetic material that they had developed over hundreds, if not thousands, of years has been largely lost with the introduction of the Green Revolution as farmers switched to HYVS. Traditional varieties have even on occasion been wilfully destroyed in order to increase the market for patented seeds (qv).

Hinkley Point
Site of Britain's largest electricity-generating nuclear complex, located on the Bristol Channel near Bridgwater, Somerset. Two Magnox (qv) reactors were opened in 1965, followed by two advanced gas-cooled reactors (qv) in 1976.

Although the two power stations have operated more successfully than some British nuclear sites, there have been some notable incidents. In 1985, for example, an escape of radioactive gas resulted in the issuing of protective tablets to 500 workers as a precaution against the inhalation of radioactive iodine.

In 1983, the Central Electricity Generating Board (CEGB) announced its intention to construct a third station. This was the follow-on to Britain's first pressurized water reactor at Sizewell (qv) in Suffolk. Opposition to the development came from more than 60 local councils and from a record 23,000 individual objectors. A public inquiry opened in October 1988 and lasted 14 months. Although the inquiry approved the new plant, its construction will depend on the outcome of a government review of the future of the nuclear industry, due to be completed in 1994. (See also: *Nuclear economics*Ⓝ.)

Holism
Holism is best seen as the opposite to reductionism, or the "analytic method" that underlies modern science. The holistic approach consists in studying complete living systems, rather than studying their component parts in isolation from each other "in controlled laboratory conditions," as modern science does. This is justified on the grounds that natural systems are more than the sum of their constituent parts. By studying the parts separately, reductionist science does not take into account the way these parts are organized.

To insist in trying to understand biological and cultural phenomena in terms of physics or molecular biology, which is still the fashion in scientific circles, is thus considered by holists to be a vain pursuit that does not enable scientists to understand the effects of the changes they are bringing about to our health, our society and to the biosphere (qv), whose true nature can only be understood in the light of a holistic view of the world.

Hormones in meat
Hormones are chemical substances secreted by the glands. Their role is to regulate such essential functions as growth, metabolism and reproduction. The endocrine system that handles hormones is highly sophisticated, delicately balanced and still not fully understood. Yet we are interfering with it by treating animals with hormonal drugs.

Such veterinary drugs are used for a number of purposes. One is to ensure that all the cows in a herd come on heat at the same time. This enables the cattleman to rationalize his breeding programme so that all the calves are born at the optimum time from the point of view of weather and pasture conditions. In the USA, a product called Lutalyse, manufactured by the Upjohn Corporation, is highly regarded for this purpose. It is a prostaglandin, a member of a group of endocrine compounds similar to hormones. Prostaglandins are only now being seriously examined. There appears to be a large number of them and they affect all sorts of biological functions, including respiration, blood clotting, digestion, blood circulation, nerve responses and reproduction.

Another purpose for which hormones, including Lutalyse, are used is as abortifacients – to induce miscarriage in feedlot heifers which do not put on enough meat to satisfy commercial requirements when in calf.

Hormones are also used for caponizing cockerels. An example is diethylstilbesterol (DES) (qv), an established carcinogen which has been blamed for a wide range of unpleasant side effects. Farmers who have come into close contact with it have developed symptoms of impotence, infertility or gynecomastia (tender breasts), and also changes in voice register. DES is even supposed to have affected the menstrual cycles of farmers' wives. Men who have eaten the necks of chicken treated with DES, and male dogs which had been fed on chicken wastes, have also shown signs of developing feminine characteristics. Such side effects led the USA to ban the use of DES implants for caponizing cockerels and to spend $10 million to remove contaminated chickens from the market.

In 1983, a new synthetic hormone that achieves its effect by blocking the production of testosterone was developed as a means of castrating young piglets without surgery.

The main use of hormones in livestock rearing, however, is as a growth promoter (qv).

Hydro-electricity

Over the last three decades, the use of hydroelectricity has grown dramatically, installed capacity increasing by 262 per cent from 149,571 megawatts in 1960 to 541,976 megawatts in 1984.

Even so, much of the hydro-electric potential of the world's rivers remains untapped. If all the rivers of the world were to be dammed, then an estimated 73,000 terawatt-hours of electricity – an output equal to that of 12,000 nuclear reactors – could be produced every year. (One tera-watt is equivalent to 10^{12} watt-hours.) Technical difficulties preclude all of that energy being exploited. Nonetheless, according to the World Energy Conference, 19,000 terawatt-hours could be tapped, as against the 1,300 terawatt-hours produced today.

For those countries that lack conventional sources of energy – and which must therefore import their fuel – the lure of hydro-power is evident. In 1984, for example, Brazil had to find $25 million a day to pay for the one million barrels of oil imported daily. Yet, as the science writer Catherine Caufield points out, the energy potential of the rivers of the Amazon Basin, excluding the Amazon itself, is 100,000 megawatts. By the turn of the century, Brazil hopes to generate 22,000 megawatts from the Amazon Basin. The Itaipu Dam on the Parana River alone generates 12,600 megawatts. By comparison, most nuclear reactors generate a mere 1,500 megawatts.

Nonetheless, large dams (*qv*) carry heavy environmental and social costs, which, especially in the tropics, invariably far outweigh the benefits of hydro-electricity. Moreover, the industries attracted to Third World countries by the promise of cheap electricity are often highly polluting. (See also: *Dams* ③.)

Incineration
Industrial Biotest
   Laboratories
Infectious diseases
Insecticides
Insulation
Integrated
   development
Integrated pest
   control
Intermediate level
   waste
International
   Commission on
   Radiological
   Protection (ICRP)
International Atomic
   Energy Agency
   (IAEA)
International
   Monetary Fund
   (IMF)
ITTO (International
   Timber Trades
   Organization)
International Whaling
   Commission
Irradiated food
Irrigation
Isotope

Junk food

Karin B
Kalkar
Kesterson reservoir
Krill

Incineration

Potentially the safest method of destroying many of the more toxic of today's hazardous wastes – particularly such substances as organic solvents, chlorinated hydrocarbons and oily wastes.

There are four major categories of incinerators: high-temperature incinerators; industrial boilers and furnaces; industrial kilns; and municipal incinerators.

Of these, only high-temperature incinerators are purpose-built for the incineration of toxic wastes. By contrast, industrial boilers burn certain toxic wastes – flammable solvents and oily wastes, for example – because they constitute a cheap and efficient fuel. In Norway and Sweden, PCBs (*qv*) and other "difficult" wastes have been successfully incinerated in kilns used for the manufacture of cement.

Effective incineration requires sophisticated equipment, including such anti-pollution devices as scrubbers (*qv*), and depends critically on good management. Properly operated, the most modern high-temperature incinerators have "destruction efficiencies" of 99.99999 per cent.

To ensure the complete and even combustion of a waste, the incineration chamber must be kept at the right temperature; the waste must be kept in the chamber for the right length of time; and there must be adequate turbulence within the chamber to ensure that the waste is well mixed with oxygen.

Failure to observe the "three Ts" of incineration carries two major dangers. First, inefficient incineration means that not all of the original waste will be destroyed; and, second, it can lead to the formation of new products, known as PICs or Products of Incomplete Combustion.

According to the US Science Advisory Board, some 24 organic compounds have been discovered in emissions from high-temperature incinerators. Most of those compounds have yet to be identified chemically, let alone assessed for their effect on human health and the environment.

Partially incinerated PCBs have

long been known as a source of highly toxic dioxins (*qv*) and polychlorinated dibenzofurans. Both chemicals are also released in significant quantities from municipal incinerators, which operate at temperatures typically 500°C (932°F) too low to destroy the plastics in domestic rubbish. Dioxins – thought to result from the incomplete combustion of plastic bone replacements – have also been found in emissions from crematoria. There is also growing concern over the high levels of heavy metals (*qv*) found in incineration sludges.

Industrial Biotest Laboratories

Private Illinois-based laboratory found to have falsified hundreds of safety tests on a wide range of products – from pesticides (*qv*) to irradiated foods (*qv*).

Investigations by the US Food and Drugs Administration revealed that safety tests on 200 pesticides had also been faked or misread. As a result, according to the US Environmental Protection Agency (EPA), 15 per cent of all the pesticides now on the market are suspect.

Some of the suspect pesticides have still to be retested and most are still in worldwide use, though Sweden and Canada banned a number because of their reliance on IBT data. In Britain, no pesticides approved for use on the basis of IBT tests have been withdrawn. Though the EPA has published a list of the suspect pesticides, Britain has refused to do so. (See also: *Cancer*ⓁⓅ, *Cancer research*ⓁⓅ.)

Infectious diseases

In spite of the successes of medical science, the incidence of infectious diseases is increasing, and many are spreading to parts of the world where they were previously unknown.

Three different factors are involved in the incidence of infectious disease. The first is the pathogen itself, the second is the host and the third is the environment in which infection occurs. Current research is concentrated on the first of these factors to the near exclusion of the others.

Humans harbour in their bodies a vast number of different microbes. In fact, the human body is made up of more microbial cells than animal cells and without these microbes our basic physiological functions would be impaired. In the course of evolution, humans have learned to live with these microorganisms and it is only in aberrant conditions that they harm them. Thus the herpes simplex virus is often acquired early in life and persists in latent form within the body. It only becomes "activated", and thereby harmful, when certain physiological disturbances occur which upset its equilibrium with the host.

Lower resistance to disease can occur for a host of reasons, such as the use of certain drugs like cortisone, exposure to various chemical pollutants and to low-level radiation, and also because of emotional disturbances.

Ironically, excessive hygiene can also be regarded as a cause of infectious disease, since it reduces resistance to microorganisms that are inevitably present and that in normal conditions are relatively harmless – indeed often essential – to the normal functioning of the human organism.

Environmental destruction is also a basic cause of infectious disease. Among other things it interferes with established relationships between parasites and their non-human hosts, which can cause them to shift their attention to human hosts. Thus bubonic plague developed as a disease of rodents, yellow fever and malaria as diseases of monkeys, and rabies of bats.

The creation of vast urban conglomerations has also provided a perfect niche for the vectors of infectious disease, including the rat that transmits bubonic plague. It has also put us in close contact with parasites that had previously established stable relationships with the animals we had domesticated. An example is smallpox, a variant of cowpox, which is a disease of cattle.

With the present trend towards urbanization (*qv*) and the development of ever-increasing mobility,

ideal conditions are being created for the rapid spread of infectious disease throughout the world. (See also: *Waterborne disease* Ⓛ③.)

Insecticides

Chemicals used to kill harmful or irritating insects, though often used against other animals, such as mites, as well.

Before World War II, the insecticides in common use were mainly inorganic poisons, such as arsenic, or natural organic products such as nicotine and derris. The development of two groups of new insecticides, the chlorinated hydrocarbons and the organophosphates (*qv*), revolutionized pest control but brought with them serious environmental problems.

Insecticides are rarely selective: they can thus harm species other than the target insect. If the predators of an insect pest are killed, then the pest problem may be made worse as natural controls on their numbers are removed. Animals at higher levels in ecological food webs are particularly at risk from the more persistent insecticides, such as chlorinated hydrocarbons, since residues pass from one species to another during predation. Examples of such damage include the decimation of birds of prey in the US and Europe, the decline of the English otter, and the deaths of seals in the Dutch Waddenzee, all of which can be attributed in whole or in part to insecticide residues.

Human beings are also at risk from insecticide poisoning, since many of these substances are highly toxic to people.

Insecticides in common use can be divided roughly into four groups: the chlorinated hydrocarbons; the organophosphates; the carbamates; and those based on or adapted from natural products. The synthetic compounds in the first three groups have caused the most environmental and health problems, but the fourth group is not without risk. Some, such as nicotine, are highly poisonous and few are selective, though modern insecticides developed from natural compounds called pyrethrins can be used against greenfly without killing their ladybird predators. Most natural insecticides, however, are not persistent in the environment.

A major problem with the use of insecticides is the development of resistance by the pests. Natural selection can rapidly produce a pest population that is unaffected by an insecticide. The amount used is then increased – which causes even more ecological damage – or an alternative found. There is only a limited number of alternatives and the development of a new insecticide takes many years; thus farmers and public health officials in some areas are facing a crisis as pests and disease-carrying insects become impossible, or very expensive, to control. The development of more subtle strategies including biological controls (*qv*) is thus seen as essential if pests are to be kept to manageable levels in the long term. (See also: *Biocides*Ⓟ, *Pesticides*Ⓟ.)

Insulation
The use of materials that are poor conductors of heat to reduce heat loss, especially from buildings. In an average uninsulated home, about 25 per cent of all the energy used for space heating is lost through the walls, 17 per cent through the roof, five per cent through the windows, and about six per cent by too frequent air changes.

Insulation has a key role to play in energy conservation (*qv*) programmes in temperate areas. (See also: *Energy conservation*Ⓔ, *Soft energy paths*Ⓔ.)

Integrated development
See: *Sustainable development*.

Integrated pest control
See: *Biological control*.

Intermediate level waste
See: *Nuclear waste*.

International Commission on Radiological Protection (ICRP)
Founded in 1928, the ICRP is responsible for advising national governments on acceptable exposures to ionizing radiation. It is composed of leading radiation

specialists from many different countries, and most countries derive their radiological standards from its recommendations. The ICRP's views on the effects of radiation on human health are largely based on continuing studies of the survivors of the atomic bombs dropped on the Japanese cities of Nagasaki and Hiroshima in 1945. The Commission also assumes that workers in industries who routinely come into contact with sources of ionizing radiation will accept a higher risk than members of the public who happen to live near nuclear installations.

In 1986, the ICRP concluded that new data from the Japanese bomb survivors showed that the chances of a person contracting fatal cancer from a given dose of radiation was about three times greater than they had previously believed. However, the Commission was reluctant to change its recommendations immediately, and was pre-empted by the British National Radiological Protection Board (NRPB). The NRPB tightened the UK standards in 1987 from a limit of 50 to an average of 15 millisieverts (mSv) per year for workers and from 1 to 0.5 mSv per year for the most exposed members of the public.

In 1991, the ICRP finally changed its own recommendations, opting for a new five-year limit of 100 mSv for workers (annual average 20 mSv) and 1 mSv per year for the public. The new limits are likely to pose problems for the operation of uranium mines (*qv*), especially in France, and for some workers in reprocessing factories, such as the UK's Sellafield (*qv*) plant.

The Commission has been regularly criticized for its conservative approach to radiological protection. Following the most recent recommendations, the UK Friends of the Earth argued that the Japanese data shows that the cancer risk from ionizing radiation is 4 to 5 times greater than the Commission maintains, and that dose limits should therefore be reduced even further. The general trend this century has been for new research on the increased

risks of exposure to radiation to be followed eventually by tighter international safety standards. (See also: *Nuclear accidents*Ⓝ, *Low-level radiation*Ⓝ, *Routine discharges*Ⓝ.)

International Atomic Energy Agency (IAEA)
The agency, founded in 1956, has headquarters in Vienna. With the membership of 113 countries and a budget of about $160 million, it has two main roles. One is to promote the use of peaceful nuclear technology through the international exchange of information. The second is to administer the Non-Proliferation Treaty (*qv*) in order to control the diversion of nuclear materials from civil to military uses.

In its first role, the IAEA has been criticized for adopting a biased approach to the problems of nuclear power. In 1991, for example, a report by the agency on the health effects of the Chernobyl (*qv*) accident concluded that most of the effects could be blamed on psychological stress, not exposure to radiation. Its findings ran directly counter to the experience of medical practitioners on the ground in the Soviet Union.

In its second role, the agency notably failed to detect the steady progress of the Iraqi government towards production of enriched uranium and plutonium (*qv*), both of which are used in nuclear bombs. Iraq is a signatory to the Non-Proliferation Treaty, but the full extent of the country's nuclear research facilities were only brought to light in the aftermath of the 1991 Gulf War (*qv*). Many critics now argue that it is impossible to effectively combine the IAEA's twin functions as nuclear promoter and nuclear watchdog. (See also: *Nuclear proliferation*Ⓝ.)

International Monetary Fund (IMF)
Institution set up, together with the World Bank, its sister body, at the Bretton Woods Conference in the US after World War II. Its purpose was to promote international monetary cooperation and

the expansion of trade, to facilitate monetary convertibility and to ensure financial stability.

The IMF is an international body with 140 members. Power resides in theory with the 21 executive directors but is, in fact, mainly exercised by the five members with the largest quota, the United Kingdom, Germany, France, Japan and, in particular, the US which has the largest quota of all. The IMF is primarily the lender of the last resort to Third World governments that are experiencing balance of payment difficulties and are in debt to private international banks. A debtor government can borrow up to the limit of its special drawing rights (SDRs) in exchange for its own currency. If this is not sufficient, it can borrow over and above its quota, but then it must accept IMF "conditionalities," imposed as part of a wide-ranging "structural adjustment programme," drawn up with the World Bank. The more the debtor country borrows above its quota, the stricter the conditionalities and the more vigorously they are enforced. If a country borrows the equivalent of double its quota, and still needs more money, then the IMF will effectively take control over economic and, indeed, social policies. Since IMF approval is critical to obtaining loans from other sources, its powers are considerable.

The "conditionalities" imposed on debtor countries by the IMF take several forms. To begin with, the debtor government is made to reduce expenditure – in particular "non-productive" expenditure on welfare, education, health and food subsidies. This has caused a great deal of hardship, particularly in the slums of the Third World where thousands of people (many of them environmental refugees (qv) from development schemes) depend on food subsidies for their very survival. It is not surprising that such policies have given rise to food riots in Peru, Turkey, Egypt and elsewhere. The debtor country is also made to reduce real wages, which clearly creates further hardships.

For example, when the Sudanese government under President Numeiri – bankrupted by increases in the price of oil and machinery during the 1970s – reluctantly capitulated to IMF demands in 1978, it was forced to devalue the Sudanese pound on four occasions in four years. The consequent increase in the cost of imports caused inflation of 40 per cent and a substantial decline in real wages. When, in 1985, the IMF insisted upon a further drop in food subsidies, popular resentment erupted in a series of street riots that precipitated President Numeiri's overthrow.

A third feature of IMF imposed policies is an insistence on the expansion of cash crops (qv) for export, at the expense of food crops grown for local consumption. This has caused still greater human misery, particularly in those countries which already suffer from serious malnutrition and famine. Yet the IMF has been uncompromising in its imposition of this conditionality. When, for example, the Sudan cut back on cotton production in order to feed its starving population, the IMF insisted on the policy being reversed before it would grant any further loans.

In order to further boost exports and, by the same token, limit imports, a debtor country is frequently required to devalue its currency. Significantly, this is as far as the IMF permits debtor countries to go in reducing expenditure on imports in order to solve their balance of payment problems. The IMF strictly prohibits the setting up of import quotas or other constraints on the import of manufactured goods from the industrialized world – even though runaway expenditure on superfluous imports is, more often than not, the main cause of the debtor country's financial plight.

Not surprisingly, critics of the IMF have accused it of placing the short-term economic interests of the industrialized world above those of debtor nations in the Third World – to the detriment of the health of millions and the ruin of the environment. (See also: *Cash crops*④③, *Development*③, *World Bank*③.)

ITTO (International Timber Trades Organization)

The ITTO was first proposed in 1977 by the Japanese, who had in mind a simple trade agreement. It was finally set up in 1983 with an additional brief of safeguarding the conservation of tropical forests. Some 45 countries became members, and votes were apportioned according to the amount of timber that each country exported or imported – which effectively meant that the more tropical forests a country destroyed, the more power it held in the organization. Any country that wished to stop logging, or ban imports, would forfeit the right to participate.

The ITTO's declared aim was to assure the long-term future of the tropical timber industry, by establishing "sustainable" forest management. However, it soon became clear that there were wildly differing opinions as to what was sustainable logging, and indeed if it was possible at all. This did not deter the ITTO from proclaiming in 1990 its "Target 2000," which resolved that all traded timber should be sustainably produced by 2000. But as the concept of sustainability has still to be defined, the target means nothing. And as there is no system of standards or monitoring agency, there is nothing to stop timber importers placing a certificate of sustainability upon their merchandise whenever they feel it appropriate.

The ITTO has consistently refused to countenance a moratorium of logging in primary forests on the grounds that logging increases the economic value of forests and thus provides an incentive for their conservation; a ban, it is argued, would encourage landless peasants to clear the forest for agricultural use. Yet the ITTO consistently ignores the fact that almost all forests are already inhabited by people who depend upon the forests for their living and for whom the forests already have value. This was graphically illustrated by an ITTO-funded project in the Chimanes region of Bolivia. About 1,500 Indians from the area marched to the capital,

Traditional irrigation
methods are slow and
laborious, but avoid the
problems of capital-intensive
schemes.

La Paz, to protest against the invasion of their lands by logging crews and their retinue of hunters and settlers. The President of Bolivia immediately withdrew the logging concessions.

The ITTO, denounced by environmentalists and ignored by producer countries, is becoming increasingly ineffectual. Its half-hearted activities are now increasingly eclipsed by the more specific, but no less suspect, proposals of the Tropical Forest Action Plan (*qv*). (See also: *Tropical timber trade*© ③.)

International Whaling Commission
See: *Whales.*

Irradiated food
See: *Food irradiation.*

Irrigation
One of the most productive forms of agriculture known to man. In the USA, for example, a Nebraskan corn farmer can produce 40 bushels of corn a year on unirrigated land, but with sprinkler irrigation that yield can be increased to 115 bushels an acre.

Not surprisingly, the UN Food and Agriculture Organization (*qv*) sees the expansion of irrigated agriculture, particularly in the arid tropics, as being vital to the battle against world hunger. In 1982, an estimated 220 million hectares (540 million acres) were

irrigated worldwide. By the end of the century, FAO hopes to have increased that area by a million hectares (2,470,000 acres).

There are good reasons to suppose, however, that, far from relieving world hunger, FAO's strategy will exacerbate the problem. It is not irrigation itself which is at fault but FAO's attempts to practise it on an intensive scale.

The modern irrigation schemes being promoted by FAO are large-scale and perennial, with two to three crops being grown on the same land year after year without respite. Drainage is rarely installed – due largely to cost – and salinization (*qv*) is near universal.

Hundreds of thousands of hectares of agricultural land are thus lost to farmers every year. Indeed, as much land is now being taken out of production due to salinization as is being brought into production through new irrigation projects.

In addition, by creating a permanent niche for the vectors of such waterborne diseases as schistosomiasis (qv) and malaria (qv), perennial irrigation projects pose a major threat to public health. Agricultural pests also thrive in perennial irrigation systems, benefiting not only from the permanently moist atmosphere but also from the presence of a permanent food supply. Irrigated agriculture also adds appreciable quantities of methane, a powerful greenhouse gas (qv), to the atmosphere, rice paddies in particular being a major source of methane.

Modern irrigation schemes are notorious for being badly managed. Problems with machinery are common and disputes over water rights are rife: bribery is frequently the only means of obtaining water in the right quantity and at the right time.

In India, only 65 of the 246 large-scale surface irrigation projects initiated since 1951 have been completed. The last people to have benefited from irrigation projects – whether in India or elsewhere in the Third World – have been the poor. Setting up large-scale irrigation projects is exorbitantly expensive – in some areas, it costs as much as $10,000 to irrigate a single hectare of land – and to earn the foreign exchange to pay the bills, irrigated land is invariably used to grow cash crops (qv) for export. Even where the project is specifically intended for peasant farmers, plantation agriculture frequently takes over. The water from Iran's Dez Dam, for example, was supposed to irrigate land belonging to small farmers in Khuzestan. In the event, however, the land went almost exclusively to foreign-owned companies, which cultivated crops for export.

The problems associated with large-scale, intensive irrigated agriculture are not new: history records the disastrous fate of the monumental irrigation schemes set up in ancient Mesopotamia. There are signs, however, that some irrigation engineers are learning the lessons of the past and rediscovering the merits of traditional techniques. Such experts are beginning to realize that successful irrigation is only possible where fallows are observed and where management is based firmly within the local community. The pressure, however, is still to build massive perennial irrigation schemes that by their very nature must be run by large bureaucracies. (See also: *Dams*③, *Development*③, *Green Revolution*Ⓐ③.)

Isotope
See: *Radioactivity*.

Junk food
Modern convenience foods not only lack nutritional quality, but their consumption contributes to a wide range of the so-called "diseases of civilization" – from tooth caries to cancer, diabetes and diseases of the bowel.

Most processed foods consist of just four basic ingredients – corn, wheat, soybean and sugar beet – which are then dressed up with additives (qv) to create artificial foods that look, taste and have the same "mouth feel" as the real thing.

The technology often owes more to heavy industry than to the kitchen. Thus Professor Ross Hume Hall of Canada's McMaster's University describes how the "salami" filling of a typical frozen pizza is manufactured from soya bean by dissolving the milled soy flour in lye and precipitating out the protein in an acid bath "in the form of fine threads that are wound on a bobbin, cemented together, dyed, flavoured and cut into hamburger-sized chunks." Additives then give the texture and taste of salami.

Since Roman times it has been known that processing foods reduces their nutritional quality – white bread being nick-named "castratus." Modern processing techniques ensure that most convenience foods have little nutritional value. After milling, for example, modern refined flour has lost up to 80 per cent of its known vitamins and minerals.

Freezing also reduces nutritional quality: when scientists at Rutgers University in the USA tested samples of frozen chicken pies, they found that the pies contained no vitamin C at all – this despite their being packed with vegetables. Even when the scientists added vitamin C, they found that 25 per cent of it had been lost after the pies had been thawed and reheated.

Though vitamins are added to "enrich" a whole range of processed foods, studies have cast doubt on the effectiveness of the practice. Thus a Canadian survey found widespread thiamine and iron deficiencies among the Canadian population despite both thiamine and iron being added to all bread sold in Canada.

Most damaging of all, food processing reduces what Ross Hume Hall has called the "biological sophistication" of food. Processed foods contain only a minute fraction of the chemicals present in natural foods: synthetic orange juice, for example, consists of just ten ingredients, while a natural orange has many hundreds.

Just as important, the molecules in natural foods have their own chemical architecture that ensures, for example, that the right nutrients are released in the gut at the right time and in the right quantities. Even the smallest adjustments to that chemical architecture can convert essential nutrients into valueless products. (See also: *Additives*Ⓛ, *Diseases of civilization*Ⓛ, *Food irradiation*Ⓛ, *Pesticides in food*Ⓛ.)

Karin B
Italian "leper" ship which hit the headlines in September 1988 after its cargo of toxic waste was refused entry into numerous European ports. The waste had been illegally dumped in Nigeria, but the Nigerian Government had forced the Italians to return it to Europe for disposal.

The same month saw three other leper ships also roaming the seas in search of somewhere to unload their cargoes. One, the *Khian Sea*, had been at sea for two years, unable to find a country which would accept its 11,000 tonnes of contaminated incinerator sludge from the USA. The waste from another, the *Zanobia*, had been carried by three ships and docked in three continents in the 14 months since it was first loaded.

According to the International Maritime Organization, leper ships are now a common phenomenon: most do not receive the media attention accorded to the *Karin B*, however, and simply dump their cargoes overboard if refused entry into a port.

The voyage of the *Karin B* highlighted the growing trade in toxic wastes from the northern industrialized countries to the Third World, where they are dumped indiscriminately. One dump in Nigeria has been found to contain 3,500 tonnes of toxic chemicals, including acidic wastes, large amounts of PCBS (*qv*), waste paints and unidentified solids. Half of the 8,000-10,000 drums at the site were corroded and experts warned that there was a real risk of a major explosion at the dump. The cost of cleaning up the site has been put at more than $1,600,000. In Guinea, 15,000 tonnes of incinerator ash from the USA were dumped on the island of Kassa, killing large areas of vegetation. The Guineans were paid $40 per tonne to dispose of the waste: in the US, the cost would have been $1,000 a tonne.

An estimated 20 million tonnes of toxic waste are dumped in the Third World annually. A 1988 study by Greenpeace International recorded 115 shipments of waste between 1986-88: the waste went to Mexico, Argentina, Brazil, Panama, Uruguay, Morocco, Senegal, Gabon, Guinea-Bissau, Somalia, Zimbabwe and South Africa. According to Greenpeace, shipments increased in the early 1980s after the USA tightened its legislation on toxic waste disposal. A second wave of shipments accompanied the introduction of stricter EC controls on waste in 1986. (See also: *Hazardous Wastes* ℗, *Export of Pollution* ℗.)

Kalkar

Prototype fast reactor (*qv*) and site of major anti-nuclear demonstrations. In 1972 West Germany, Belgium and Holland began construction of SNR-300 at Kalkar, on the German side of the border with Holland. Comparable in size to the British prototype fast breeder reactor at Dounreay (*qv*), Kalkar has so far failed to obtain a licence to operate because of concern over its safety. Its costs have risen from an initial estimate of $800 million to more than $3,500 million – the plant barely escaped cancellation in 1982 and 1983.

Kesterson reservoir

Californian reservoir, built in 1971, and now thoroughly polluted by contaminated drainage water from the irrigated farmlands of the Central Valley Project. In particular, the reservoir's 12 ponds now contain high levels of selenium – a natural element which, though essential for animals in trace quantities, is toxic in large doses. Other pollutants in the water include pesticides, salt and toxic wastes.

Kesterson lies on a major migration route for birds and, in 1971, was declared a national wildlife refuge. Studies have shown high rates of malformation among birds at the reservoir.

The contaminated water entered Kesterson via the San Luis Drain. Alarmed at the extent of selenium pollution, the US Department of the Interior (DOI) ordered Kesterson reservoir to be closed in March 1985. In addition, farmers were ordered to find alternative means of draining 42,000 acres served by the San Luis Drain. The drain itself was plugged in 1986.

Plans to clean up the reservoir are still under discussion. The only safe long-term solution, say environmentalists, is to remove the bottom mud altogether. The cost could be as high as $146 million.

According to the DOI, nine other areas in six other states suffer from potentially dangerous levels of selenium.

Kesterson is not the only wildlife site in the USA to be affected by pollution. Nationwide, ten other reserves have been identified as having contaminant problems – and a further 74 are under investigation. (See also: *Hazardous wastes* ℗, *Salinization* Ⓐ.)

Krill

A shrimp-like crustacean (*Euphausia superba*), which grows to a maximum size of about 6cm (2 inches) and is found in most of the Southern Ocean south of the Antarctic Convergence. It plays an essential role in Antarctica's marine ecosystem, being a major source of food to many species of fish, animals and birds. These include fin fish, six species of seals, several species of great whales and more than 50 bird species.

Estimates of the total biomass of krill, and the annual rate of production, are difficult to make due to the complex variables involved. Exploitation of krill, however, for which the USSR is 90 per cent responsible, has risen from an exploratory four tonnes in 1961-2 to more than 520,000 tonnes in 1982.

Such heavy exploitation must be reduced until more is known about the rate at which krill populations can regenerate. Catches for 1983 and 1984 fell to 233,800 and 128,329 tonnes respectively. From 1985 to 1987 the catch averaged 338,000 tonnes. This suggests that krill stocks are highly unstable and may be heading for collapse – in the same way as happened with Antarctic fin fish.

The depletion of the Antarctic ozone layer (*qv*), which shields organisms from solar ultraviolet radiation, may also threaten the krill population. Phytoplankton, the microscopic plants that are krill's staple foodstuff, have been found to be highly sensitive to ultraviolet rays. If the plankton decline, so will the krill, causing the collapse of the entire ecosystem of the Southern Ocean. (See also: *Antarctica* Ⓒ, *Extinction* Ⓒ, *Overfishing* Ⓒ, *Whales* Ⓒ.)

Land disposal
Land reform
Landfill
Leachate
Lead
Leukemia clusters
Lindane
London Dumping
 Convention
Love Canal
Low level radiation

Land disposal

According to the Organization of Economic Co-operation and Development (OECD), more than 70 per cent of the hazardous waste (*qv*) generated by its 24 member states (which include the USA, Great Britain, Germany, the Scandinavian countries, and Australia) is disposed of on land. In most countries, the figure for municipal wastes is even higher – though there are notable exceptions, Switzerland, for example, incinerating 90 per cent of its municipal wastes.

The principal methods of land disposal are landfill (*qv*), surface impoundment, deep-well injection (*qv*) and storage in underground mines. All three methods pose a major threat to groundwaters and surface water supplies.

In the US, the greatest volume of hazardous wastes (58.7 per cent, according to a 1981 survey) were until recently disposed of via underground injection, with 34.9 per cent dumped in surface impoundments and 5.5 per cent in engineered landfills. Amendments to the Resource Recovery and Conservation Act, however, have virtually banned new landfills and surface impoundments, and severely limited the use of deep-well injection. In Britain and many other OECD countries, however, landfill and impoundment remain the major form of land disposal.

Land reform

During the 1960s and 1970s, it was generally agreed by development and aid agencies that the root cause of soil degradation and deforestation was the rapid rise in population. But by the beginning of the 1980s some organizations were suggesting that land tenure systems could also have a significant influence upon the environment. In 1981 Oxfam published a short report, entitled "Land for the People," that signalled a decisive shift in their public policy. They pointed out that land ownership in the Third World was very highly concentrated: in South America, 2 per cent of the farming population controlled 47 per cent of the land; in India, 22 per cent held 76 per cent of the land. Because most aid was directed towards landowners, the ultimate effect was to widen the gulf between the well-off landowners and a rising tide of landless labourers.

The environmental effects of this concentration of wealth were graphically illustrated throughout the 1980s by the rapid increase of deforestation in the Amazon. Brazil is by no means an overpopulated country – in the 1970s it had a ratio of 2.3 acres of cropped land per person, which is higher than in the USA – but there are great disparities of wealth among its inhabitants. A very small section of the population owns a large proportion of the land. Large-scale agricultural projects, the introduction of mechanization and other forms of agricultural "rationalization" forced millions of peasants off the land, either into shanty towns or into the unexploited parts of the Amazon, where they have participated in the large-scale clearance of forest areas.

This pattern has been mirrored in many Third World countries. It has become commonly accepted that to prevent a continuous influx of poor peasants into ecologically fragile areas, some kind of land reform is necessary.

The call for land reform is nothing new. Countless governments have come to power on manifestos of land reform, only to renege on their promises, more often than not because of the fierce opposition from existing landowners, who usually wield considerable political power. It is not surprising that the more successful programmes have tended to evolve during periods of social upheaval. The most impressive case is China, where it was shown that a combination of peasant agricultural techniques and cooperative infrastructure can feed enormous numbers on a small area of land. Of capitalist countries, Japan, Taiwan and South Korea all benefited from land redistribution measures in the aftermath of World War II, which have contributed to their economic success.

In the light of past experience, it appears that the opposition to land reform from vested interests can only be surmounted by some degree of social upheaval, even violence. For this reason many development agencies have shied away from the issue – land reform is uncomfortably close to radical politics. But as the Oxfam report points out, violence is already an integral part of land tenure relations in Third World countries. Countless peasant families have been forcibly removed from their lands, seen their homes burned or been murdered by rapacious landlords. In India, 20 per cent of all crime is linked to land ownership. Poverty and environmental degradation are intimately linked to oppressive social conditions, and they are unlikely to be eradicated without some degree of conflict. (See also: *Cash crops*Ⓐ③, *Population*③.)

Landfill

Method of waste disposal, used to dispose of most of the world's domestic and hazardous wastes.

At its most primitive, landfilling consists of no more than tipping waste into a hole in the ground. Modern "sanitary" landfills, however, are specially engineered, the waste being tipped into prepared cells and covered daily.

Numerous pollution incidents – most notoriously Love Canal (*qv*) – have made the landfilling of hazardous waste the subject of bitter controversy.

Several countries have already outlawed the use of "dilute and disperse" sites for the disposal of hazardous wastes. Since such sites make no effort to prevent wastes from seeping out of the landfill, all too often the wastes simply migrate undiluted into local groundwaters (*qv*). One US survey found that of 50 sites studied, 40 had contaminated groundwaters. Nonetheless, dilute and disperse sites remain the most common form of landfill in the world.

Fears over groundwater pollution have led several countries to limit the landfilling of hazardous wastes to "containment" sites, the aim being to prevent the migration of leachate (*qv*) from the landfill. In France, only sites with a base of impermeable material 5m (16 feet) thick are permitted to take "special" wastes.

But containment sites have been plagued by problems. Certain chemicals – particularly industrial solvents – can transform even clay liners into sieves. Synthetic materials are no more reliable. A 1980 study of four "secure" landfills in New Jersey discovered that the liners at all four leaked, one within months of being installed.

A further problem, common to all landfills, is the potential build-up of explosive gases, particularly methane. In 1989, it was estimated that 1,390 landfill sites in England and Wales alone pose a risk of explosion – 756 of them within 250m (820ft) of housing. In 1986, gas from one such landfill ignited blowing up a nearby bungalow. Some scientists see the generation of methane from landfill sites as a major potential contributor to the greenhouse effect (*qv*), methane being a potent greenhouse gas (*qv*). According to H.G. Bingemer and P.J. Crutzen of the Max Planck Institute for Chemistry in Mainz, Germany, landfills worldwide contribute between 30 and 70 million tonnes of methane a year to the atmosphere.

The landfilling of hazardous wastes has been severely restricted in the Netherlands following a spate of pollution incidents. In France, it is seen as "a necessary and technical acceptable solution" – but only "in the short term" and only for wastes of low toxicity. In the USA, landfilling untreated hazardous wastes was phased out altogether in 1990. A ban on the land disposal of liquid wastes is already in force.

Britain, however, insists that, if properly sited and managed, landfill is a safe means of hazardous waste disposal. Confidence in that position has been somewhat eroded by two reports from the Hazardous Waste Inspectorate (HWI), an official watchdog agency, both severely critical of the standard of management at British landfills. The Chemical Industries Association has also expressed concern about standards, though, like the HWI, it remains committed to landfill.

Others are less sanguine. In 1989, the Natural Environment Research Council told a House of Commons Committee: "The problems of gas and leachate generation and of co-disposal, and the considerable uncertainty about the future behaviour of many landfills, suggest that a new approach to waste disposal is required. We should no longer accept landfill as a convenient means of reclaiming derelict land if the long-term behaviour and stability of each site cannot be predicted and assured. Landfilling (in the true sense of backfilling inconvenient holes in the ground) should thus be reserved for materials which are essentially inert and non-toxic, with predictable long-term stability, both physical and chemical. The implication of this suggestion is that degradable domestic wastes should not go directly to landfill, but ought to be sorted, recycled, reclaimed, used as fuel, and composted by encouraging accelerated biodegradation, to form an inert end-product which could then be used to landfill."

Health surveys of those living near hazardous waste landfills have shown higher-than-expected rates of cancer. In rural Louisiana, an area of the USA that has a disproportionate number of old landfills, the cancer rate is nearly a fifth higher than in other parts of the country. (See also: *Co-disposal*Ⓟ, *Hazardous waste*Ⓟ, *Leachate*Ⓟ.)

Leachate

The liquid that drains from a waste dump when water percolates through the waste, picking up polluting materials as it does so. The water may be from rain or from streams flowing over or through the surface. Poor landfill (*qv*) management can give rise to large volumes of leachate.

The composition of leachate depends on the age of a dump, with fresh refuse producing the strongest leachate. Very high biochemical oxygen demands (see

BOD) are characteristic of fresh refuse leachate which, coupled with high levels of ammonia and sometimes heavy metals, result in massive pollution if the liquid enters streams in any quantity. Older leachates have lower BODs, but still have large amounts of dissolved ammonia, a species especially toxic to fish.

Leachates from industrial waste sites may contain a wide range of pollutants such as heavy metals, solvents, ammonia, phenols and cyanides, though they may have lower BODs than those from domestic waste sites.

The migration of leachate from both domestic and industrial landfills has led to serious contamination of groundwaters (qv) in many parts of the world.

In Britain, most of the research done into the movement of leachates has dealt with industrial waste sites. Limited studies have been used to justify the widespread landfilling of domestic and industrial wastes in sites where leachate is intentionally allowed to migrate from the site, relying on natural processes of "attenuation" to render it harmless. Considerable disquiet has been expressed at this view and in Germany, much of the USA, Italy and the Netherlands, sites where leachate is collected and treated are the rule. Britain, too, is moving in this direction, helped by the success of several leachate treatment plants. (See also: *Hazardous waste*Ⓟ, *Landfill*Ⓟ.)

Lead

A poisonous heavy metal that has been in widespread use for thousands of years. A powerful neurotoxin, even in trace quantities, it is currently used in batteries, alloys, shot, paints and gasoline, and as a building material.

Lead plumbing, particularly in soft-water areas, causes raised lead levels in drinking water and, in some instances, poses a serious threat to human health. A British survey, carried out in 1975-76, revealed that between seven and eight per cent of water samples taken from taps in England exceeded the EC limit for lead in drinking water. In Scotland, the corresponding figure was 34.4 per cent. Though steps were subsequently taken to reduce lead levels in the worst affected areas, hundreds of thousands of homes in Britain still have water with lead levels that exceed the EC safety standard. To ensure that all drinking water sources in Britain complied with that standard would cost between \$1,500 million (£937 million) and \$5,000 million (£3,125 million).

The addition of tetra-ethyl lead to gasoline in order to prevent engine knocking has resulted in the universal distribution of lead in the environment, with particularly high concentrations occurring in urban air and dust. A recent study in Turin showed that at least 30 per cent of the lead in the blood of people living there came from gasoline.

Levels of lead in food are also raised by airborne lead. Indeed, such is the pervasiveness of lead that a 1975-76 study found few places left in the British Isles where leafy vegetables could be grown with lead levels below those considered fit for consumption by babies. The problem of lead in food is aggravated by the use of lead solders in food cans – a practice now being phased out in some countries.

Acute lead poisoning causes stomach pains, headaches, tremor, irritability and, in severe cases, coma and death. Much controversy surrounds the effects of low levels of lead on the developing brains of children. Lead is known to affect the nerves and the brain at very low concentrations and many authorities now accept that levels of lead commonly found in the blood of urban children are having a small but significant effect on their mental functioning.

In the USA, research at Harvard Medical School in Boston has found that the mental development of babies is affected by blood lead levels as low as ten micrograms per decilitre. More than a quarter of babies born in urban areas in the USA are exposed to such levels.

Lead-free gasoline has been available in the USA since 1975 and its use has been encouraged by strict car-emission standards. In West Germany, the lead content of gasoline was severely limited from 1976, and the German government now intends to phase out leaded petrol altogether. In Britain, it took a major campaign by environmentalists and doctors before the Government announced in 1981 that the lead limit for gasoline would be reduced from 0.4 grammes per litre to 0.15 grammes per litre by 1985. Britain is opposed to an outright ban on leaded gasoline, but preferential taxation has been introduced to promote its use. Lead-free gasoline is now required to be available in all EC countries. (See also: *Car emissions*ⓁⓅ, *Heavy metals*ⓁⓅ, *Water quality*ⓁⓅ.)

Leukemia clusters

Significantly higher-than-expected rates of leukemia in local areas. The most notorious cluster in Britain is near the Sellafield (qv) nuclear complex in Cumbria.

In November 1983, Yorkshire TV broadcast "Windscale – the Nuclear Laundry," having unearthed evidence that the cancer and leukemia rate among young people living near Windscale (now renamed Sellafield) was ten times higher than expected. Bootle and Waberwaite, villages that should have had no more than one case of cancer in children under 18 over a 30-year period, had instead four cases in 20 years: whereas Seascale, just one and half miles from Sellafield, had had 11 cases of childhood cancer since 1950. The chances of there being 15 childhood cancers in the three villages rather than the expected three cases was no more than one in 50,000 – a very low probability indeed.

The British government responded by setting up an independent advisory panel, headed by Sir Douglas Black, to investigate. Black concluded that a link with Sellafield discharges was possible but unproven. The report gave a "qualified reassurance" to local people.

The report has been criticized, first, because seven cancer cases were left out of the analysis.

Secondly, many children may have spent much longer in the sea near Sellafield than Black's assumption of 25 hours per year. Thirdly, Black's conclusions as to the induction of cancer were based wholly on the International Commission on Radiological Protection's (qv) model of the relationship between radiation dose and cancers – a model that has been criticized for underestimating the carcinogenic potential of radiation by a factor of ten to 20. Fourthly, as was later revealed, Black was himself misled over the atmospheric discharges of uranium from the Sellafield plant. British Nuclear Fuels, the operators of the plant, had told him that between 1952 and 1955 only 400g (14oz) of uranium had been released. In fact, 20kg (44lb) had been discharged.

In 1988, a government committee, set up on the recommendation of Sir Douglas Black, overturned his findings and concluded that the leukemia cases "must be assumed to be connected with the (Sellafield) plant unless proven otherwise". The report also linked a five-fold excess of childhood leukemias near Dounreay (qv) to radiation. In 1989, the families of 18 children from the Sellafield area were granted legal aid to sue British Nuclear Fuels Ltd, the operators of the plant, for causing their children's leukemia. The most recent study into leukemia around Sellafield was conducted by Professor Martin Gardner on behalf of the Medical Research Council and published in 1990. Gardner's team found a correlation between workers at the plant who had received an exceptionally high radiation dose and the development of leukemia in their children. Men who had received more than 100 millisieverts of radiation in their working life had a six to eight times greater chance of producing a child with the illness. This led to the startling theory that the men had actually passed on the cancer to their children by way of their sperm. It also added weight to demands for reductions in the doses allowed to nuclear workers.

There have been similar reports linking nuclear plants and leukemia in other countries. A study in the USA by the Massachusetts Department of Public Health concluded that adults living within a ten-mile radius of the Pilgrim nuclear plant between 1978 and 1983 had a four times greater risk of contracting leukemia. In 1991, an excess of childhood leukemia was reported round the Krummel nuclear site near Hamburg in Germany.

A high incidence of cancer among people living near the Rocky Flats nuclear weapons plant in Colorado is also considered to be linked to amounts of plutonium and other radionuclides in the local topsoil. (See also: *Radiation health effects* Ⓝ Ⓛ.)

Lindane
See: *HCH*.

London Dumping Convention
The Convention on the Prevention of Marine Pollution by Dumping of Waste and Other Matter – better known as the London Dumping Convention or LDC – came into force in 1975. An international treaty, covering all the world's oceans, its main aim is to control the dumping of wastes from ships and aircraft. It was originally signed by 33 countries. Others (notably Belgium) have ratified the treaty in recent years.

The convention specifically prohibits the dumping of certain "black list" substances into the sea, except in trace quantities. The black list includes organohalogen compounds; mercury and mercury compounds; cadmium and cadmium compounds; persistent plastics and other persistent synthetic compounds; crude oil, fuel oil, heavy diesel oil, hydraulic fluids and lubricating oils, if taken on board for the purpose of dumping; high-level radioactive waste (qv) or other radioactive material, where deemed unsuitable for sea disposal by the International Atomic Energy Agency (qv); and materials produced for biological or chemical warfare.

In addition, there is a "grey" list of substances that may be dumped only with a specific permit. Grey listed substances include arsenic, lead, copper and zinc; organosilicon compounds; cyanides; fluorides; and pesticides (qv) and their by-products.

In recent years, signatory nations to the LDC have clashed over several issues, notably ocean incineration (qv) and the dumping of nuclear waste. Thus, in 1985, 25 countries, led by Australia, Spain and New Zealand, voted for an indefinite ban on the dumping of nuclear wastes at sea. The proposal was opposed by six countries, including the USA, Britain and France. When the vote was passed, Britain insisted that the resolution was not legally binding and announced that it would continue to view ocean dumping as a possible option for nuclear waste disposal. (See also: *Heavy metals* Ⓟ, *Ocean dumping* Ⓟ, *Oslo Treaty* Ⓟ.)

Love Canal
Dump site in Niagara City, New York, that gained notoriety as America's first major dumping disaster.

First excavated in the late 19th century, as part of a hydroelectricity and industrial project planned by an eccentric entrepreneur called William T. Love, Love Canal was used by the Hooker Chemicals and Plastics Corporation as a dump for its chemical wastes from the early 1940s to 1952. More than 43,000 tonnes of waste, much of it carcinogenic, was dumped in the canal.

In 1953, Hooker Chemicals sold the site to the local Board of Education for one dollar, on condition that the company was absolved of future liability for any injury that might result from the chemicals in the dump. A school was built on the site, followed by a housing estate.

In 1977, the dump was found to be leaking. Tests revealed the air, soil and water around the dump site to be heavily contaminated with a wide range of toxic and carcinogenic chemicals. At first, the local authorities refused to act, but in April 1978 the New York State Commissioner for Health ordered the evacuation of some 240 families. The dump was cordoned off and the site declared a Federal Disaster Area – the first time in the history of the USA that a national emergency has been declared as a result of chemical pollution. This action was only taken following the ceaseless protests and activities of a local citizen's group, comprised mostly of women and led by Lois Marie Gibbs (who subsequently went on to found the Citizens Clearinghouse on Hazardous Wastes, one of the most effective anti-waste campaigning groups in the USA).

Later, in 1980, after further studies had revealed the pollution to be more extensive than previously thought, still more families were evacuated.

Three other Hooker dumps in the Niagara Falls area are now known to be leaking. Wastes from one, at Hyde Park, are oozing directly into the Niagara River, the source of drinking water for some six million people. The site contains the largest deposit of dioxin (qv) in the world. A second dump, at Bloody Run Creek, is also leaking. It is sited just across the road from a water-treatment plant serving 100,000 people.

Quite apart from Hooker's dumps, there are 212 other hazardous wastes sites in the Niagara Falls area, containing an estimated total of eight million tonnes of waste, including one tonne of dioxin (qv).

Some $14,000 million-worth of law suits have been filed against Hooker. (See also: *Hazardous waste*Ⓟ.)

Low level radiation
See: *Radiation and health.*

Magnox reactor
Malaria
Malathion
Malnutrition
Maralinga
Marshall Islands
Medfly epidemic
Mediterranean
Mendes, Chico
Mekong River Project
Mercury
Michigan disaster
Microchip pollution
Micropollutants
Minamata
Mineral resources
Moderator
Molluscicides
Monoculture
Monofilament nylon nets
Monosodium glutamate (MSG)
Montreal Protocol
Mururoa
Mutagens
Mutual defence agreement
Mutualism

Magnox reactor
Nuclear reactor that uses natural uranium metal fuel, encased in a magnesium alloy cladding (hence the name "magnox"), using graphite bricks as a moderator (qv) and carbon dioxide to take the heat out of the reactor core.

During the 1950s and 1960s, 11 Magnox power stations were built in Britain, including two (at Chapelcross, Dumfriesshire, and Calder Hall, Cumbria) specifically designed to extract plutonium (qv) for nuclear weapons. In addition, Britain has exported two Magnox stations, each consisting of a pair of reactors; one went to Japan in 1965 and one to Italy in 1962. France also developed a similar design for its first programme of ten reactors, but switched to pressurized water reactors in 1969.

Early Magnox reactors in Britain had steel pressure vessels, but the last two to be built – at Oldbury in Gloucestershire and Wylfa in Anglesey – were concrete. After the Chernobyl (qv) accident, some Magnox reactors were criticized for having inadequate, or no, secondary containment (qv). At the time, fears that the Magnox reactors could suffer a Chernobyl-scale accident were dismissed by Britain's nuclear industry. However, in 1989, a report by the Central Electricity Generating Board (CEGB) admitted that such an accident could indeed occur, although it dismissed the probability as extremely low – one in a million. However independent experts have criticized the report's assumptions and argue that the probability of such an accident is far higher than stated, and that reactor engineers would have far less time to bring the reactor under control than the CEGB estimates: perhaps minutes, rather than the four hours claimed by the Board.

With an average thermal efficiency of 25.8 per cent, Magnox reactors have never been able to compete with large modern coal-fired stations, whose efficiency is 36.1 per cent. Their electrical output is modest because they use natural, rather than enriched, uranium as fuel, and they were downrated in 1969 by an average of 18 per cent because of corrosion problems.

The Magnox reactors were originally built for 25 years' operation but most of them have now been running for nearly 30 years. In 1989, the Magnox station at Berkeley, Gloucestershire, was closed because it was judged that it would be too expensive to carry out vital safety improvements. The only Scottish civil Magnox station at Hunterston has also been shut down. Nuclear Electric, successor company to the CEGB, has said it wants to extend the operating lives of the remaining Magnox stations to 35 or 40 years. However, their age, failure to meet modern safety standards and serious corrosion problems make the continued use of these stations particularly hazardous. (See also: *Advanced gas-cooled reactor*Ⓝ, *Pressurized water reactor*Ⓝ.)

Malaria

One of the most widespread and lethal diseases in the world. It kills at least one million people a year and at any given moment 160 million people suffer from it.

Swamps and stagnant pools are ideal breeding grounds for malarial mosquitoes. Irrigation ditches, water storage ponds, and the marshy shores of reservoirs are also favoured breeding grounds. Not surprisingly, by creating permanent and vastly expanded habitats for the anopheles mosquito, irrigation schemes have greatly contributed to the spread and incidence of malaria.

Once established, malaria is extremely difficult to control. Draining mosquito breeding grounds is one solution – but this can have severe ecological effects and is clearly not an option in areas under irrigation. A more common method of eradication is to spray breeding grounds with insecticides. Again, the ecological costs are high: moreover, the success of spraying programmes generally proves temporary. Indeed, in many areas, the problem has been exacerbated. In Sri Lanka, for example, the emergence of the more virulent strain of malaria,

Plasmodium falciparium, has been directly linked to spraying programmes. Mosquitoes also have a remarkable ability to develop genetic resistance to insecticides. In 1981, the World Health Organization reported that 51 species of mosquito were resistant to one or more insecticide.

Resistance is also growing to anti-malarial drugs. Resistance to chloroquine is now recorded in ten South American countries, ten African countries, and nine South-East Asian countries. Resistance to Fansidar, a drug used in chloroquine-resistant areas, is widespread throughout Vietnam, Kampuchea and Manomar (Burma). Fansidar-chloroquine resistance has also been reported in West Papua and along the coasts of Kenya and Tanzania. (See also: *Dams*Ⓛ③, *Insecticides*Ⓟ, *Pesticides*Ⓟ, *Wetlands*Ⓒ.)

Malathion

An organophosphate (*qv*) used to kill a variety of insect pests in agriculture, public health and the garden. Although it is not generally considered very toxic to humans, those susceptible to organophosphates should avoid its use. Malathion is unselective and is harmful to bees, and to fish and aquatic life in general. (See also: *Pesticides*Ⓟ.)

Malnutrition

A word that means "bad feeding" and thus both overeating and undereating. Where malnutrition is caused by a chronic lack of nutrients, it leads to listlessness, damage to the immune system, impairment of mental functions, and, if severe enough, to death. At the other end of the scale, excess eating causes obesity, heart disease, and other "diseases of civilization" (*qv*). An imbalanced diet also causes malnutrition and can result in such deficiency diseases as beri-beri (lack of thiamine), rickets (lack of vitamin D) and pellagra (lack of niacin).

Between 1970 and 1980, the number of people in the Third World not getting enough to eat rose by 14 per cent to a total of 340 million people. Since then, according to the World Bank,

their numbers have risen inexorably and continue to do so. Today, estimates of the number of people "chronically deprived of the food necessary to enjoy an active life" vary between 512 million and 730 million. Though malnutrition in Africa has received the lion's share of publicity, Africa is not the worst affected continent. A 1987 UNICEF report on world hunger notes: "In the last two years, more children have died in India and Pakistan than in all the 46 nations of Africa together. In 1986, more children died in Bangladesh than in Ethiopia, more in Mexico than in the Sudan, and more in Indonesia than in all eight drought-stricken countries of the Sahel."

Although infant mortality resulting from malnutrition is highest in the Third World, it is by no means restricted to developing countries. In the USA, for example, a succession of reports throughout the 1980s highlighted the extent of malnutrition in this, the richest country in the world. One report estimated the number of malnourished children at over 12 million. Low incomes are the most immediate cause of hunger-related malnutrition in both the US and the Third World. But corrosive as the effects of poverty undoubtedly are, the problem is more deep-rooted than a lack of cash.

In the slums of the USA and other Western countries, malnutrition is as much a symptom of social alienation as it is of outright poverty. Surveys confirm that, all too often, what money is available is spent on junk foods of dubious nutritional value, on alcohol and narcotics, and on such trappings of affluence as television sets, videos and tape recorders.

In the Third World, the lack of cash is a more immediate cause of malnutrition than in the industrialized world, where welfare payments provide a cushion between poverty and outright starvation. Nonetheless, their poverty can also be seen as a symptom of a deeper problem; in this case, the social and ecological disruption caused by the introduction of the market economy.

Previously, though they had no cash, traditional peoples were well capable of feeding themselves. Indeed, anthropological studies repeatedly show a decline in nutritional standards when traditional peoples begin to work for wages and to grow cash crops. Where such peoples are still independent of the market, nutritional standards are high, with diets generally being varied and healthy.

In effect, the very development programmes being touted as the solution to Third World malnutrition often lie at the roots of its spread. Examples include large-scale dams (*qv*) and agricultural projects aimed at promoting the Green Revolution (*qv*). (See also: *Development③*.)

Maralinga

Site in the South Australian desert that was used by Britain from 1952 to 1957 to test atomic bombs, with "minor" trials continuing until 1963. During the period of testing, scientific integrity and the health of servicemen and the Australian population were sacrificed to the political urgency of developing a credible nuclear force. The operation to clean up the site after testing had stopped was totally inadequate. Britain claims to have been discharged from obligations to the site under agreements signed in 1968 and 1979. Australia claims that Britain did not fulfil its obligations because the site is still contaminated. (See also: *Atomic tests③*.)

Marshall Islands

Group of 30 atolls in the Pacific used by the USA as a nuclear test site from 1946 to 1958. Seventy atmospheric tests took place, the bombs being exploded on the atolls of Bikini and Enewetak.

Throughout the test programme, scant regard was paid to the health of the Marshalese or their way of life. The inhabitants of Bikini and Enewetak were forcibly removed from their homelands and resettled on two barren atolls which proved unable to support them. Malnutrition was rife on the atolls.

Other islanders were evacuated when their atolls became too radioactive for human habitation. Many are now dying of cancer.

Few warnings were given on the dangers of radiation. The inhabitants of Rongelap Atoll were exposed to fall-out from the "Bravo" hydrogen bomb test for three days before they were evacuated. Many suffered symptoms of acute radiation sickness.

Three years later, the islanders were allowed to return to Rongelap – even though radiation levels were still ten times higher than those on uncontaminated islands. An official memorandum records: "The habitation of these people on the island will afford most valuable ecological radiation data on human beings."

Other islanders fared no better. In 1978 – less than ten years after they had been allowed to return home – the inhabitants of Bikini were again evacuated. The islanders were found to be taking in dangerous levels of plutonium-239, caesium-137 and strontium-90 through their food. The US Department of Energy now estimates that it will be another 50 years before Bikini will again be safe for human habitation. (See also: *Atomic tests③*, *Radiation and health①③*.)

Medfly epidemic

The epidemic of Mediterranean fruit flies – or "medflies" – that hit California in the early 1980s, causing millions of dollars' worth of damage to fruit crops, provides a classic example of how biological control can go disastrously wrong.

The control programme involved the release of sterile medflies to disrupt the breeding cycle, a technique that had worked remarkably well with other insect pests in the past. However, one batch of supposedly sterile males from a laboratory in Peru had been improperly treated: as a result more than 100,000 fertile medflies were released onto crops.

Eventually, the then Governor, Jerry Brown, agreed to permit the aerial spraying of malathion (*qv*) – despite protests from local residents. The governor's action was in response to a Federal threat to quarantine all California fruit produce. (See also: *Biological control④⑤*.)

Mediterranean
See: *Regional seas.*

Mendes, Chico
Francisco (Chico) Mendes Filho was leader of the Brazilian rubbertappers' movement and an internationally-respected campaigner to save the tropical rainforests. On the night of December 22nd 1988, Mendes was shot dead at his home in Xapouri Acre, in the northwest of Brazil. The prime suspect for the murder, a wealthy landowner named Darli Alves da Silva, later fled to Bolivia, after ordering his son to hand himself over to the police.

Mendes led the Acre-based "Alliance of Forest Peoples," uniting the region's rubber tappers (*seringueiros*) and Indians against the destruction of the rainforests. Led by Mendes, the rubber tappers developed a form of passive resistance, known as the *empate*, defending the rainforest with their lives by forming human chains against both local ranchers and the police.

Mendes lobbied for collective land-use, and for government-owned "extractive reserves" where tappers could extract latex, brazil nuts and medicinal plants for sale. Twelve reserves are now created in five Brazilian states, covering 2 million hectares (5 million acres) of rainforest.

In 1987, Mendes visited the United States where he lobbied congressional staff and officials of the Inter-American Development Bank (IDB) over the funding of a proposed extension to the Trans-Amazonian highways from Porto Velho in Rondonia to Rio Branco in Acre. Shortly after his visit, the IDB temporarily suspended $65 million worth of loans for the project until environmental protection measures were implanted. The asphalted highway to Porto Velho had already brought in its wake a rush of speculators and ranchers, along with their armed henchmen, forcing an estimated 10,000 families into Bolivia, and an equivalent number into the slums of Rio Branco.

Mendes was one of 1,000 rural workers and trade unionists in Brazil to have been murdered since 1980. Only three per cent of the suspected killers have been jailed. (See also: *Amazonia*③, *Tropical forests*③.)

Mekong River Project

Prospects of a peace settlement in Cambodia and increased foreign aid to the Indochinese countries have recently given new impetus to plans to "harness" the Mekong River – the heart of one of the most biologically diverse watersheds in Asia – with massive dam projects.

Under the plans, up to 11 multipurpose dams may be built to generate up to 20,000 megawatts of electricity and provide irrigation, flood control and improved navigation. The dams would displace up to 350,000 people and disrupt the habitats of more than 100 known species of migratory freshwater fish, the chief source of protein for the majority of the 52 million residents of the lower Mekong basin.

Initial attempts to dam the river's tributaries have met with large amounts of determined resistance from villagers who would lose farmland or fisheries as a result. For example, plans to build the Kaeng Sua Ten dam on the Yom tributary were put on hold after massive demonstrations in 1989.

Planners at the agency sponsored by the United Nations known as the Mekong Committee, however, insist that dams are an idea whose time has come. They say the dams are needed to meet a doubling in electricity demand forecast by Thailand's electricity authority. Opponents claim that these estimates have been inflated. They add that the dams would interfere with the Mekong's annual floods, which provide farmland with fertile silt and create seasonal lakes and swamps used as spawning grounds by fish.

Environmentalists are particularly concerned about the proposed 600MW Nam Theun 2 dam on a Laotian tributary of the Mekong. Export of electricity from the dam to Thailand is one of the few ways Laos could significantly boost its foreign income. But Nam Theun 2 would flood 300sq km (185sq miles) of forest, grasslands and wetlands, and endanger further thousands of square kilometres of prime tropical forest by bringing in migrants. (See also: *Dams*③, *Resettlement*③.)

Mercury

Mercury is a highly toxic heavy metal (*qv*) which has caused considerable damage to human health and the environment as a result of its misuse.

Mercury attacks the nervous system. Small doses cause irritability, nervousness and headaches, while large doses cause convulsions, coma and death. It is toxic when swallowed or if particles of mercury compounds are inhaled. Mercury metal is easily absorbed through the skin and its vapour is highly toxic.

Most inorganic mercury compounds are poisonous, but organic mercury compounds, formed when mercury compounds combine with certain organic molecules, are even more so. These organic mercury compounds are soluble in fat, which means they accumulate easily in the body and so penetrate readily into the nerves and brain. Methyl mercury, one such organic compound, is also teratogenic (*qv*). Under certain conditions, methyl mercury can be formed in the environment from inorganic mercury and organic matter, a potentially extremely dangerous phenomenon.

Like all heavy metals, mercury can accumulate up food chains and species such as fish and birds of prey at the top of the chain may contain large quantities.

A major use of mercury compounds, which still continues, is as a seed dressing to prevent the growth of moulds. Hundreds of cases of mercury poisoning were caused in Iraq when dressed seed was cooked and eaten by mistake and the use of such dressings has also been the cause of many wildlife casualties.

The most famous mercury pollution incident was at Minamata Bay in Japan when mercury discharged by a factory was passed up the marine food chain to fish, which formed the staple diet of local people. Brain damage, delirium and death were caused while exposed women produced deformed babies. The form of mercury involved was methyl mercury.

Mercury metal is still in use in thermometers, barometers and even children's toys. Spillage of even small quantities of this metal in a warmish room can cause mercury poisoning as the material vaporizes.

In Amazonia (*qv*), the continuing (though now illegal) use of mercury by goldminers to separate gold from mined ores is causing severe pollution problems. In Rondonia, where gold production increased from 4kg (8.8lb) a year in 1974 to 3,600kg (8,000lb) a year in 1984, fish have been found with mercury levels four times in excess of the World Health Organization's safety limit. Mercury levels in the eggs of one species, the acari-bodo, were nearly eight times the WHO limit. In 1989, tests of Kayapo Indians and gold prospectors revealed mercury levels in blood, urine and hair above WHO safe limits. It is estimated that more than 1,800 tonnes of mercury have entered the Amazon ecosystem as a result of gold prospecting.
(See also: *Heavy metals*℗, *Minamata*℗.)

Michigan disaster

Mass poisoning of cattle in Michigan resulting from a fire-retardant being accidentally packaged as a cattle feed. The fire-retardant contained polybrominated biphenyl (PBB), a highly toxic chemical which is closely related to polychlorinated biphenyls (PCB) (*qv*).

The contaminated feed was fed to tens of thousands of farm animals, causing stillbirths, abortions, tremors, anorexia, liver damage, abscesses and other symptoms of poisoning. Some affected animals were buried in mass pits. Others were used as animal feed, thereby recycling the poison.

It was nine months before the cause of the poisoning was discovered. By then, nine million people in Michigan had eaten contaminated meat and dairy products. In 1982, a study by New York's Mount Sinai School of Medicine revealed that 97 per cent of the population were contaminated with PBBs – the highest levels being found in children and men. (See also: *Cancer*ⓁⓅ.)

Microchip pollution

The use of microchips in electronic devices is bringing a number of environmental benefits, but, unfortunately, the industry itself has caused health and pollution problems and may continue to do so if adequate controls are not established. Toxic chemicals are used, the effects of which are not always fully understood, and even well-understood chemicals, handled carelessly, have caused pollution that could have been prevented.

In California's Silicon Valley, massive solvent pollution of groundwater has occurred because storage tanks built to hold these materials were badly designed and leaked. Water supplies have had to be taken out of use because of toxic and carcinogenic contamination, while adverse health effects have been claimed by people living in the vicinity.

In a semiconductor plant in Massachusetts, production workers have suffered from increased headaches, sore throats and nausea, which have been blamed on the chemicals used. More serious was the finding that women working in the production area were more likely to miscarry than workers working in non-manufacturing areas of the plant such as offices. The exact cause of this effect has not been discovered, but the company concerned has encouraged women of childbearing age to work elsewhere in the plant.

Silicon, the basis of the microchip, is not harmful in the form in which it is manufactured for use in microelectronics, but some other materials which are used in smaller amounts are poisonous. Arsenic and selenium are potentially harmful, but their properties are reasonably well understood. Some other substances in increasing use, such as gallium and germanium, have not been distributed or studied so widely and much less is known about their toxicological and environmental properties. (See also: *Chlorinated solvents*Ⓟ, *Groundwater*Ⓟ.)

Micropollutants

Some 1,200 unidentified chemicals have been detected in public drinking water supplies. Little is known about the effects on health of these "micropollutants". In 1975, the World Health Organization (WHO) reviewed the safety data on 289 compounds commonly present in drinking water and found that no toxicological data of any sort existed for more than half of them.

Six years later, a British study came to the same conclusion: of the 343 compounds it identified, "most" had never been evaluated for safety.

Among the micropollutants that scientists have identified are chloroform, benzene, trichloroethylene and carbon tetrachloride – all suspect or proven carcinogens. Ironically, many micropollutants result from the chlorination (*qv*) of water supplies to protect public health. Certain organic pollutants – some of natural origin, others industrial – react with chlorine to form trihalomethanes (THMS), several of which – chloroform, for example – are suspected of causing cancer (*qv*) in humans. Though micropollutants are present only in low concentrations, repeated small doses may well cause chronic toxic effects.

Some countries have taken steps to minimize exposure to THMS. Municipal water treatment plants in the USA are required to use granulated active carbon to remove THMS from drinking water. In Germany, the government has limited the concentration of THMS in drinking water to 25 microgrammes per litre – and many German treatment plants are now using ozone instead of chlorine as a disinfectant. (See also: *Drinking water*, *Water quality*ⓁⓅ.)

Minamata

Fishing village in Japan whose inhabitants suffered an epidemic of nervous diseases from eating fish contaminated by industrial discharges from a nearby chemical plant owned by the Chisso Corporation. Victims suffered convulsions, blindness, brain damage and, in some cases, death. The Minamata tragedy was one of the first incidents to alert people to the dangers of chemical pollution.

The first cases of Minamata disease were diagnosed in 1953. By 1966, 43 people in Minamata had died and a further 68 were permanently disabled – mainly from cerebral palsy. By 1983, more than 300 people had died and nearly 1,500 were officially recognized to be suffering from the disease – though 6,000 claimed to have been affected.

The cause of the disease was methyl mercury poisoning. Initially, it was thought that the mercury (*qv*) had been discharged in inorganic form and had been transformed by marine organisms into the more toxic methyl mercury, an organic form of mercury. Later, it emerged that Chisso had in fact been discharging methyl mercury directly into Minamata Bay – though biotransformation undoubtedly compounded the problem.

Though Chisso paid token damages to Minamata victims ($160/£100 to adults and $48/£30 to children), it consistently denied responsibility for the disaster. Those who received compensation did so only after signing a document that precluded them from taking further legal action. (See also: *Bioconcentration*Ⓟ, *Mercury*Ⓟ.)

Mineral resources

Modern industrial societies consume vast amounts of energy and raw materials. It has been estimated, for instance, that an average American will use, directly and indirectly, during the course

Unfettered market forces combine to devastate land and workers in a Brazilian tin mine.

of his or her life, some 1,600 tonnes of various materials, all of which have to be extracted from the earth, processed and delivered – that is, about 50 times more resources than are used by an average Indian.

Are there enough resources in the world to support the resource-intensive way of life of the First World and, at the same time, enable people in the Third World to increase their consumption of materials, which they would have to do if they are to develop? How long, in fact, are the Earth's mineral resources likely to last?

It can be argued that if we are willing to pay a higher price for mineral resources, more can be made available through new explorations. This is only true up to a point. Thus the massive increase in the price of oil (*qv*) in 1973 has not made very much more oil available. On the contrary, it has encouraged us to use less of it.

Indeed, only a few countries, such as Japan and West Germany, could have afforded to pay for oil at $36 a barrel for very long, since at that price, in many countries, it was absorbing a significant part of foreign earnings. The same must be true for many minerals; once their price has reached a certain level, many of their uses will cease to be economic.

It can also be argued that, with the development of the "service economy," and with the increased use of plastics and of new technologies such as microelectronics, the demand for minerals will fall. This is probably true. It would also fall, of course, if there were a major economic slump. However, if consumption continues to increase at the current rate, shortages should begin to occur early next century; by then, most Third World countries will also be suffering serious shortages of land, water, food and firewood, making the pursuit of an industrialized way of life difficult to continue.

Moderator
See: *Fission*.

Molluscicides
Chemicals used to kill snails, mussels and other animals with shells. There are two applications of these chemicals that have environmental significance: disease control and anti-fouling treatments for yachts.

In slow-moving tropical freshwater, snails frequently carry the parasite that causes the crippling disease schistosomiasis (*qv*). One of the measures by which this disease is controlled is the destruction of the snail host by the application of molluscicides to the water. Copper sulphate and a pentachlorophenol derivative were originally used but these tended to kill other forms of life. More selective compounds are now available.

Molluscs of a different kind have proved to be a nuisance to yacht owners. To prevent their clinging to the bottoms of boats anti-fouling paints, toxic to the animals concerned, have been developed. The principal compound used is tributyl tin and its use has caused serious problems to other organisms, notably oysters. (See also: *Biocides*Ⓟ, *Waterborne diseases*ⓁⒶ.)

Monoculture

The cultivation of large stretches of a single crop, which is harvested all at once. It is a necessary feature of modern mechanized farming and clearly the best way to reduce labour costs, make the maximum use of expensive machinery, and maximize marketing efficiency.

In terms of the environment, however, monoculture is the least desirable agricultural strategy, with few of the advantages of traditional polyculture.

Polyculture minimizes vulnerability to pests by providing the smallest niche for pests affecting specific crops. What is more, if rotation is practised, then this niche is reduced both in time and space. When monoculture is introduced, then the niche is maximized and the pest population expands to occupy it as fully as possible. If, as is usually so with modern agriculture, the same crop is grown year after year, then the massive niche provided for the pest becomes a permanent one, encouraging the pests' proliferation.

Polyculture, especially when it involves the cultivation of many different strains of the same crops, also provides insurance against droughts, heavy rains, frosts, and pest infestations. The reason is that while some crops, or strains of a particular crop, are affected, many others are likely not to be. Monoculture, by contrast, is highly vulnerable to discontinuities of all sorts because it consists of only one crop.

Polyculture also often involves growing crops that are complementary, such as cereals interspersed with legumes, the latter providing the nitrogen which is needed to grow the former. Crops of different height are also grown, the higher ones providing shade for the lower ones and also helping to keep down weeds.

In addition, the different crops grown provide effective cover to the soil and reduce loss of soil moisture. Hedgerows (*qv*) and windbreaks also help provide protection from the winds, reduce moisture loss, and help prevent erosion.

Not surprisingly, though yields of specific crops may not be high, total yields of all the different crops grown are often higher than those obtained when monoculture is practised. This is not surprising, since under monoculture all the subtle devices for maintaining soil fertility, soil structure and soil moisture, and for reducing vulnerability to pests and other discontinuities, are sacrificed to short-term economic efficiency.

In partial compensation, more nutrients in the form of artificial fertilizer and trace elements are added, as well as pesticides (*qv*). However, these have adverse ecological consequences, and make no contribution to the maintenance of soil structure, which can only deteriorate.

Moreover, the tendency, under a regime of monoculture, to leave the soil bare between crops, especially during the rainy winter months as now occurs in the North American cornbelt, must lead to erosion (*qv*). (See also: *Organic farming* Ⓐ.)

Monofilament nylon nets
See: *Drift nets.*

Monosodium glutamate (MSG)
An additive (*qv*) used as a flavour enhancer. It has only a slight flavour on its own, but when added to food it stimulates the taste buds and so deceives consumers into thinking that the foods have more flavour than they really do.

Worldwide, MSG is probably used in more than 15,000 different processed food items. It is also added to some animal feeds to stimulate appetites. By the mid-1960s, the Japanese were producing 63 million kg (140 million lb) of MSG a year, and the Americans were consuming some 20 million kg (45 million lb) annually, equal to more than a kilogramme per person per year. Since then consumption has increased rapidly.

For much of the last 25 years, MSG has been among the more controversial additives. During the early 1960s, evidence emerged that MSG could not only have profound effects on the chemistry of the brain, but also that high doses could provoke undesirable changes in the brains of mice. There was further evidence that glutamic acid (to which MSG is closely related) may concentrate in the placental fluid of pregnant women. Furthermore, in the late 1960s, studies revealed that in some (but not all) tests, MSG and glutamic acid damaged the reproductive processes of rabbits and chickens, though in previous tests on rats no problems had emerged. In the late 1960s, some direct human evidence indicated that, on an empty stomach, glutamates can provoke a range of sub-lethal effects – from headaches to respiratory difficulties and muscular tightness.

Several official bodies have recognized that MSG can provoke some symptoms of discomfort and intolerance. MSG has been particularly popular with some Chinese restaurants, and customers and doctors came to recognize what has been called Chinese Restaurant Syndrome, which is attributed to MSG.

Official bodies have generally argued that since glutamic acid is a normal component of proteins, it, along with MSG, can be adequately metabolized as long as the digestive system is not overloaded. They conclude a "safe level" for daily intake can be established. MSG is thus permitted and used in the UK, the US and many countries of the EC. In the UK, it has been recommended, however, that MSG should not be included in the manufacture of commercial baby foods. (See also: *Acceptable daily intake*ⒻⓁ, *Flavourings*Ⓛ.)

Montreal Protocol
International agreement, drawn up at Montreal in 1987, in which the world's leading industrialized nations agreed to halve their consumption of CFCs (*qv*) and halons –

two of the most damaging ozone-depleting substances – by 1991. Within months of the Protocol being signed, however, further evidence concerning the persistence of CFCS in the atmosphere made it clear that the agreed measures were hopelessly inadequate. In June 1990, delegates from nearly 100 countries met in London and agreed to phase out the use of CFCS and halons by the year 2000.

A major stumbling-block at the London conference was the position of developing countries, who were reluctant to deprive their fledgling industries of the cheap CFCS that had for so long been available to the industrialized nations, or to become dependent upon the West for a new generation of sophisticated and possibly expensive chemicals. It was finally agreed that $240 million, part of a $1,000 million global fund for the environment, should be allotted to Third World countries to help them bring in alternatives to CFCS, and that these countries should have their deadline ex-

tended 10 years to 2010.

Ratification of the treaty has been slow. By summer 1991, 71 nations had ratified the original 1987 Protocol, but only ten had ratified the revised 1990 London agreement; and only $10 million of the $53 million due had been paid into the fund, barely enough to pay for all its administration costs. Meanwhile companies such as ICI, while advertising their commitment to the environment, had been unloading stocks of halons in Third World countries that had not already signed the treaty. In India, sales of halons rose from 39 tonnes in 1987 to 315 tonnes in 1990.

Nevertheless, the Protocol has demonstrated an encouraging willingness on the part of the international community to formulate solutions to urgent environmental problems. It now remains to be seen whether, at the next review of the Protocol in 1992, the deadline for phasing out the use of ozone-depleting substances will be brought forward, and whether nations will seal the agreement

and follow it up with money and action. (See also: *CFCs*℗, *Ozone layer*℗.)

Mururoa

Nuclear test site in French Polynesia in the South Pacific. It was established in the face of bitter opposition from the local Territorial Assembly after Algerian independence prompted France to move its previous nuclear test site from the Sahara.

Testing began in 1966, with 41 above-ground tests being carried out in the first nine years (France did not sign the Partial Test Ban Treaty). The testing programme was condemned by the UN conference on the human environment at its 1972 Stockholm Conference (*qv*) and, with France undergoing diplomatic pressure from Pacific states and from environmental groups such as Greenpeace (whose yacht *Vega* was illegally attacked and detained on the high seas by the French navy), and with legal action being taken at the International Court of Justice, the testing programme was

France's independent nuclear force has resulted in many atmospheric tests at Mururoa.

moved underground in 1975. More than 80 underground tests have been carried out – the latest being on May 6 1987.

President de Gaulle, visiting the island in September 1966, refused to delay a test for a change in wind direction towards the uninhabited Southern Ocean. Consequently, all the islands as far away as Western Samoa (3,000 km/1,800 miles) received high levels of radiation.

Underground testing has proved hazardous also. The island has sunk more than 1.5m (5ft) since testing began and a crack 35-50cm (14-20in) wide and 1km (1,100yd) long has developed in the atoll beneath sea level. Radioactivity has been leaking into the ocean for several years. Particularly damaging was a bomb which was detonated, after it had stuck half-way down its test shaft, in the coral rather than in the underlying basalt bedrock. A large slab of the internal wall of the atoll was dislodged and the resulting tidal wave injured seven people on the beach. The north beach of the atoll was contaminated in 1975 by several kilogrammes of plutonium, after a series of tests. The authorities attempted to "bury" the plutonium under a layer of asphalt. In March 1981, however, a tropical storm tore apart the asphalt covering, washing radioactive debris into the sea.

Radioactivity from the tests (either leaking into the sea or from fallout) is reconcentrated in the seafood that forms the staple diet of the people of the Pacific. No one knows how many have developed cancer, however, since the French refuse to disclose the health statistics for French Polynesia since the tests began. Attempts to set up an independent inquiry have come to nothing. In the 1981 French elections, Mururoa became a major political issue and François Mitterrand promised the anti-nuclear and environmental groups that the testing programme would be reviewed. The decision to continue testing came just four days after the review began.

The widely scattered popula-tion, subject to colonial rule, and hindered by press and radio censorship, have only recently begun to mount organized opposition to the testing. Despite growing worldwide condemnation, however, France looks set to continue its testing programme. (See also: *Atomic tests*Ⓝ, *Underground nuclear tests*Ⓝ.)

Mutagens

Chemicals that cause mutations in the offspring of living organisms. A mutation is a change in the chemical structure of the genetic material of an organism and though a few mutations may be advantageous, most are harmful or neutral in effect. Chemicals capable of combining with DNA – the chemical that carries genetic information – are often muta-genic; a common example is the insecticide dichlorvos (*qv*). Mutagens are often carcinogens (*qv*) as well, a fact used as the basis of the Ames test, which uses bacteria to screen chemicals for possible carcinogenicity. Ionizing radiation is one of the best documented mutagens.

Screening for mutagenic prop-erties is still not mandatory in most industrial countries, despite 1,000 new chemicals entering the market each year. (See also: *Radiation and health*ⓁⓃ.)

Mutual defence agreement

Signed by the UK and US Governments in 1958, the Agreement for Co-operation on the Uses of Atomic Energy for Mutual Defence Purposes governs the exchange of fissile materials for military purposes between the two countries.

Much controversy surrounds the origin of the British plutonium exported to the USA. Until 1986, the government denied that any plutonium from civil nuclear reactors had been used for mutual defence purposes. However, investigation by independent physicists, aided by information released under the US Freedom of Information Act, revealed that up to seven tonnes of plutonium may have been exported and used in US weapons manufacture, a significant proportion of that plutonium coming from civil Magnox reactors. This use of civil plutonium contravenes the Non-Proliferation Treaty (*qv*) to which both Britain and the USA are signatories.

The agreement was renewed in 1984 for ten years. (See also: *Magnox reactors*Ⓝ, *Nuclear proliferation*Ⓝ.)

Mutualism

Theory of the interdependence of all living things.

The idea of the world as a "vast cooperative enterprise" is an ancient concept. The principle was embodied in the "Oeconomy of Nature," a term first used in 1658 by Sir Kenelm Digby, before becoming, a century later, the title of Linnaeus's famous essay.

"By the Oeconomy of Nature," Linnaeus wrote, "we understand the all-wise disposition of the creator in relation to natural things, by which they are fitted to produce general ends and reciprocal uses." He saw living beings as "connected, indeed so chained together that they all aim at the same end, and to this end a vast number of intermediate ends are subservient."

Eighteenth-century naturalists also adopted this view of our planet, but with the industrial revolution the accent shifted from cooperation or mutualism to competition and aggression.

Thus Adam Smith, Thomas Malthus, Herbert Spenser, Charles Darwin and T.H. Huxley, Darwin's most distinguished disciple, each saw competition and the "struggle for survival" as the natural tendency among living things. Huxley regarded cooperation as something so totally foreign to our planet that it had to be introduced by man – via the agency of scientific, technological and industrial progress.

Ecology developed very much as a reaction against this view of the world as atomized, random, and in perpetual flux. But after World War II, which accentuated human aggression and triggered off an unprecedented euphoria for economic development, the accent among the ecological community and theoretical biologists shifted once more towards competition and aggression.

To quote Professor Boucher, author of *The Biology of Mutualism*, "twentieth century ecology . . . has continued the tradition of seeing antagonistic interactions as the basis of community organization."

Professor Rickless, author of a famous textbook, makes the same point. The notion of competition, he writes, "as a major organizing principle in ecology, is so widely accepted that it has achieved the status of a paradigm."

It is only in the last few years that this assumption has even been questioned. It has been found that the evidence for competition as the driving force of nature is more than slim.

That competition serves a function is clear, but it may by no means be the ubiquitous force it is supposed to be, still less the only tool for assuring the evolution of species and hence the structure of the biosphere.

In the 1970s there was a sudden resurgence of interest in mutualism. Boucher, in an article written jointly with the ecologists Drs. James and Keller, for instance noted "that gut flora are involved in breaking down cellulose and related substances in mutualism with many vertebrates as well as with termites and other arthropods. Urea is broken down and its nitrogen recycled by rumen bacteria and by the fungal components of some lichens."

Interest in mycorrhizae – the fungi that live in mutualistic association with the roots of plants – was also revived. Mycorrhizae increase the ability of plants to extract minerals from the soil, and in return are provided with photosynthate. Many trees will not grow without mycorrhizae.

Interestingly, an increasing number of parasitic or predatory relationships have turned out, on closer examination, to be mutualistic. Thus the ecologist Professor McNaughton has pointed out that the normal view of the relationship between grazers and grass is false. He identifies nine different ways in which this relationship can be regarded as mutualistic. They include evidence that grazing increases the water-use efficiency of grass, and that saliva may increase grass growth by as much as 50 per cent above control levels.

Boucher sees present theories of mutualism as "still basically mechanistic, mathematical, fitness-maximizing, and individualistic." This seems inevitable. A realistic theory of mutualism belongs to a holistic or really ecological paradigm and is irreconcilable with today's reductionistic and mechanistic science.

Boucher refers to the difficulties ecologists have experienced in this respect: "While arguing that nature is an integrated whole and that everything is connected to everything else, we continued researching with theories that said that communities are no more than sets of individual organisms. The problem, in other words, is one of cognitive dissonance – the difficulty of working with two sets of ecological ideas, based on different fundamental assumptions and ultimately in conflict."

Narmada Valley
    Project
Nitrate
Nitrite
Nitrosamines
Nomadic pastoralism
Non-Proliferation
    Treaty
North Sea
Nuclear accidents
Nuclear economics
Nuclear proliferation
Nuclear waste
Nuclear winter

Narmada Valley Project

India's Narmada Valley Project is one of the largest and most controversial development programmes ever undertaken in the world. Over the next 50 years, 30 major dams, 135 medium-sized dams and 3,000 smaller dams are to be built on the Narmada and its tributaries. The project will cost tens of billions of dollars.

In 1985, the World Bank (*qv*) approved $450 million in funding for the first dam to be built, the Sardar Sarovar. The Sardar Sarovar will be followed by the Narmada Sagar dam. The dams have been vigorously opposed by environmentalists throughout the world.

Twenty million people inhabit the Narmada River basin, which stretches more than 1,300km (800 miles) from the Arabian Sea to the heart of India, passing through the north-eastern states of Gujarat, Maharastra and Madhya Pradesh. Hindus consider the Narmada to be the holiest of all rivers: even the Ganges is said to travel to the Narmada every year, disguised as a cow, in order to purify itself in the river's waters.

Of the planned major dams, five are hydroelectric, six multi-purpose and 19 are for irrigation. According to the Narmada Valley Development Agency (NVDA), the project, when completed, will irrigate 50,000sq km (19,000sq miles) of land, and supply 2,700MW of electricity. The NVDA claims that 11,500,000 local villagers will benefit, in addition to millions of others in the cities.

But the ecological and social costs of the project are devastating. The project will submerge 3,500sq km (1,300sq miles) of forest – 11 per cent of the forest in the Valley – 200sq km (77sq miles) of cultivated land and some 400sq km (150sq miles) of grazing land. As much as 40 per cent of the land to be irrigated by the project is "black cotton soil," and is thus particularly susceptible to waterlogging and salinization (*qv*).

According to the Institute of Urban Affairs, New Delhi, one million people will be displaced by the dams, though some put the figure at nearer 1,500,000. Many of those who will be moved are tribal peoples, who have cultivated the forests for centuries. Because they have no title to land, they will not receive compensation. This is not only in contravention of the International Labour Organization's convention on tribal rights, but of the World Bank's own guidelines on tribal peoples. There are few who doubt that the resettlement programme spells cultural death for these tribal people.

In the face of growing international concern over the adverse environmental and social impact of the Narmada Project, the World Bank temporarily suspended its funding for Sardar Sarovar pending a full review of "resettlement and rehabilitation" plans. As a result, the Indian government commissioned an environmental impact statement from the Department of the Environment in New Delhi. The review was strongly critical of the resettlement programmes for both dams.

Nonetheless, on April 14 1987, Prime Minister Rajiv Gandhi announced that the Narmada Valley Project would proceed. The decision was purely political: after a series of electoral defeats throughout India, Gandhi needed to secure Gujarat and Madhya Pradesh for his Congress party.

In late 1988, the World Bank announced that continued funding for Sardar Sarovar would be conditional upon improving the resettlement programme for oustees. The local state governments were given until March 30 1989 to produce detailed resettlement plans acceptable to the bank – or further credit for the dam would be suspended. However, the deadline was subsequently extended to June 30 1988, and then to July 1990 – this despite a highly critical report by the bank's own appraisal mission on the inadequacies of the resettlement programme.

In June 1990, Japan, which had already given $20 million towards the project, refused any further funding. In September 1990, the Indian government declared its intention to proceed with the scheme, even if all foreign finance was withdrawn. The World Bank then announced that it would continue to fund the project, on the grounds that by doing so it would be in a better position to minimize the impact of the dam. In June 1991, however, continuing criticism from local people and NGOs forced the Bank to take the unprecedented step of appointing an independent investigator, Bradford Morse, to review the whole project.

Meanwhile the construction of the dam has continued unabated, and by the summer of 1991 its wall was high enough to cause a backwater build-up in the event of a flood. In January 1991, the state government of Maharastra started felling a 3,000-hectare forest inhabited by tribal peoples to provide land for some of the villagers displaced by the dam. Ironically, this land is part of the catchment area for an earlier dam, the Ukai, which has been silting up because of deforestation. Felling was suspended by order of the District Court; then recommenced after the State successfully appealed to the High Court in Bombay. While the negotiations continue, a large number of the "oustees" have vowed that they will never move from their homes, saying that they would prefer to stay and drown. (See also: *Dams*③, *Development*③, *Resettlement programmes*③.)

Nitrate

A naturally occurring substance that is essential for plant growth. Nitrate itself is not particularly poisonous to humans, but if converted into nitrite (*qv*) or nitrosamines (*qv*) it can present a health risk.

Large quantities of nitrate, in animal manures and more particularly in artificial fertilizers, are added to growing crops to improve yields, but often lead to pollution.

Nitrate is highly soluble and easily washes off fields into rivers, where eutrophication (*qv*) may result. It can also be carried down through the soil by percolating water and may contaminate groundwater to dangerous levels.

In Britain, an estimated 1,500,000 people are now exposed to nitrate levels in drinking water that exceed the limit of 50 milligrammes per litre (mgl) set by the EC. Initially, Britain tried to exploit loopholes in the EC directive, which came into force in 1985, to allow 52 water sources in the Anglian, Thames, Yorkshire and Severn-Trent areas to be exempted from having to comply with the new limits. However, in 1989 the government undertook to meet the EC standards in most areas by 1993 and in the rest by 1995. The 1995 deadline did not satisfy the commission, which angered by the delays in implementing the directive, announced in September 1989 that Britain would be taken to the European Court for breaching the directive, subsequently ruling that Britain was in breach of the directive. (See also: *Artificial fertilizers*Ⓐ⒫ , *Groundwater*Ⓟ.)

Nitrite

A substance found in the soil and formed in the human gut by the action of bacteria on nitrate (*qv*). It forms part of the nitrogen cycle and is converted to nitrate, which is absorbed by plants. In humans it can cause problems.

Nitrite combines with the red blood pigment haemoglobin. This prevents the blood from carrying oxygen around the body efficiently, and if this happens to a significant degree the body may suffocate from within, a condition called methaemoglobinaemia. This is rare in adults, but occurs in babies and small children who absorb excessive amounts of nitrate in drinking water and made-up feeds. Babies are particularly at risk because conditions in their digestive system favour the rapid formation of nitrite from nitrate. They also have a type of haemoglobin in their blood which combines especially readily with nitrite. Methaemoglobinaemia can be fatal and doctors in areas where nitrate levels in water are high are warned to be on the lookout for it. Nitrite may also present a cancer risk. (See also: *Cancer*Ⓛ Ⓟ, *Carcinogen*Ⓕ Ⓛ Ⓟ, *Nitrosamines*Ⓛ Ⓟ.)

Nitrosamines

Chemical compounds formed when nitrites react with certain organic nitrogen compounds in an acid solution. More correctly called "N-nitrosamines," they have been shown to cause stomach cancer in laboratory animals and there is growing concern that they may also do so in humans who absorb nitrite (*qv*) or nitrate (*qv*) in their diet. (See also: *Cancer*Ⓛ Ⓟ, *Carcinogen*Ⓕ Ⓟ, *Nitrate*Ⓐ Ⓛ Ⓟ, *Nitrite*Ⓛ Ⓟ.)

Nomadic pastoralism

For many years, nomadic pastoralism has been denigrated as both unproductive and environmentally destructive, the nomads themselves commonly being described as ignorant, irrational and unproductive.

To improve productivity, vast sums have been spent on livestock management programmes, intended to transform pastoral nomads into settled cattle ranchers. Almost without exception, the projects have proved unmitigated failures.

Well-digging programmes have led to overgrazing (*qv*), while bans on the burning of grassland prior to grazing have increased the habitat for tsetse fly and reduced the nutritional quality of dry-season grasses.

Attempts to prevent pastoralists moving their herds from one area to another have also failed. During periods of drought, mobility enables the pastoralists to exploit those few areas where the rains fall. As Michael Horowitz, Professor of Anthropology at the State University of New York, points out, research in the Ferlo region of Senegal reveals that such is the variation in local rainfall that in 1972 (a year of catastrophic drought) "a herder locked into the Ferlo without the right to move would have lost 100 per cent of the herd." Nonetheless, the fencing of rangelands continues: under the World Bank's (*qv*) Senegal Project, for example, herders will be forbidden to stray from their allotted grazing units.

In the light of the abject failure of modern ranching programmes, traditional practices appear increasingly sound by comparison. (See also: *Desertification*Ⓐ Ⓒ ③, *Development*③.)

Non-Proliferation Treaty

The Treaty for the Non-Proliferation of Nuclear Weapons was signed by the USA, USSR and UK (the depository signatories) in 1968, and came into force in March 1970. One hundred and thirty-seven other states have also signed to date.

Among the states with nuclear weapons, China has not signed. Notable non-signatories among the states without such weapons are India, Israel, South Africa, Pakistan, Argentina and Brazil, all countries with known nuclear competence. (See also: *Nuclear proliferation*Ⓝ, *Nuclear safeguards*Ⓝ.)

North Sea

Opinion is deeply divided over the health of the North Sea. An official Dutch Government report, prepared for a 1987 conference of European environment ministers on the protection of the North Sea, calls it "one of the most polluted seas on Earth" and warns that if its state is allowed to deteriorate further, "significant environmental changes could be expected well into the 21st century." Britain disputes that view, arguing that the pollution is limited to "hot spots" on the margins of the sea and that in general the North Sea is "a wholly healthy body of water."

In 1984, some 5,570,000 tonnes of industrial waste were dumped directly into the North Sea, together with 5,100 tonnes of sewage sludge, and 97 million tonnes of dredge material. Other sources of pollutants included wastes discharged via rivers, the atmospheric deposition of wastes from land-based sources, and emissions from the 93,677 tonnes of waste incinerated at sea.

As a result, the North Sea received 6,020 tonnes of copper; 31,070 of zinc; 7,840 of lead; 2,830 of chromium; 840 of cadmium; 3,740 of nickel; and some 45 tonnes of mercury. In addition, some 25,000 tonnes of hydrocarbons were either dumped or discharged into the sea, principally from ships and oil rigs; between 744kg (1,600lb) and two and a half tonnes of chlorinated hydrocarbons – PCBS (*qv*), DDT (*qv*), dieldrin (*qv*) and the like – entered the sea from various sources; and 250,000 tonnes of inorganic nitrogen entered from atmospheric sources, mainly car exhausts and fossil-fuel power stations. Radioactive discharges from the Sellafield reprocessing plant on Britain's Cumbrian coast also added to the total pollution load, the radionuclides making their way into the North Sea via the north coast of Scotland. The estimated input of caesium-137 in 1984 amounted to 2,000 terabecquerels (2,000 million million becquerels).

Britain is one of the few countries in Europe still dumping sewage sludge at sea. Britain also contributes the highest inputs of radioactive isotopes, atmospheric nitrogen and hydrocarbons. Though only trace quantities of the most toxic heavy metals are permitted in sewage sludge, the 5,180,000 tonnes dumped by Britain in 1984 contained half a tonne of mercury and three tonnes of cadmium.

The effects of pollution are most evident along the eastern coast of the North Sea. There, PCB pollution is responsible for the high rates of infertility and miscarriages that have decimated local seal populations and for mass poisonings among eider, spoonbill, herring gull and tern. Dutch surveys have revealed increased rates of disease amongst flounders, dab and plaice caught off the eastern North Sea – 11 per cent showing evidence of liver cancer, ulcers and finrot. A marked increase in skin disease has also been observed amongst dab caught near a site used for the dumping of titanium dioxide wastes. A more recent study has revealed that 40 per cent of flatfish in certain parts of the North Sea have cancer. Although official British figures show only 11 per cent of the fish caught in the Thames estuary to be diseased, a 1987 Greenpeace survey found that 34 per cent of floun-

ders in the Thames estuary are affected by clots and tumour-like growths. More recently, in 1988, an epidemic, ascribed by environmentalists to pollution, decimated seal (*qv*) colonies throughout the North Sea. Britain denies that pollution is necessarily the cause of the problem.

Controversy also surrounds the cause of the algal blooms (*qv*) – the so-called "red tides" – which increasingly affect coastal waters. Denmark, Norway, Belgium and Germany all blame the blooms on the eutrophication (*qv*) of coastal waters as a result of the increasing quantities of nitrogen and other nutrients entering the sea via sewage, agricultural run-off and atmospheric depositions. Once again, Britain is the odd man out, claiming that a clear-cut relationship between nutrient enrichment of the sea and the algal blooms has yet to be established.

Until 1987, Britain consistently opposed stricter controls on the dumping of wastes at sea. In 1984, British officials effectively stymied a West German proposal to halt the dumping of all persistent and bio-accumulative waste into the North Sea. Whereas Britain appeared content to delay action until there was firm evidence of pollution, her neighbours on the other side of the North Sea argued that further delay was irresponsible. As one Dutch scientist put it, "By the time we have conclusive evidence of pollution, it might be too late to do anything about it. We may have passed the point of no return."

Although Britain still insists on the merits of its "wait and see" approach, it has nonetheless accepted the need for pollution controls in the North Sea. In 1987, at a conference which it hosted in London, Britain joined eight countries in endorsing an agreement to cease the dumping of all "harmful industrial wastes" by the end of 1989; to control the discharge of dangerous substances via rivers; to employ "the best available technology" to reduce radioactive discharges; and to "reduce the input of nutrients which have harmful environmental consequences." Under the

agreement, the incineration of toxic waste at sea would be "greatly reduced" by 1991 and ended by 1994. At a subsequent conference in 1990, Britain promised to end sewage dumping by 1998, but extended its deadline for dumping industrial waste until 1993. There was general agreement among participants to halve emissions of dangerous chemicals by 1995, but once again Britain was alone in refusing to make the same commitment for phosphate and nitrate inputs, arguing that they did not contribute to the problem. There was considerable delay in the signing of the final agreement because of Britain's insistence that it should retain the right to bury nuclear waste under the sea in constructed cabins. The UK's record during the formation of a North Sea agreement has earned it a reputation as "the dirty man of Europe." (See also: *Fish stocks*©℗, *London Dumping Convention*, *Ocean dumping*℗, *Ocean incineration*℗, *Oslo Treaty*℗, *Sub-lethal pollution*℗.)

Nuclear accidents

From its inception, the civil nuclear industry has always insisted that nuclear reactors, unlike nuclear weapons, are clean and safe. Indeed, until the early 1980s, the industry refused to acknowledge that radiation from reactors had ever caused a death. In addition to dismissing as remote the chances of a major accident occurring at a reactor, the industry has consistently denied that the health effects of reactor accidents – however serious – could ever compare with the devastation caused by a nuclear bomb.

Minor accidents involving relatively small releases of radioactive material occur all the time at nuclear installations. But what are the risks of a major accident? In 1957, the US Brookhaven National Laboratory put the probability of the most serious accident conceivable occurring in a nuclear plant at less than one per 1,000,000 years of reactor operation. Such an accident would lead to 3,400 deaths, 43,000 injuries and would cause $7,000 million worth of damage to property.

An update of the Brookhaven report, published in 1964, conceded that the effects of an accident at a 1,000MW reactor sited within a city could be worse than previously estimated, leading to 55,000 prompt deaths and 70,000 injured. However, the report's estimate of the probability of such an accident occurring remained unchanged.

Ten years later came the WASH 1400 Report, better known as the Rasmussen Report, which gave the chance of a major accidental release of radioactive material from a nuclear reactor as one in 1,000 million years of reactor operation.

Such calculations are of course highly suspect. As Nobel Laureate Professor Liebe Cavalieri writes, "The case of the Oak Ridge Research Reactor accident is one example of how misleading probability calculations can be. In this accident there were seven sequential failures, each involving redundancy of three parallel elements, for a total of twenty-one failures, the absence of any one of which would have prevented the incident. Three of the seven were personnel failures: an experienced operator threw wrong switches in three separate rooms; another operator failed to report finding any of these errors; and so forth. The others were design or installation errors in a reactor with an outstanding performance record. The probability of the event was calculated to be one in 100 billion billion. The event 'was almost unbelievable,' but it happened. Again, in the complex nuclear reactor accident that occurred in 1970 at the Dresden II reactor, the most generous assessment of the probabilities of the separate events could not raise the overall probability above something like one in a billion billion. Yet, here again, it happened."

A number of serious accidents have already occurred to nuclear installations, notably those at Kyshtym in the USSR in the winter of 1957; at Windscale (*qv*) in Britain in 1957; at Three Mile Island (*qv*) in the USA in 1979; and, in 1986, at Chernobyl (*qv*).

These four serious accidents have occurred within the space of 30 years and make nonsense of the Rasmussen Report's official calculations. Indeed, some officials at the US Nuclear Regulatory Commission now estimate the chance of a reactor in the USA suffering a core meltdown before the end of the century at 50:50. This fits with the experience to date. Since the USA possesses about a quarter of the world's reactors, we may see several more serious nuclear accidents before the end of the century.

The possibility of a serious nuclear accident today is indeed only too real. The operation of any reactor is a delicate balance between too little and excessive reactivity. Unleash the normal control mechanisms restraining the nuclear chain reaction and the power can increase phenomenally in a matter of seconds.

At Chernobyl, the power rose to at least 480 times maximum operating power before the reactor exploded. Should the gas circulatory system in a British advanced gas-cooled reactor (*qv*) fail, followed by a failure to scram, an even more devastating accident than Chernobyl could result within seconds.

Similarly, according to calculations by Dr. Richard Webb, author of the highly respected book *The Accident Hazards to Nuclear Power Plants*, a super prompt critical accident in a fast reactor could lead to an explosion of up to three kilotonnes TNT equivalent or more.

Since Chernobyl, it has become increasingly difficult for supporters of nuclear power to maintain the fiction that major nuclear accidents are so improbable as to be not worth worrying about. Instead, there is an acceptance that accidents will occur and the emphasis is now on ways in which their consequences can be mitigated. As the prestigious science journal *Nature* wrote at the time of Chernobyl, "The important question is not so much how accidents like these can be prevented but how we can live with them safely." (See also: *Chernobyl*Ⓝ Ⓟ, *Three Mile Island,*Ⓝ Ⓟ, *Radiation and health* Ⓛ Ⓝ.)

Nuclear economics

A major argument used to promote nuclear power has been that it produces cheap energy. Early hopes were based on the expectation that, although nuclear power stations would be more expensive to build than those using coal or oil, their running costs would be extremely low. Instead of having vast tonnages of coal to move around, for example, there would be small quantities of uranium (*qv*). Fewer workers would be employed. Maintenance costs were expected to be minimal. At one time it was even hoped that nuclear reactors would increasingly provide the power for vehicles and ships as well as for generating electricity.

After the 1973 Middle East crisis, nuclear power was given a further boost as an alternative to unreliable (and expensive) supplies of oil. An ambitious projection by the UK Atomic Energy Authority showed more than 100 large nuclear stations being built in Britain alone by the end of the century.

Three things have happened to ruin those optimistic dreams. First, in some countries the construction costs of nuclear plants have proved to be much higher than was expected. Plants have taken longer to build and there have been unforeseen technical problems. Second, running costs have been much higher than predicted. Increased safety demands and regular equipment breakdowns have been compounded by the expensive problem of dealing with nuclear waste (*qv*). In the UK, for example, the cost of handling nuclear waste at the Drigg site near Sellafield (*qv*) rose in just three years from £30 to £1,000 per cubic metre. The cost of decommissioning (*qv*) power stations has also escalated. The third factor is that the crisis over fossil fuels has proved less dramatic than was expected. Supplies of oil from the Middle East have been supplemented from other countries, and there are ample global supplies of coal.

Experience has varied around the world. In the USA, which has the largest number of reactors, the worsening economics of nuclear power have been one of the main reasons why no new station has been ordered since 1978. Costs have risen so dramatically, especially since the extra safety demands made after the 1979 accident at Three Mile Island (*qv*), that some companies have faced bankruptcy. One financial magazine described the failure of the US nuclear industry as "the largest managerial disaster in business history."

In Japan and France, on the other hand, which have poor supplies of their own fossil fuels, it is still claimed that nuclear power makes good economic sense. The French, in particular, by launching a massive building programme, have benefited from the savings that flow from a factory production line of nuclear reactors. However, the claimed low price of French nuclear electricity has only been achieved at the expense of massive subsidies from the government.

State financial support for the nuclear industry, based on its perceived strategic or military significance, has been a crucial factor in nuclear economics in many countries. Such support has helped, for example, to keep the British nuclear industry going, despite some disastrous management and development decisions in the 1960s and 1970s. It has also succeeded in hiding the industry's real financial state from public examination.

In 1988 and 1989, however, in the run-up to the privatization of the UK's electricity generation and supply network, the economics of nuclear power were revealed to be so unreliable that it was the only part of the system not eventually sold to private investors. In 1989, the government decided that all existing nuclear power stations would remain in state hands, and that there would be no finance for further construction after the partially completed pressurized water reactor (PWR) (*qv*) at Sizewell (*qv*) in Suffolk. A review of the nuclear industry's prospects is

promised in 1994. This effective moratorium on nuclear construction has cast a shadow over the whole future of nuclear power in Britain.

It is clear that judgements on which energy source to pursue cannot be made on economics alone. Environmental and safety factors must play an important part. Nonetheless, nuclear power has now lost its claim to be a cut-price panacea.

Nuclear proliferation

The spread of nuclear weapons to countries that do not already have a military nuclear capacity. In the USA, the USSR and the UK, civil nuclear power was a spin-off from the technology developed to produce fissile plutonium for the purpose of making weapons. The risk of nuclear proliferation arises from the ease with which it is possible to do the reverse; to derive fissile plutonium from civil nuclear facilities.

Reprocessing (*qv*) spent nuclear fuel is a necessary step in the development of nuclear weapons. The Non-Proliferation Treaty (NPT) (*qv*) attempts to control the destination of reprocessed plutonium, the aim being to expose any attempts at proliferation while actively encouraging civil nuclear development.

Attempts to limit the "nuclear club" began in earnest after France joined it in 1960 and China in 1964. The NPT was ratified in 1970, and in 1974 India (a non-signatory) became the first state to explode a bomb whose fissile material had been manufactured using imported civil nuclear equipment. The equipment in question was a research reactor supplied to India by Canada. After the test, Canada broke off further cooperation.

Europe's attitude to proliferation has been more cynical than that of the USA or Canada; within two years of the Indian test France had sold a large reprocessing plant to Pakistan and another to South Korea (though neither deal was completed after US pressure on France), and Germany had concluded an enormous contract with Brazil involving eight reac-

tors, an enrichment plant and a reprocessing plant. Earlier, Germany and France both provided reactors and technology to South Africa, and France sold nuclear equipment to both Israel and Iraq. By the late 1970s, Brazil, Argentina, Taiwan, India, Pakistan, South Africa and Israel (the last two possibly working together) had developed facilities for the separation of plutonium, and Pakistan was also developing technology to build a uranium bomb, using technical data stolen from Holland and equipment bought in Western Europe.

Twenty-nine non-nuclear weapons countries have power reactors and at least 100kg (220lb) of separable plutonium. Twelve also have reprocessing plants; six of these have not signed the NPT. With so many locations holding fissile material, the danger is not only that states will make nuclear weapons, but also that nuclear material can be stolen, and made into "do-it-yourself" bombs using laboratory-scale reprocessing.

Clearly, attempts to limit membership of the nuclear weapons club have failed. A range of smaller countries either have atomic weapons or hold themselves ready to make them at short notice. Many of these countries have refused to submit their facilities to nuclear safeguards laid down by the International Atomic Energy Agency (IAEA) (*qv*) via the NPT. Even signatories to the NPT, such as Iraq, have continued to develop a nuclear weapons capability. Following the 1991 Gulf War, Iraq was found to have substantial facilities for production of highly enriched uranium.

Members of the EC also have to submit their civil nuclear facilities to EURATOM safeguards. Until June 1986 the UK government refused EURATOM inspectors access to the Magnox reprocessing line at Sellafield (*qv*), because it is both a military and a civil facility. Even when a EURATOM inspection was permitted, inspectors were not allowed to make their findings public. As the result of the threat of court action by the EC, the UK stopped reprocessing civil and military spent fuel in the same run at Sellafield, a practice that is known as co-processing. They are now treated separately, and inspectors are allowed access when the plant is treating civil fuel.

Nuclear waste

The nuclear industry worldwide is generating an appalling legacy of radioactive wastes. The properties of those wastes vary enormously, but many are highly radioactive and toxic, and many will remain radioactive for hundreds of thousands of years.

Nuclear waste embraces a great range of material, from lightly contaminated overalls, to uranium (qv) mill tailings, to the fiercely radioactive liquid high-level waste that is produced by reprocessing. By the turn of the century, the worldwide inventory of high-level wastes is projected to reach 150,000 million curies.

The production of wastes starts at the first stage of the nuclear fuel cycle – with the mining of uranium (qv). In the USA, it has been calculated that radon emissions from mill tailings could cause 4,000 cancer deaths a year.

Mill tailings apart, the amount of radioactive wastes produced by a nuclear power programme depends critically on whether reprocessing (qv) or long-term storage is practised. A large pressurized water reactor (PWR) (qv) produces 11 cubic metres of irradiated fuel per gigawatt per year. If stored, this is the only volume to be dealt with. If reprocessed, 6.25 cubic metres of high-level waste, 40 cubic metres of intermediate-level waste and 600 cubic metres of low-level waste are produced from the original 11 cubic metres of spent fuel.

At the end of the first year after extraction from the reactor, the irradiated fuel still contains, in highly concentrated form, 270,000 times more radioactivity than the ore from which it was derived. Even after 10,000 years, one kilogramme would contain, gramme for gramme, 18 million times more radioactivity than the lambs that Britons were forbidden to eat as a result of Chernobyl (qv).

High-level wastes are generally stored in stainless steel tanks, constantly agitated and cooled. In the USA, the main storage centre is Hanford (qv), a site that has a notorious record for accidents involving waste. Between 1945 and 1973, some 422,000 gallons of liquid waste containing 500,000 curies of radioactivity had leaked out of the tanks. Tritium and ruthenium have been detected in the groundwater; strontium-90 and iodine-131 in the Columbia River; and plutonium-239 in the soil. The levels of plutonium were 5,000 times the permissible level.

In the UK, high-level wastes are stored at Sellafield (qv). Ultimately, the aim is to solidify the waste in glass through a process known as vitrification. The process is intended to reduce the volume of waste and to make it easier to handle. Several US and Australian researchers are strongly critical of vitrification, warning that the glass blocks will disintegrate at some time in the future.

Even assuming vitrification works, the problem of a long-term repository for high-level wastes remains unresolved – and, many would claim, insoluble. In both Europe and the USA, the nuclear industry talks of burying waste in deep underground sites, but the search for stable geological sites has proved difficult. Indeed, uncertainties over geological faults, the inability to predict future geological movement, and the possibility of earthquakes make it impossible to guarantee the integrity of any site for the length of time that the waste must be kept isolated.

In the USA and the UK, low-level wastes are buried in shallow burial grounds, while in Germany they are consigned to an abandoned salt mine. All the sites have experienced problems.

In the USA, three out of six sites have been closed down due to contamination problems or breaches in transportation regulations. The West Valley site in New York State was closed after tritium contaminated local groundwater, and the Maxey Flats dump in Kentucky after plutonium was found to have migrated three-quarters of a mile off site within three years of the site opening. At Barnwell, South Carolina – one of the three sites still operating – movement of both cobalt-60 and tritium have been detected.

The only available dump site in Britain for disposing of solid low-level waste is at Drigg, adjacent to Sellafield. The site, which is almost full, is designed to allow its wastes to drain into the Irish Sea, on the grounds that they will be rendered harmless through "dilution and dispersal" (qv).

Before 1983, most low-level waste produced in Britain was dumped at sea. The practice was halted after a ban was imposed by the National Union of Seamen.

The ban was accompanied by an international moratorium – consistently opposed by Britain – under the London Dumping Convention (LDC) (qv) on all future dumping of nuclear waste at sea. Apart from Britain, the only other countries using ocean disposal were Belgium, the Netherlands and Switzerland. The accumulated radioactivity dumped between 1967 and the ban in 1983 amounted to some one million curies, 90 per cent of it originating from the UK.

Discharges of low-level nuclear waste into the sea from land (as opposed to dumping from ships) escape the LDC moratorium, and such waste is still discharged by both Sellafield and Cap de la Hague (qv).

The British Government and the nuclear industry are under considerable pressure to find acceptable disposal routes for intermediate-level and low-level waste. In 1987, vociferous local opposition at every site chosen for investigation finally caused the government to call off its search for a shallow dump site. In 1991, however, NIREX, the body responsible for overseeing nuclear waste disposal, announced that it had decided to build an underground "repository" for waste at Sellafield (qv), with Dounreay (qv) in Scotland as a back-up option. The 800-metre-deep repository at Sellafield – a massive series of linked shafts and caverns – would cost up to £3.5 billion to construct, and receive low- and intermediate-level wastes over a period of 50 years. Environmental groups argue that Sellafield has been chosen because it is already a nuclear site with a receptive local public, but is geologically unsuitable to provide a stable resting place for the waste over the lengthy timescales that will be involved.

Similar arguments have accompanied the proposed construction of large subterranean waste dumps in Sweden and the USA. A plan to excavate Yucca Mountain in the Nevada Desert to house some of the large quantities of US waste has consistently foundered on geological objections. (See also: *Radiation and health* Ⓛ Ⓝ Ⓟ, *Radioactivity* Ⓛ Ⓜ.)

Nuclear winter

A major nuclear exchange could cause rapid cooling over much of the Earth as dark clouds of smoke and dust generated by the explosions and consequent fires spread far beyond the combatant nations. This nuclear winter may last from days to months, possibly even years, causing widespread harvest losses which, when combined with the almost inevitable breakdown in international trade, would threaten the survival of much of the world's population.

A single one-megatonne nuclear warhead has the potential to ignite 400sq km (150sq miles) if detonated over an urban or industrial area. A 6,000-megatonne exchange could cause fires over 250,000sq km (96,000sq miles) – about half the area of the 1,000 largest cities in the likely combat zone – and 20,000 to 250,000sq km (7,700 to 155,000sq miles) of rural areas, depending on the season of the exchange. A third to one-half of the smoke generated by these fires would promptly fall out or form "black rain," as happened after the atomic bombing of Hiroshima in 1945. Of the remainder, up to 50 per cent might consist of carbon-based soot less than one-thousandth of a millimetre in diameter. The precise proportion of soot would depend on the locations targeted – city fires would generate more soot than forest fires.

It is the soot component of the smoke that would produce a marked cooling at the Earth's surface. The size, shape and chemical composition of these particles make them unusually strong absorbers of incoming solar radiation while permitting outgoing radiation from the Earth to pass through relatively unhindered. Thus, a cloud of sooty smoke has the potential to warm the atmosphere where the bulk of the cloud lies and to create cold, dark conditions below.

Assuming war takes place in the northern hemisphere, the nuclear winter effect would be greater in the northern summer. At this time of the year, the amount of sunlight normally reaching northern latitudes is at a maximum and the potential for disturbance is greatest.

The acute sensitivity of crops and many natural ecosystems during the growing season means that a spring or summer war could effectively wipe out production even if the temperature drop is at the less extreme end of the range of possibilities. For example, a temperature drop of only 5°C (9°F) over the growing season is sufficient virtually to eliminate grain production throughout the northern hemisphere. Potato production in Poland and Russia would cease and, in England, yields would be cut by half. Livestock and animals would be without their thick winter coats for protection. Coniferous trees in Canada are able to tolerate temperatures of −70°C (−158°F) in the winter but may die if temperatures fall below −10°C (−50°F) during the growing season.

The survivors of the war would face a dark, cold, polluted environment and the likelihood of severe food shortages. Depending on the scale of the population losses during the conflict itself, food stocks might – if they could be distributed – support the survivors through the initial months, but the possible continuance of cooler temperatures into the next growing season combined with a lack of the technology that underpins modern farming practices could mean that food supplies would run short before long.

Following a nuclear war that took place outside the summer months, the initial temperature drop would not be as severe. However, if the cooling persisted into the growing season, mass starvation may only have been postponed.

For Third World nations south of the combat zone, the possibility of nuclear winter adds a new dimension to prospects for survival. In the northern sub-tropics and the tropical zone, the initial temperature reductions are likely to be less severe than those experienced to the north, though they may still be of the order of 5° to 10°C (9° to 18°F) in the case of a summer war. However, the lower natural climatic variability in these regions means that plants and animals are even less well adapted to cope with cooler conditions. During the growing season, a single day of temperatures below 15°C (41°F) would destroy the rice harvest – the staple food for more than 1,000 million people. In Africa and South-East Asia, harvest failure could also result from a weakening of the monsoons due to reduced heating of the Tibetan Plateau. With the possible loss of grain production in North America – currently provider of 90 per cent of the world's food surplus – a food shortfall could not be made up and the affected nations would be thrown back on their own limited reserves. The Sahel is already suffering widespread famine and no reserves would be available. India's food reserves could not support her population for more than a few months.

Cold streams of air penetrating into the tropics and beyond as dense clouds pass overhead would threaten the two-thirds of the world's species of plants, animals and microorganisms that live within 25 degrees of the Equator. Since there is no distinct seasonal cycle in the tropics, ecosystems would be vulnerable whatever the season of the war. The destructive potential of cold outbreaks in lower latitudes is illustrated by the impact of the freezing winds that occasionally affect Florida – five such events between 1977 and

1985 caused huge losses of vegetable crops, and fruit and fish stocks. Damaged trees took years to recover. Periodic cool temperatures spreading from the south into the Amazon Basin – "friagems" – are responsible for the deaths of large numbers of birds and fish even in the present-day. More than a week of freezing temperatures in rainforest areas could kill all the vegetation above ground and the impact of this would cascade through the food chain, adversely affecting virtually all forms of life.

The 15 per cent of the world's population living south of the Equator would fare better than those in the north. Even at the more extreme range of possibilities, temperature reductions alone are unlikely significantly to affect crop yields over the southern hemisphere.

Many uncertainties surround the predictions of the climatic change that might be induced by nuclear war and it is not possible to estimate the effect except in the most general terms. Nevertheless, it is clear that nuclear war threatens the existence of most of the world's population. Nuclear winter effectively draws all nations into the nuclear debate.

Ocean dumping
Ocean incineration
Ogallala Aquifer
Oil
Organic farming
Organophosphates
Oslo Treaty
Overfishing
Overgrazing
Ozone layer
Ozone (tropospheric)

Ocean dumping

Prodigious quantities of dredged spoils, sewage and industrial waste are dumped every year directly from ships into the world's oceans. The major dumping grounds are the Atlantic and the North Sea (qv), direct dumping now being banned in most regional seas (qv). Proponents of ocean disposal argue that wastes are quickly rendered harmless through dilution and dispersal (qv). But many dumping grounds throughout the world are now severely contaminated, with high levels of pollutants in bottom sediments and in fish.

The dumping of heavy metal wastes and persistent or carcinogenic wastes is banned in all seas under the London Dumping Convention (LDC) (qv), the international treaty that governs dumping in the world's oceans. The Oslo Treaty (qv), which oversees dumping in the North Sea, has similar provisions. Nonetheless, many tonnes of heavy metals and persistent or carcinogenic wastes are still dumped quite legally under provisions which allow for waste consignments to contain "trace quantities" of banned substances. A moratorium on the dumping of nuclear waste (qv) at sea has been in force since 1983.

Hundreds of drums of highly toxic and radioactive wastes – dumped before the LDC was introduced – still lie in the world's oceans. Some of that waste was dumped at deep ocean sites on the assumption that the deep ocean was "a tranquil abyss," the sea bed being utterly devoid of currents. Recently, however, researchers at the Woods Hole Oceanographic Institute in the USA have discovered that the deep oceans experience violent underwater storms, which literally scour the sea floor of sediment, transporting large volumes of silt from one area to another. The effects on the drums of waste that have been dumped in the deep oceans is unknown, but even if they survive the battering of the storms, they must eventually rust, leaking their contents into the sea.

Professor Gunnar Kullenberg,

chairman of the main UN expert group on marine pollution, describes current studies of marine pollution as "primitive." "We take each substance separately and then try to estimate what effects it may have. We are not yet able to consider something as complicated as synergistic effects," he told *Siren*, a United Nations Environment Programme newsletter, in 1983.

Sea dumping is a prime example of the "out of sight, out of mind" approach to waste disposal. It is surrounded by long-term uncertainties and has already caused considerable damage, particularly to fish stocks (*qv*). Alternative methods of disposal for all the wastes currently dumped at sea exist on land, though such alternatives are undoubtedly costly. According to Britain's Water Authorities Association, for example, it would cost $187 million in new equipment and running costs were Britain to agree to a ban on sewage dumping at sea. Industry, too, argues that a ban on sea dumping of its wastes would have a severe recessionary impact, diverting investment from production and undermining competitiveness.

Such arguments, however, ignore both the jobs that would be created through pollution and the savings that would be made through the recycling (*qv*) of materials currently dumped at sea. More important still, they overlook the very real long-term costs that are even now being incurred through dumping.

Those long-term costs are hard to quantify in cash terms, but they are likely to be high. For we are in danger of disrupting an ecosystem whose health is vital to our survival.

Ocean incineration

At present, only four countries – Germany, Belgium, Great Britain and France – regularly incinerate wastes at sea, burning an average of 100,000 tonnes a year. Though the US Environmental Protection Agency (EPA) has said that it sees ocean incineration as playing an important role in reducing America's burgeoning inventory of hazardous waste, it has yet to sanction waste incineration within US waters.

Proponents of ocean incineration argue that it is an environmentally sound, economic, and safe technology. That view is not shared by the Oslo Commission, the body that oversees the Oslo Treaty (*qv*), the European Commission, and a sizeable lobby within the London Dumping Convention (*qv*) which has sought to introduce an international ban, though these attempts are being resisted by the USA and several other countries.

Unlike land-based incinerators, incineration ships are not equipped with scrubbers (*qv*) to trap unburned wastes, which are thus emitted directly into the atmosphere. Though research burns show a destruction efficiency of 99.99 per cent, that still leaves one tonne of unburned waste entering the environment for every 10,000 tonnes burned. The danger is that such waste will be concentrated by marine organisms and thus find its way into the food chain. Among the wastes that have been emitted during trials are unburned polychlorinated biphenyls (PCBs) (*qv*) and heavy metals.

The second danger of ocean incineration lies in the possibility of a major accident, followed by a leak. Though Chemical Waste Management put the risk of such an accident at one in 24,000 years, accidents do happen. The results could be catastrophic. In 1983, at the time when the EPA was considering licensing waste burning in US waters, a study warned that a discharge of 500,000 US gallons of liquid PCBs – less than half a ship's cargo – would contaminate the "upper foot of the entire Gulf of Mexico . . . with 2.5 parts per billion of PCB." Since phytoplankton, the very basis of the marine food chain, live in that upper foot of Gulf water, the resulting pollution would arguably "be sufficient to deteriorate all life in the Gulf of Mexico" – an area of some 1,507,000sq km (582,000sq miles).

Ocean incineration is scheduled to end in the North Sea in 1994. (See also: *Hazardous waste* Ⓛ Ⓟ, *Incineration* Ⓛ Ⓟ.)

Ogallala Aquifer

The largest source of groundwater in the USA. It stretches from southern South Dakota to northwest Texas and is a classic example of a resource that has been grossly over-exploited.

The 30 years following World War II saw a dramatic expansion in irrigated agriculture in the Great Plains, an expansion that was made possible only through "mining" the groundwaters of the Ogallala. Between 1944 and 1978, according to the Washington-based Worldwatch Institute, the area under irrigation in the six states most dependent on the Ogallala rose from 21,000sq km (8,100sq miles) in 1944 to more than 80,000sq km (30,800sq miles) in 1978. In the Great Plains as a whole, some 95,000sq km (36,700sq miles) of irrigated agriculture – one fifth of the irrigated cropland in the USA – is watered by the Ogallala.

Since 1940, more than 500 cubic km (120 cubic miles) of water have been withdrawn from the Ogallala. The result has been the gradual depletion of the aquifer, with some areas of Kansas, Texas and New Mexico now down to half their reserves. Indeed, a recent study suggests that some of the older irrigated areas of the High Plains of Texas will only be able to continue pumping for a decade or so at the most. At current rates of pumping, some 20,000sq km (7,700sq miles) are expected to be forced out of production by the end of the century. Already, both Oklahoma and Texas have lost 18 per cent of their irrigated farmland. In Colorado, Kansas and Nebraska, almost 6,000sq km (2,300sq miles) have now been taken out of production. The depletion of the aquifer has caused considerable disquiet and even anger in the USA. (See also: *Groundwater* Ⓐ Ⓟ.)

Oil

The most important trend in energy (*qv*) use since the war has been increasing world dependence on oil. By 1973, the world had become dependent on oil for 41 per cent of its energy needs, consuming 56 million barrels a day. After the first energy shock of the 1973 Middle East price rise, a deliberate attempt was made to reduce oil consumption by adopting energy conservation (qv) measures and by switching from oil to other sources such as nuclear energy.

As a result, North America succeeded in reducing its oil consumption from 18,600,000 barrels a day to 16,600,000 in 1984; Western Europe from 15,200,000 to 12,300,000 and Japan from 5,500,000 to 4,600,000. During this period, both the Eastern Bloc and the Third World, however, actually increased their consumption from 17,900,000 to 25,300,000 barrels a day.

Since 1973, total oil dependence has thus only fallen worldwide to 35 per cent of all energy sources. World oil consumption in 1984 was 57 million barrels a day, which is just slightly higher than in 1973.

How long can the world continue to use energy at that rate?

The accepted measure of world oil resources is "proven reserves." In 1950, these stood at 76,000 million barrels. Each year new discoveries are added and "production" subtracted. By 1973, proven reserves had increased to 664,000 million barrels. In the years since, intensive exploration has increased this figure by some five per cent only.

It seems reasonable to suppose that global oil reserves have never been more than 1,600,000 to 2,400,000 million barrels. Of this, we have already used up some 500,000 million barrels and 700,000 million barrels have been discovered and constitute present proven reserves. This means that there remain between 400,000 and 1,200,000 million barrels yet to be discovered.

If we continue to make the appropriate effort to discover new reserves, and continue to consume oil at something like the 1985 rate of consumption of 21,000 million barrels a year, then oil resources could last between 50 and 88 years. Increased energy conservation could, of course, make a difference, so could a switch, for some end-use pur-poses, to renewable sources of energy – but, in spite of the present oil glut, it would be grossly misleading to suppose that our present oil consumption can be maintained for very long. (See also: *Exxon Valdez* ℗, *Gulf War*℗.)

Organic farming

Farming without the aid of artificial fertilizers (qv) or synthetic organic (qv) pesticides (qv). Such farming has been the norm since agriculture first began. Over the past 40 years, however, all but a small number of farms in the industrial world have abandoned organic agriculture in favour of intensive chemical farming. The move has been encouraged by international organizations such as the UN Food and Agriculture Organization (FAO) (qv), and heavily subsidized by nearly all national governments.

The principles of organic farming lie in the maintenance of soil fertility through careful husbandry, the recycling of agricultural wastes, and the use of natural forms of pest management and weed control.

Soil fertility is affected by the supply of a variety of nutrients in the soil, its structural composition, its water-holding capacity, its aeration, and its capacity to absorb heat.

By using farm wastes in the form of manures, composts and mulches, organic agriculture permits a wide selection of nutrients to be returned to the soil and there is a congruence between the rate of plant nutrient uptake and nutrient release from organic wastes. Bulky organic wastes improve the structure of the soil, while the nutrients they contain increase its fertility. When fallowing is adopted, deep-rooted weeds can bring minerals up from the sub-soil to remineralize the cropland.

Crop rotation, an essential feature of organic agriculture, ensures that different levels of soil are exploited and no particular level overexploited. When green manure crops, such as mustard or comfrey, are included in the rotation and ploughed back into the soil, its organic content is further increased. The introduction of leguminous plants (that is, those with nitrogen-fixing bacteria on their root nodules) such as clover or field beans into the rotation maintains the necessary level of nitrogen in the soil. Rotation also avoids creating a permanent niche for pests, thereby reducing the need for pesticides.

Polyculture, another essential feature of organic farming, also reduces the need for pesticides by reducing the size of the niche available for pests affecting specific crops.

Quite apart from being uncontaminated by chemicals, organically grown food has greater nutritional value than chemically grown food, not least because organic fertilizers do not increase the water content of food to the same degree as artificial fertilizers.

Organic farming has the additional advantage of not polluting surface waters and groundwaters with fertilizers and pesticides, and of being sustainable.

Revenue from organic farms is lower than that from conventional farms – but so are the costs. With non-organic farmers now being hit by the increasing cost of inputs and by falling yields – the result of the inevitable degradation which the excessive use of chemicals inflicts on the soil – organic farming must become increasingly economic.

A recent study conducted by the US Department of Agriculture (USDA) shows that organic farming presents a viable agricultural proposition for the USA. The study found that organic farmers use less energy and more labour per unit of produce than their conventional counterparts. More important, they are also two and a half times more productive per unit of energy consumed than conventional farms. As yet, the US authorities have still to act on the conclusions of the report.

American farmers now owe some $216 billion to the banks, mainly in loans taken out to buy the chemical inputs and machinery necessary for modern mechanized farming. Unable to service their debts, many are going bankrupt. To those who remain in business, organic farming, with its low costs, is proving increasingly attractive. (See also: *Artificial fertilizers*ⒶⓅ, *Pesticides*ⒶⓅ.)

Organophosphates

Organophosphorus compounds – sometimes loosely known as organophosphates – are powerful insecticides and acaricides. They were discovered during research into nerve gases.

Organophosphates exert their toxic effects by inhibiting acetylcholinesterase, a substance that is involved in the transmission of signals along the nerves. As a result, the nervous system of a poisoned animal suffers massive disruption. Nausea, vomiting, twitching, stomach cramps and diarrhoea lead to convulsions, coma and death in badly poisoned humans. Organophosphorus compounds are the most common cause of insecticide poisoning and can enter the body by mouth, through the skin or as a vapour.

Chemicals that exert this type of effect are known as cholinesterase inhibitors and some people are particularly sensitive to them. Thus very small doses, to which most people would not react, produce uncomfortable and sometimes dangerous symptoms. Organophosphorus compounds have proved most dangerous to people who come into direct contact with them through their work, such as farmers and those involved in timber treatment. By law, farmers in Britain have had to use organophosphates in sheep dips and for the treatment of warble fly infestations. In 1990, a new pressure group, known as the Pesticide Exposure Group of Sufferers (PEGS), revealed that the use of organophosphorus compounds in sheep dips had produced serious side effects in more than 2,500 British farmers. There are fears that organophosphates also damage the health of animals, and their use is prohibited under organic production standards. Some people believe that there may be a connection between the use of organophosphates for warble fly eradication and the development of BSE (*qv*) in cattle.

Organophosphorus compounds have produced devastating effects on wildlife owing to their high toxicity and low selectivity. However, they are not as persistent in the environment as the chlorinated hydrocarbon compounds, such as DDT (*qv*), chlordane (*qv*), and dieldrin (*qv*). (See also: *Circle of poison*ⓁⓅ③, *Dichlorvos*Ⓛ, *Fenitrothion*Ⓛ, *Malathion*Ⓛ, *Parathion*Ⓛ, *Pesticides*Ⓐ, ⓁⓅ.)

Oslo Treaty

Signed in 1972 by the major North Sea states, the Oslo Convention governs the dumping of wastes in the North Sea and the North-East Atlantic. The treaty came into effect in 1974. (See also: *North Sea*Ⓟ, *London Dumping Convention*Ⓟ.)

Overfishing.

See: *Fish stocks.*

Overgrazing

The overstocking of land with grazing animals – cattle, goats or sheep, for example – can all but eliminate edible plant cover, particularly when the animals are clustered in small areas, such as around a waterhole, or kept on the same land for a long period. Eventually, the land is laid bare. The soil is then vulnerable to severe erosion (*qv*), excessive compaction and, ultimately, desertification (*qv*).

Traditional pastoral nomads avoided the problem of overgrazing by ranging extensively over large areas. Overstocking, however, has become a problem as nomads have been encouraged to build up their herds as part of livestock development schemes. At the same time, many rangelands have been converted to plantations in order to grow crops for export, thus reducing the extent of available pastures. Well-digging programmes, too, have encouraged the harmful concentration of animals.

Nomads are well aware of the forces that lead to overgrazing. Indeed, in West Africa, one group, the Illabakan Tuareg of Niger, went so far as to request that the Niger Government close down a new well that had been built in their area. Another group, the Wodaabe of Bernou, are reported to be opposed to all new well-construction programmes.

Overgrazing is now fairly general throughout the dry tropics, especially where traditional pastoralism is being replaced by intensive livestock-rearing schemes geared to the export market, as in Botswana for instance. There is now a growing consensus that only a reduction in livestock numbers, together with a return to traditional pastoralism, can prevent widespread desertification. (See also: *Carrying capacity*ⒷⒸ, *Desertification*③Ⓡ, *Hamburger connection*③ⒶⒸ.)

Ozone layer

The discovery in 1984 of a hole in the stratospheric ozone layer over Antarctica was totally unexpected. Although scientists had warned for a decade that chlorofluorocarbons (*qv*) could damage the ozone layer, their theories were disputed, especially by the chemical industry, and little action was taken to reduce the use of CFCs. The ozone hole, which in October 1987 reached the size of the USA and the depth of Mount Everest, shocked even ozone scientists who had expected ozone to be gradually depleted worldwide, rather than to dramatically disappear over one region. In 1991, NASA satellite research, carried out over the previous 12 years, revealed that ozone had been depleted twice as fast as had previously been estimated; even temperate regions, including the Mediterranean and the southern USA were affected.

The complexity of the chemistry of the stratosphere, the zone between roughly 15 and 50km (9 to 30 miles) above the earth, seriously hampers understanding of the processes of ozone depletion and Sherry Rowland, one of the first scientists to realize the potential of CFCs to destroy the ozone layer, admits that as the experts failed to predict the appearance of the ozone hole, there is no reason to suppose that they will accurately predict the future rate of ozone destruction. As CFCs can last for more than 100 years and take around a decade to reach the stratosphere, the outlook for ozone is bleak indeed.

The extreme cold of the stratosphere during the Antarctic winter creates the conditions under which drastic losses of ozone can occur. A feedback mechanism between ozone depletion and the greenhouse effect (*qv*) which may already be exacerbating both problems, is that as heat which would normally escape into space from the earth is trapped by increasing levels of greenhouse gases in the troposphere (between the earth's surface and the stratosphere), the stratosphere will cool making the conditions more favourable for ozone depletion. As ozone is depleted, less heat in the form of ultraviolet light is absorbed by the ozone layer, which therefore cools further, creating the conditions for more ozone depletion. In January 1989, the stratosphere above the Arctic, normally too warm to allow an ozone hole to appear, recorded its lowest temperature for at least 25 years and an Arctic ozone hole was observed for the first time, with characteristics similar to the much larger hole in the southern hemisphere.

Two other greenhouse gases (*qv*) which also affect ozone are nitrous oxide and methane. Nitrous oxide (N_2O) like CFCs, is stable until it reaches the stratosphere where it breaks down to form nitric acid (NO), which attacks ozone in a similar fashion to the chlorine monoxide (ClO) released by CFCs. Methane, on the other hand, actually increases the amount of ozone in the tropopause (the boundary between troposphere and stratosphere) and may therefore mask ozone depletion at higher altitudes. Changing the relative concentrations of ozone could have implications for climatic stability.

The main importance of the ozone layer is in protecting life on earth from the harmful effects of short-wave ultraviolet (UV) radiation. The ozone layer absorbs most of the solar UV-B radiation (radiation with a wavelength between 290-320 nanometres). UV-B in small doses causes sunburn and some skin cancers in fair-skinned people. The US Environmental Protection Agency suggests that there might be an extra 200,000 deaths from skin cancer in the USA alone over the next 50 years. One scientist predicts that space suits and glass-domed cities will be necessary in the next century if the process of ozone depletion is not stopped. UV-B also causes eye cataracts and suppresses the immune system in humans of all races and probably other species. Its effects on crops are only beginning to be researched, but of 200 plants which have been tested, two-thirds showed sensitivity to UV-B. Soybeans suffer a 25 per cent decrease in yield when UV-B is increased by 25 per cent. The most serious effects of increased UV-B may be in the oceans. The productivity of phytoplankton, the microscopic animals upon which the rest of the marine food chain depends, has been shown to be sensitive to increased UV-B, as have certain species of fish larvae. The oceans are a major source of human protein and plankton are also important because of their role in absorbing the major greenhouse gas carbon dioxide; thus another positive feedback between ozone depletion and the greenhouse effect may take hold.

At present the ozone layer prevents any solar UV-C radiation (wavelength 240-290nm) from reaching the earth. UV-C can destroy DNA and protein, the basic building blocks of life. It is not known what effects prolonged exposure to UV-C will have upon humans or ecosystems. (See also: *Greenhouse effect*℗, *Chlorofluorocarbons*℗, *Montreal Protocol*©.)

Ozone (tropospheric)
The ozone layer (*qv*) in the stratosphere protects the earth from the harmful effects of ultraviolet (UV) radiation. The ozone in the troposphere, 0–15km (0–9 miles) above the earth, is produced when volatile organic compounds such as hydrocarbons from vehicle exhausts combine with nitrogen oxides in sunlight and is toxic to both animals and plants. It is a major greenhouse gas (*qv*).

A recent study has shown that half the population of the USA is exposed to levels of ozone above the levels recommended by the Environmental Protection Agency. The short-term effects of exposure to ozone include irritation of the eyes, nose, throat and lungs. Little is known about the long-term effects, but animal tests have shown biochemical and structural changes in lung tissue. The World Resources Institute has described low-level ozone as the air pollutant of greatest national concern to agriculture in the USA and estimates that US crop yields are reduced by 5-10 per cent due to present ozone concentrations. (See also: *Greenhouse effect*℗, *Greenhouse gases*℗.)

Paraquat
Parathion
Patented seeds
Paving over
PCB
PCDF
Pentachlorophenol
Permaculture
Pesticides
Pesticides in food
Phenoxy herbicides
Phosphates
Plant-breeders' rights
Plutonium
Polychlorinated
    biphenyls (PCB)
Polychlorinated
    dibenzo-furans
Population
Population control
Population explosion
Post harvest losses
Preservatives
Pressurized water
    reactor
Price-Anderson Act
Proposition 65

Paraquat

A contact herbicide that is widely used in agriculture, horticulture and gardening around the world. It differs from most other herbicides in that it is highly toxic to mammals. It has been responsible for more poisonings, many of which have been fatal, than any other weedkiller. Less than a teaspoonful of the concentrated material is likely to prove lethal if swallowed, and paraquat is also absorbed through the skin.

In the environment, paraquat is often regarded as fairly harmless since, once sprayed, it adheres so tightly to soil particles that it is not free to poison other plants. New crops can thus be sown soon after paraquat has been sprayed. But this is not invariably true: some soils do not hold on to paraquat so tightly and it can drain into rivers where it is extremely toxic to fish. Paraquat residues on vegetation may also be hazardous. Hares in England have frequently been poisoned by eating sprayed plants.

In some countries spraying with paraquat is replacing the plough as a means of soil preparation. Stubble and weeds are sprayed and new seed is placed in the soil almost immediately by direct drilling. This does not disturb the soil structure, and is economical, but the use of large quantities of paraquat in this way is giving rise to concern about the effects on the environment.

In Britain, concentrated paraquat is listed as a poison and may be bought only by professionals, though a dilute preparation is on general sale. The USA restricts its use to licensed operators and it is severely restricted in Sweden, Finland, Denmark, the Philippines, New Zealand, Turkey and Israel. It is widely used in the Third World, where it is also said to be the preferred method of suicide. (See also: *Herbicides*Ⓟ.)

Parathion

One of the most toxic insecticides in general use. It is an organophosphate (*qv*) and has been involved in many cases of human poisoning and damage to wildlife.

Because recovery from the effects of parathion is slow, repeated exposure to small amounts can have a cumulative effect. Parathion is restricted in the UK and the USA on environmental and health grounds, but continues to be used in Third World countries, where it has often caused serious, sometimes fatal, poisoning.

Parathion is not as persistent in the environment as the chlorinated hydrocarbon (*qv*) insecticides, but dangerous residues can remain for some time. Serious toxic effects have occurred when workers have handled oranges sprayed with parathion nearly three weeks previously. (See also: *Pesticides*ⒶⓅ.)

Patented seeds

In 1964, the British Parliament passed the Plant Varieties and Seeds Act. Further acts were passed in the following years: namely the European Communities Act in 1972 and the Seeds National Lists of Varieties Act 1973. In the US the Plant Protection Act and the Senate Bill S.S.23 were passed in 1970.

The aim of such legislation is to give plant breeders rights over the plant varieties that they develop and enable them to collect royalties on the sale of the seeds for as long as 30 years. In the UK, the Acts also provide for the establishment of a list of approved seeds, and make it a criminal offence to sell seeds that do not appear on the list. It is relatively expensive to register a seed, since it costs about £500 ($800) to prove that it is a distinct variety and hence eligible for patenting. It then costs a further £800 ($1,280) a year to keep it on the list and, in addition, a plot must be sown with the variety and inspected every year by a representative of the Ministry of Agriculture, for which a further payment is required. If the variety is to stay on the list, then at least 5,000 packets must be sold every year. For small family seed companies, such payments can prove crippling.

The net effect of the legislation has been to condemn traditional, often local, varieties of fruit and vegetables to extinction (*qv*), only those varieties produced on a large scale by large companies being allowed to survive. The legislation has encouraged large multinational companies to buy up increasing numbers of traditional seed houses. For companies manufacturing fertilizers and pesticides, control over the plant breeding process is becoming increasingly important because it allows research to be concentrated on developing varieties that grow well only when provided with large quantities of artificial chemicals. With the advent of biotechnology (*qv*), the multinationals are now working on the identification of plant genes that impart resistance to specific herbicides so that the seeds and herbicides can be sold as packages, thus increasing overall sales.

The seed business has become so important to the agrochemical industry that companies such as Shell, ICI, Ciba-Geigy, DuPont, Monsanto and Bayer have all bought up formerly independent seed companies. Multinational seed houses now control about a quarter of seed sales in the North, and 5-10 per cent of sales in the Third World market.

A driving force behind these new developments is the International Union for the Protection of Plant Varieties (UPOV) in Geneva. Financed by multinational companies that have recently bought up the traditional seed companies, UPOV has close relations with various European Ministries of Agriculture and is backed by the United Nations.

The UPOV has persuaded the EC that a large number of non-patented traditional varieties should be banned on the grounds that they are not really distinct varieties, but simply synonyms that are very nearly alike. Lawrence Hills of the Henry Doubleday Research Association in England has shown, however, that many of these varieties are genetically distinct and have different advantages such as resistance against different diseases.

For a variety to be listed, it must be distinct in shape and form, uniform in its genetic structure, and it must be stable – that

is, it must breed true. However, as Lawrence Hills points out, if these criteria were adopted in the Third World practically "all the local varieties would become illegal." The reason is that "each one is a gene pool in itself, a centre of genetic diversity which is as unexplored as the botanic treasures of the Amazon."

The seeds that are replacing traditional varieties require large amounts of artificial fertilizer and pesticides, products that are manufactured by the companies now involved in patenting seeds. The new varieties tend to be F1 and F2 hybrids, whose main feature is that they cannot be re-grown: farmers cannot keep the seeds from one year to plant the next, but must buy new seeds.

An effect of the new legislation will be a reduction in the quality of life. Traditional varieties – bred for their flavour, their storage qualities and nutritional value, and adaptability to local climatic conditions – are rapidly being replaced by new varieties that are often tasteless, of low nutritive content, and not particularly well adapted to local conditions. The massive genetic loss, moreover, will make humanity correspondingly more vulnerable to plant epidemics and any changes in the climate. (See also: *Green Revolution*Ⓐ③, *Seed-pesticide connection* Ⓐ③.)

Paving over

Worldwide, vast areas of highly productive land are lost to roads, factories, housing development, shopping centres, car parks and other forms of urban development – a process known as "paving over."

In the USA, 31sq km (12sq miles) of farmland are lost to concrete every day and 11,315sq km (4,360sq miles) go out of production every year, one-third of which is prime agricultural land.

In Britain, some 5,000sq km (1,900sq miles) of land were lost between 1933 and 1963. Much of that land was of the highest quality. Since the 1960s, the rate of farmland loss has accelerated.

In the Third World, too, the loss of prime agricultural land to

urban sprawl is a growing problem. In Egypt, some 4,000sq km (1,500sq miles) of fertile land in the Nile Valley were lost to urban expansion between 1955 and 1975 – more, that is, than the 3,700sq km (1,400 sq miles) brought into production through reclamation projects and irrigation schemes.

Paving over can also deprive city dwellers of "green belts" set aside to provide them with space for recreation.

PCB
See: *Polychlorinated biphenyls.*

PCDF
See: *Polychlorinated dibenzo-furans.*

Pentachlorophenol

A general biocide (*qv*) that has been used against fungi, algae, molluscs and other organisms throughout the world. It is a chlorinated hydrocarbon (*qv*) and persists in the environment, where it can accumulate in food webs. Pentachlorophenol is carcinogenic and teratogenic. It is restricted in Canada, New Zealand and the USA but is still available in the UK to people untrained in its correct usage.

Permaculture

The term permaculture, first coined by Bill Mollison in the 1970s, is derived from the words "permanent" and "agriculture." Permaculture is not so much about specific farming techniques (such as how to grow cabbages, raise livestock or make compost) as about creating a system in which the elements of the landscape and the plants and animals in the system interact in the most efficient way. Ideally, the output from one part of the system becomes the input to another part, the different parts interacting and complementing each other in such a way that energy input is reduced and yields are increased.

In moving away from a dependence on annual cropping patterns, and in particular by using tree crops, permaculture systems mimic natural ecosystems. They not only have a diversity of species and varieties, but also a diversity in the ages and heights of crops. One of the key differences between organic farming and permaculture (which can, and often does, employ organic techniques) is that permaculture systems are more consciously designed to minimize the use of energy. This is achieved by greater use of perennial crops (which also improves diversity), and by deliberately designing farms and farming systems so that energy requirements are minimized.

Permaculture was first developed in Australia as a way of revitalizing land that had been degraded and eroded by conventional farming practices. The permaculture concept has spread rapidly, both in the northern industrialized countries and in the Third World. The term has also taken on a wider meaning as permaculturalists have applied their philosophy to the wider problems of industrial society. Many advocates of permaculture systems are now as concerned about the design of cities, the use of water and energy, the exploitation of forests and the treatment of "wastes," as they are about the design of sustainable agricultural systems. (See also: *Organic Farming*.)

Pesticides

A term used more or less as a synonym for biocides. Included in this category are herbicides (*qv*), insecticides (*qv*), fungicides (*qv*), acaricides (which kill mites), nematocides (which kill nemotode worms), molluscicides, and rodenticides.

The world pesticide market for 1990 was about $24 billion. The top 20 agrochemical companies account for around 94 per cent of the total global market. Production figures by weight are more sparse. The 1985 world production of pesticides was estimated at 3,000,000 tonnes by the World Health Organization. This was a doubling in production since 1975. It has been estimated that global growth in pesticide usage between 1988 and 1993 will be 20 per cent, but for Africa it is likely to be about 200 per cent.

Unfortunately, pesticides cause widespread pollution of the environment, seeping into our rivers, killing off fish life, and contaminating groundwater, drinking water, and food, most of which now contains pesticide residues.

Though levels of pesticides in the general environment are usually low, pesticides tend to concentrate as they move up the food chain, a phenomenon known as bioconcentration (*qv*). The consequences for wildlife and human health are severe. Our body fats also now contain pesticides, as do ova and spermatazoa. A World Health Organization (WHO) study in 1987 warned that human breast milk is now seriously contaminated with pesticides and other chemicals that could have serious effects on the health of our children. The WHO experts even recommend that, in certain areas, breast feeding should be avoided.

Most modern pesticides are synthetic organic (*qv*) chemicals, a category that includes many known or suspected carcinogens (*qv*), mutagens (*qv*) and teratogens (*qv*). It has been suggested that 49 pesticides in current use in the UK are possible carcinogens, 61 suspected mutagens and 90 possible allergens. In the UK, 38 pesticides in use are banned or restricted in other countries.

Unfortunately, the literature on the health effects of pesticides is scanty. To date, the US Environmental Protection Agency (EPA) has been able to establish the harmlessness of only 37 of the more than 600 active ingredients used in the 45,000 different formulations at present marketed in the USA. This means that precise and reliable information is available on little more than five per cent of all the pesticides used in the USA.

In 1972, a WHO expert committee on insecticides concluded that there were about 500,000 cases of pesticide poisoning a year, causing 9,000 deaths. Since then pesticide use has increased by 50 per cent and it is now estimated that there are more than a million cases of poisonings a year, leading to about 20,000 deaths. This figure does not take into account long-term health effects.

At least one-quarter of the pesticides exported from the USA to Third World countries have been banned or severely restricted, or have never been registered for use in the USA. There is little if any control on the use of these poisons in the Third World – or, as the Bhopal (*qv*) tragedy demonstrated, on their production.

The pesticide industry argues that pesticides are essential for feeding the world. The standard claim, originally made by Dr. Norman Borlaug, the father of the Green Revolution (*qv*), is that without pesticides, world food production would fall by 50 per cent, causing starvation.

This seems unlikely. Indeed, since the introduction of modern pesticides in the 1940s, crop losses in the USA have increased rather than decreased, from an estimated 32 per cent to 37 per cent. This is probably largely due to changing farm practices, with much bigger farms, ever-greater stretches of monoculture (*qv*), the cultivation of high-yielding varieties (HYVS) (*qv*) that are particularly vulnerable to pests, and the greatly reduced farm labour force. It can also be partly attributed, however, to problems inherent to the use of pesticides: notably, their tendency to increase pest infestations by killing off predators that previously controlled target species, and the latter's tendency to develop resistance to pesticides. This problem is particularly acute in the tropics where conditions are most favourable for pest infestation.

Such factors have given rise to what has been termed the "pesticide treadmill" with farmers being forced to use ever greater amounts just to keep crop losses at a given level. What, then, would be the real cost of dispensing with pesticides?

A study undertaken at Cornell University concluded in 1978 that without pesticides financial losses would be about nine per cent higher, while food crop losses, in terms of food energy, would be about four per cent higher. This is a long way from the pesticide industry's 50 per cent claim. In any case, pesticides are mainly used in the Third World for the cultivation of cash crops.

The use of pesticides should not be considered on its own, but as part of the modern farming system, which also requires HYVs, fertilizer (*qv*), elaborate farm machinery and irrigation (*qv*) water – a system which, because of its prohibitive cost and its adverse social and environmental effects, cannot be maintained for very long. (See also: *Desertification*Ⓐ, *Erosion*Ⓐ, *Salinization*Ⓐ, *Seed-pesticide connection*Ⓐ③, *Tropical agriculture*Ⓐ.)

Pesticides in food

Much of our food routinely – and lawfully – contains dangerous levels of pesticides which pose an increased risk of cancer, neurobehavioural damage and other health problems.

In the USA, according to the National Academy of Sciences, legal levels of residues from just 28 common pesticides could be causing cancer in as many as six out of every thousand persons. Most at risk are children, who typically consume more fruit and vegetables than adults. With this increased intake comes greater relative exposure to the pesticides present in food. Experimental studies have also shown that children are frequently more susceptible than adults to carcinogens and neurotoxins.

A recent study by the Natural Resources Defence Council (NRDC) estimates that between 5,500 and 6,200 of the current population of American pre-school infants may eventually develop cancer solely as a result of their exposure before eight years of age to eight pesticides commonly found in fruits and vegetables.

According to the report, children currently receive unacceptable levels of the potent carcinogen unsymmetrical dimethylhydrazine (UDMH), a breakdown product of the pesticide daminozide, and the carcinogenic fungicides captan (used on strawberries and other fruits), chlorathalonil (used on fruits, vegetables and peanuts), folpet (used on grapes, apples and melons), and ethylene

thiourea (ETU), a constituent of the fungicide mancozeb (used primarily on tomatoes, potatoes, and apples).

The NRDC warns that its study "may significantly underestimate" both the extent to which pre-school children are exposed to pesticides in food and the health risks of such exposure. The report points out that:
- 40 per cent of the pesticides classified by the government as posing "a moderate to high" health hazard cannot be detected by the residue monitoring techniques used by the Federal Drugs Administration;
- No account was taken of exposure to pesticides in products other than fruit and vegetables;
- The study looked only at the health risks incurred during the first five years of a child's life. The total lifetime cancer risk will be clearly greater, since exposure to residues does not stop when one goes to school;
- The extent to which many of the pesticides are used has been grossly underestimated by the authorities, thus making a nonsense of many official carcinogenic risk assessments. According to the EPA, for example, only 5 per cent of apples are treated with diminozide; but the manager of one major company privately admitted that 10-11 per cent of the US apple crop is sprayed, whilst independent tests reveal that 30 per cent of the apples in one large supermarket chain had been treated;
- The study reviewed only 23 of the 300 pesticides that can be used legally on food. Of the 66 pesticides deemed to be potentially carcinogenic by the US Environmental Protection Agency, only 6 were evaluated by the NRDC;
- Most of the 600 active pesticide ingredients used in the US "have not been tested according to modern testing requirements, or the test data are unacceptable by today's standards." In 1984, the US National Academy of Sciences concluded that the safety date for 90 per cent of the pesticides available on the US market was insufficient to fully assess their health hazards.

The report concludes: "Our nation's children are being harmed by the very fruits and vegetables we tell them will make them grow up healthy and strong." It recommends that parents should wash produce carefully, peeling it when appropriate, and (where possible) switch to organically grown food.

In Britain, where more than 1,000 million gallons of pesticides are used by farmers and growers every year, the problem is equally acute. In 1989, the Ministry of Agriculture, Fisheries and Food (MAFF) released the results of a nationwide survey of pesticide residues in food. The Ministry was forced to admit that "there is no such thing as a pesticide-free food in Britain." The report revealed that food was still contaminated with DDT (*qv*), despite a ban on its use; that babies are likely to exceed the World Health Organization's acceptable daily intake levels for organochlorines (*qv*) if they drink baby milk prepared from cow's milk; that the residue levels of many pesticides exceed official maximum residue limits (MRLs); that 58 per cent of infant rusks sampled contained organophosphates (*qv*); and that 67 per cent of white bread samples were contaminated with pesticides. Many known carcinogens were among the residues reported, including lindane (*qv*), dieldrin (*qv*), pentachlorophenol, malathion, captan, parathion and others.

Although MAFF claimed publicly that its findings provided "a reassuring overall picture," leaked documents reveal that MAFF officials have expressed grave concerns over the inadequacies of current residue testing for both pesticides and their breakdown products. Many pesticides are never even tested for their residues. MRLs have still to be established for a range of common pesticides (tecnazene, widely used on potatoes, is one); monitoring is inadequate; and several pesticides which are set to be withdrawn in the USA on safety grounds are not even being reassessed in Britain.

A frequent excuse for inaction over pesticide residues in food has been to claim that residues are present at such low levels that they are unlikely to be harmful. However, as Peter Snell of the Food Commission pointed out: "There is a substantial body of medical opinion which believes that since cancer is caused at the level of the individual cell, there is no safe level for a carcinogen." (See also: *Pesticides.*)

Phenoxy herbicides
Among the first of the modern herbicides (*qv*) to be developed in the 1940s. They interfere with plant growth causing the plant to overgrow and die.

The two main phenoxy herbicides are 2,4-D (*qv*) and 2,4,5-T (*qv*), the former being used against general weeds and the latter against woody weeds.

For many years it was thought that these chemicals were virtually harmless to humans, since large doses were required to produce immediate symptoms of poisoning. But in the late 1960s concern was expressed that long-term and more subtle harmful effects may result from exposure, particularly to 2,4,5-T. There is now considerable evidence linking phenoxy herbicides to such rare cancers as soft-tissue sarcoma and malignant lymphomas.

There has been considerable controversy over whether it is the herbicides that are harmful or the dioxins (*qv*) that contaminate some of them during manufacture. A variety of different chemicals is involved and it seems that the herbicides themselves, even if dioxins are absent, may be carcinogenic. Recent research has suggested that this may well be so with 2,4-D, which does not contain dioxins.

Despite concern about their environmental effects, most phenoxy herbicides remain in unrestricted use. (See also: *Pesticides*ⓛ ⓟ.)

Phosphates
Phosphates are essential nutrients for plants but, like many other such substances, they can cause serious pollution if present in excessive quantities. The principal effect is eutrophication (*qv*), which occurs when phosphates, together with nitrates (*qv*), enter lakes or slow-moving rivers in large quantities.

There are three main sources of phosphate pollution. Some runs off agricultural land, since phosphates are major constituents of fertilizers. Naturally occurring phosphates that enter sewage also contribute, but the main source is phosphate water softeners used in synthetic detergents. These enter waterways in sewage discharges and have caused problems in many parts of the world. As a result, attempts have been made to restrict their use. Unfortunately, however, some of the substitutes suggested have proved to be more hazardous than the material they were intended to replace.

In eastern England, where the Norfolk Broads suffer serious phosphate pollution, a plant has been built to remove phosphates from sewage before it is discharged into the local river and this may be the first of many. (See also: *Artificial fertilizers*Ⓐ ⓟ, *Eutrophication*ⓒ ⓟ.)

Plant breeders' rights
See: *Patented seeds.*

Plutonium
The first, and most significant, man-made or "trans-uranic" element to be created. The first tiny sample was produced at Berkeley University in February 1941. Four years and $2,000 million later, a few kilogrammes had been made, enough to fuel two atomic bombs. The first of these was tested over the desert in New Mexico, the second over Nagasaki.

Even before plutonium actually existed, it was known that it would be capable of fission (*qv*) with somewhat better characteristics as a bomb material than uranium-235.

Plutonium was, and is, made in nuclear reactors, by bombarding uranium-238 with neutrons. The uranium-238 transmutes to plutonium-239 by absorbing a neutron into its nucleus, and is extracted from the reactor fuel by a chemical process called reprocessing (*qv*). Plutonium can itself be used as fuel, or part of the fuel, for conventional, or thermal, nuclear power reactors, or alternatively as fuel in fast breeder reactors (*qv*). However, because of high costs and concerns over safety, political interest in fast reactors has waned somewhat.

Countries that reprocess civil reactor fuel have growing stockpiles of plutonium, which present obvious proliferation and pollution risks. Until 1986, a total of 75 tonnes of "civil" plutonium had been separated from spent reactor fuel around the world, much of this produced at the Sellafield (*qv*) plant as part of the British programme of Magnox (*qv*) reactors. (See also: *Nuclear waste*Ⓝ, *Nuclear proliferation*Ⓝ, *Radiation and health*Ⓝ, *Radioactivity*Ⓝ.)

Polychlorinated biphenyls (PCB)
First synthesized in 1881, polychlorinated biphenyls have been used commercially since the 1930s, their low flammability, high heat-resisting capacity and low electrical conductivity making them valuable compounds in a wide range of products – from fluorescent light bulbs to hydraulic fluid and, most important of all, electric transformers and capacitors. Though the toxic effects of PCBs were first documented as early as 1936, it was not until the late 1960s – following a major pollution incident in Japan – that their dangers became widely appreciated.

PCBs are immensely stable compounds and can be destroyed only through incineration at temperatures above 1,200°C (2,200°F). Incomplete incineration can lead to the formation of new, and often more toxic, compounds, notably PCDFs and dioxins (*qv*).

PCBs have not been manufactured in Britain since 1977, when Monsanto – the sole UK manufacturer – ceased production. In 1980, the British Government implemented a 1976 EC directive that banned the use of PCBs except in sealed equipment. As a result of that ban, little new equipment containing PCBs now comes on to the market.

But while the EC directive has helped curtail the production and use of PCBs, next to nothing has been done by European governments to combat the threat posed

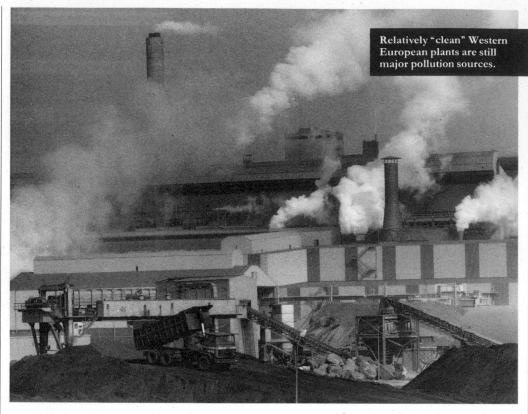

Relatively "clean" Western European plants are still major pollution sources.

by PCBs in old and often dilapidated equipment. It is estimated that 90 per cent of Britain's 20,000 transformers are in such a poor state of repair that they regularly leak PCB insulating fluid.

Within the decade, most of the PCBs now in use will wear out in both industrial and developing countries. Of the estimated 1.2 million tonnes of PCBs ever produced, 31 per cent is thought to have entered the general environment, 20 per cent ending up in the oceans and 11 per cent in soil and sediments. The rest is in use, held in storage or dumped in landfills. In Britain alone, an estimated 600 tonnes of PCBs leak out of landfills every year. According to a 1988 report by Professor Joseph Cummins of the University of Western Ontario: "If the PCBs held in the Third World alone entered the seas, they would probably prove sufficient to cause the extinction of a wide range of marine mammals, if not all." The danger is not so much from direct dumping

(although this is a serious concern in itself) as from atmospheric transport, recent research suggesting that 98 per cent of the PCBs in the ocean enter via the atmosphere. Even the remotest regions are now contaminated. Rainwater in northern Saskatchewan, for example, has been found to contain 17 times the level of PCBs permitted in drinking water in Ontario. Cummins has urged an international agreement under which PCB manufacturers would have to buy back the Third World's stock of PCBs and ensure their safe disposal. (See also: *Cancer*①℗, *Carcinogen*①℗, *Incineration*℗.)

Polychlorinated dibenzo-furans
A common contaminant of commercial polychlorinated biphenyls (PCBS) (*qv*), polychlorinated dibenzo-furans are far more toxic. Indeed, many now believe that PCDFS are responsible for the most harmful effects of PCBs.

Tests carried out in the late 1960s using three commercial

brands of PCB – Clophen A 60, Phenoclor DP 60 and Aroclor 1260 – revealed that Clophen and Phenoclor were much more toxic than Aroclor. Suspicions that Clophen and Phenoclor were contaminated with some chemical that was more toxic than PCB itself were confirmed when further analysis of the Clophen and Phenoclor samples revealed the presence of tetra- and pentachlorodibenzofurans, two of the most toxic furan isomers.

The presence of PCDF contaminants in PCBs is generally thought to result from the PCBs having been heated. (See also: *Dioxin*℗, *Incineration*℗.)

Population
Since the beginning of the 19th century, the world's population has increased five-fold. Currently, 220,000 new babies are born every day – 150 every minute, one every half second.

Ninety per cent of the growth predicted to occur before the end of the 21st century will be in the Third World. Africa alone is predicted to pass the 1,000 million mark by 2010.

In the industrial world, population growth is declining, some countries having zero growth rates. Even so, as the World Commission on Environment and Development (*qv*) (the Brundtland Report) points out, "the population in North America, Europe, the USSR, and Oceania is expected to increase by 230 million by the year 2025, which is as many people as live in the USA today."

According to the UNFPA, the world population is expected to stabilize at around 10,000 million people by the end of the 21st century. But even at current population levels, more than half of the 5,000 million people in the world today live in a state of grinding poverty, suffering from endemic malnutrition and continually hovering on the brink of starvation.

Under the present economic system, the carrying capacity (*qv*) of many areas of the world has already been exceeded – in many cases, irreversibly so. Indeed, delegates at the Second International Conference on The Environmental Future, held in Reykjavik in 1977, predicted that 1,000 million people will die of starvation before the end of the century as a result of current economic policies. The present famines (*qv*) in Africa and South East Asia lend credibility to this view.

But more people could be fed if radical changes were made in the use of land and resources.

For example, millions of square kilometres of the best arable land in the Third World are currently used to grow cash crops (*qv*) for export to the industrialized world. Were that land to be used to grow crops for local consumption, it would not only alleviate hunger but would also reduce the pressure on the environment by relieving displaced peasants of the need to encroach onto marginal lands.

Equally, a less materialistic way of life in the industrialized countries would greatly reduce the environmental impact of rising population levels in both the industrialized world and the Third World. High living standards in the industrialized world ensure that a single western child has about a forty times greater impact on the resources of the world than a child born in the Third World.

In the absence of such reforms, however, there is little chance of a "civilized" solution to the problem of population growth.

The role that can be played by family planning (*qv*) is limited. The notion that, with sufficient economic growth, a demographic transition (*qv*) will occur is largely an act of faith, and the economic growth is, in any case, unlikely to materialize. (See also: *Zero population growth*①.)

Population control
See: *Family planning.*

Population explosion
In historical terms, the current population "explosion" is a very recent phenomenon. For 90 per cent of the time that humans have lived on Earth, the human population remained very low, a generally accepted estimate being around five million people.

During that time, humans lived in hunter-gatherer bands, but with the adoption of farming, some 10,000 years ago, the population began to rise. By 500BC, it had reached an estimated 100 million, rising to 500 million by 1300.

The next major spurt in population growth occurred with the coming of the industrial revolution, the population passing the 1,000 million mark in the early 19th century. Since then, as economic and industrial development has spread, the population has increased at a phenomenal rate, moving from 4,000 million in 1975 to 5,000 million in 1987.

Several explanations have been suggested to account for this population growth. The best known, first put forward by the Reverend Thomas Malthus in the 18th century, is that populations inevitably breed up to their food supply: increasing yields have thus brought increasing numbers.

The theory, though popular, has little basis in fact. Though the output of food has undoubtedly risen, particularly in the last 40 years, the availability of food in those countries where population growth has risen fastest has actually declined so far as the poorest sections of society are concerned. The increased production has largely gone for export, and has thus been at the expense of food grown for local people.

In addition, anthropological studies make it clear that traditional societies do not breed up to their available food supply. On the contrary, a wide range of strategies – from natural contraceptives to taboos on sex during lactation – are exploited to control population numbers.

A second explanation is that improved medical treatment and sanitation have greatly reduced mortality, thus allowing more people to survive into old age. Undoubtedly this is true, but it is not a sufficient explanation. Disease and ill-health were not the only constraints on population growth prior to the age of modern pharmaceuticals.

A third explanation – the one that best accords with the data – is that population growth is a direct result of the social insecurity bred by the development process. In traditional societies, people derive a sense of identity and belonging from their extended family, their lineage, their clan and their community: there is thus less need to invest in children to acquire security. This factor has been exacerbated by the tendency of the development (*qv*) process to bring about an increasing domination of men over women, which in turn leads men seeking to boost their status and power by demanding more children, particularly sons.

By destroying those traditional supports, economic development (*qv*) not only ferments the alienation that leads people to seek children, but also breaks the traditional controls on procreation. The inevitable result is an upsurge in population. (See also: *Contraception*①, *Demographic transition*③, *Family planning* ①③, *Population*③.)

Post harvest losses

According to the UN Food and Agriculture Organization (*qv*), about 30 per cent of the food produced in the Third World is now lost during storage to pests and mould. This is probably an overestimate: nonetheless, high losses do occur and the problem is undoubtedly serious.

Post-harvest losses are officially attributed to primitive food storage methods, the solution apparently lying in the introduction of new capital-intensive technology, much of which involves the increasing use of pesticides.

In fact, traditional food storage techniques are extremely efficient. Indeed, it now appears likely that the high losses incurred during storage are primarily the result of modern agricultural technology and production processes. This is the view of Dr. Martin Grenley of the Institute of Development Studies at the University of Sussex: "It is the changing structure of production operations associated with increases in land productivity and seasonal changes in cropping patterns that critically affect the level of losses rather than the inefficiency of traditional systems."

In particular, blame has been placed on the high moisture content of modern cereals. This is partly due to the fact that the new varieties frequently mature before the end of the rainy season, partly to lack of artificial drying facilities, and partly to their genetic structure, which makes drying difficult. The high levels of artificial fertilizer required by modern varieties have also been incriminated, since plants whose critical carbon/nitrogen balance has been disrupted by exposure to nitrogen fertilizers are known to react by taking up more water.

For some, the high water content of modern cereals is an advantage. As Dr. Anne Bergeret of France's National Centre for Scientific Research notes, "Dealers have always been tempted to sell a percentage of water or dust for the price of grain." However, if losses during storage are anything like as high as FAO states, the price humanity must pay for such dubious commercial practices is a high one. (See also: *Development*③, *Green Revolution*Ⓐ③, *High-yielding varieties*Ⓐ③, *Pesticides*Ⓟ.)

Preservatives

A group of food additives (*qv*) used to inhibit the rate at which bacteria will grow and reproduce in food products. While many bacteria are benign, a few, such as botulism and salmonellae, can be fatal. Preservatives can thus protect the health of consumers, which is not true of other types of additives.

In Britain and the EC, 47 different preservatives are permitted, and they all have E numbers (*qv*) ranging between E200 and E297 a sequence that includes colourants and flavourings.

While many preservatives are almost certainly safe, some are suspect. There is some evidence that benzoic acid and the benzoates (E210 to E219) may provoke occasional symptoms of acute intolerance, while sulphur dioxide (E220) and the sulphites (E221 to E226) may well cause adverse effects for asthma sufferers.

In the main, however, concern centres on sodium nitrite (E250) and sodium nitrate (E251). These are widely used in many processed and cooked meat products, such as bacon, ham and salami. The nitrate (*qv*) decays into nitrite (*qv*), and sodium nitrite can combine with food constituents during the cooking process and in the digestive tract to form chemicals called nitrosamines (*qv*) which are notorious carcinogens (*qv*). The official position is the levels at which nitrosamine compounds are formed are too low to pose any significant hazard. Some consumers prefer not to take the risk. (See also: *Cancer*Ⓛ.)

Pressurized water reactor

First developed by the Westinghouse Corporation as a reactor for nuclear submarines, the pressurized water reactor (PWR) is now the most widely used nuclear power plant design in the world. In 1990, there were 239 in operation, 66 under construction, and 65 being planned. The first PWR was built at Shippingport, Pennsylvania, and commenced operating in 1957.

PWR fuel consists of pellets of uranium dioxide enriched to three per cent U-235. The core is contained within a steel pressure vessel filled with ordinary water at up to 150 atmospheres pressure. The water serves as both moderator (*qv*) and coolant, circulating through the core and the steam generators. The high pressure prevents the water from boiling, even though temperatures are in excess of 300°C (570°F).

The PWR's steam temperature, and thus its efficiency, is low. Nevertheless, the power density is high and a loss of coolant – for instance through a stuck-open valve, as happened in the Three Mile Island (*qv*) accident – can lead to fuel melting and threaten the integrity of the pressure vessel, the heat being provided by fission product decay. The first PWR in Britain is being built by Nuclear Electric at Sizewell (*qv*) in Suffolk to a Westinghouse design.

Price-Anderson Act

A serious accident at a nuclear plant could cause damage in the region of billions of dollars. Consequently, US electricity utilities were initially slow to order nuclear reactors because they were unable to find private companies prepared to insure them against an accident. The Federal Government therefore passed the Price-Anderson Act of 1957 which limits corporate liability in a reactor accident to $60 million, and total liability to $560 million. The Act was renewed in 1967 and is still in force. In 1987, however, the Energy and Commerce Committee of the US House of Representatives recommended a new ceiling of $7,000 million. Many Democrats argued that electric supply companies should be made liable for unlimited damages in the event of negligence. A proposal to provide unlimited compensation under international law for victims and the environment following a nuclear accident was presented to the International Atomic Energy Agency (IAEA) (*qv*) by the Australian government in 1991. It was opposed by the USA, Britain and Belgium. The USA argued that such an agreement would "remove the incentive to develop the nuclear industry." (See also: *Nuclear accidents*Ⓝ.)

Proposition 65

Known technically as the "Safe Drinking Water and Toxic Enforcement Act," Proposition 65 was adopted by Californian voters in a state referendum in November 1986. Despite opposition from Governor George Deukmejian, and from industry (which spent $4,500,000 in an attempt to stop the Act), the proposition was passed by a 2-to-1 majority.

The proposition requires the Governor of California to publish a list of chemicals that are known to cause cancer or birth defects. Under the new legislation, it will become illegal knowingly to allow "significant" amounts of any of the listed chemicals into any source of drinking water. The Act uses a stricter definition of "significant" than that employed in federal food contamination laws.

Citizens will have the right to sue companies they suspect of infringing the new regulations but, in sharp contrast to legislation that existed before, it will be up to the accused companies to prove their innocence. The burden of proof has thus been shifted dramatically.

The implications of Proposition 65 for the siting of factories and waste disposal facilities are far-reaching. In particular, the new law will force industrial plants away from water sources and hasten the end of landfill as a means of waste disposal. (See also: *Cancer*ⓁⓅ, *Groundwater pollution*Ⓟ, *Hazardous wastes*Ⓟ.)

Radiation and health
Radioactivity
Rainbow Warrior
Rainforest
Recycling
Reforestation
Regional seas
Reprocessing
Resettlement
    programmes
Rhine
Rocky Mountain
    Arsenal
Routine radioactive
    discharges

Radiation and health

The ability of radiation to damage human health is well established. At high doses – such as those received by the firemen who died during the Chernobyl accident (*qv*) – radiation causes vomiting, loss of hair, bleeding and death. It is also one of the best-documented environmental carcinogens (*qv*) known to humanity. But controversy surrounds the effects of low levels of radiation on health.

The living environment is bathed in radiation from a variety of sources, both natural and artificial. Every second of the day, human beings are bombarded with some 100,000 cosmic ray neutrons and 400,000 secondary cosmic rays, about 30,000 radioactive atoms that disintegrate in the lungs, and 200 million gamma rays from soil and building materials. Finally, radiation from the diet leads to about 15 million potassium-40 atoms and about 7,000 natural uranium atoms disintegrating inside the body every hour.

That astronomical number of hits, totalling on average some 60,000 a second, will give a radiation dose of 1,870 microsieverts, or five times lower than the one rad of X-rays that used to be given up until the 1960s in producing a radiographic picture of bones.

In industrial societies, people are increasingly exposed to radiation additional to background radiation. Airline crews, for instance, can virtually double their annual radiation dose by increasing their exposure to cosmic radiation, which becomes more intense the higher the altitude. Radiation workers in nuclear installations can receive doses during normal operation that are five or even 25 times natural background. People living near nuclear installations may suffer increased radiation. Those, for instance, who consume relatively large quantities of locally caught fish and shellfish will receive greater-than-normal radiation if the sea is contaminated with radionuclides

Do low levels of natural and

human-made radiation constitute a health risk, or can the body cope with the levels currently found in the environment?

The International Commission on Radiological Protection (ICRP) (qv) bases its assessment of radiation damage on the premise that radiation is always potentially harmful, however small the dose. The commission also assumes a straight-line relationship between the radiation dose and the probability of cancer induction, getting data for the high-dose end of the graph from what happened to the victims of the Hiroshima and Nagasaki atom bombs.

Some radiation biologists believe that as radiation levels increase, the body's repair mechanisms become overloaded, and, therefore, the risk of damage at high levels is greater than at low levels. Others believe that low doses of radiation are particularly pernicious, since they stimulate repair mechanisms which then operate imperfectly and allow deranged cells, which would otherwise be destroyed by higher doses of radiation, to survive. The deranged cells transform into malignant cells, which proliferate until they have formed a mass sufficiently large to be detected as a tumour.

Historically, acceptable levels have had to be progressively reduced. Thus the level acceptable for people working within the industry was set at 73 rems in 1931, a level which was reduced to 50 rems in 1936, 25 in 1948, 15 in 1954 and five in 1958. The new levels recommended for radiation workers by the ICRP in 1990 were an average of 20 millisieverts (mSv) per year, with a yearly maximum of 50mSv. (Ten millisieverts is the equivalent of one rem under the old system of units.) In Britain, the annual dose officially considered acceptable for the most exposed members of the public is now 0.5mSv.

A number of studies around operating nuclear power stations and reprocessing (qv) sites have recorded a much higher incidence of cancer, especially leukemia, than the official correlation between radiation and health effects

would suggest likely. These include the leukemia cluster (qv) discovered around the Sellafield plant in Britain. These studies have prompted further investigations into other ways in which radiation may affect the human body. For example, some critics of the nuclear industry, such as the US scientist Dr. Rosalie Bertell, assert that radiation has a fundamental effect on the immune system. (See also: *Atomic tests*Ⓝ, *Radioactivity*Ⓝ.)

Radioactivity
The atoms of certain elements are inherently unstable and liable to transform into other elements through the expulsion of particles from the nucleus.

The period of time for half the number of atoms in a given mass of the element to transform is known as the half-life. After 10 half-lives about one-thousandth of the original mass is left, the remainder having transformed into a new element, which itself may or may not be radioactive and unstable.

The half-life of a radioactive substance is individual and specific. Uranium-238, the commonest isotope of uranium found in nature, has a half-life about equal to the present age of the Earth, namely 4,500 million years; uranium-235, the fissile isotope of uranium, has a half-life of 710 million years; polonium-214, one of the decay products of uranium-238, has a half-life of 1,160 micro-seconds. Fission products resulting from nuclear reactors have a whole range of different half-lives; three important ones, iodine-131, caesium-137 and strontium-90, have half-lives of eight days, 30 years and 28.1 years respectively.

Depending on the element and its isotope, radioactive decay can take different forms. Some isotopes give out alpha radiation (qv), while others give out beta radiation (qv) or gamma radiation (qv). When uranium-238 undergoes spontaneous radioactive decay with the loss of an alpha particle, thorium-234 is created, which is also radioactive and has a half-life of 24 days. The thorium

then disintegrates and proactinium-234 is created. After a further twelve more transformations of one element into another, lead-206 is left, which is stable and not radioactive.

The different particles and rays that comprise the radioactivity of elements have different characteristics, depending on their size and energies. Gamma rays require a substantial slab of lead or concrete to stop them penetrating. Alpha particles, on the other hand, are ponderous and have poor penetrating powers. Beta particles are intermediate with regard to their effects and are capable of penetrating through a centimetre or more of living tissue. The radiation levels that are emitted by these rays and particles can cause damage to body cells. (See also: *Radiation and health*ⒸⓃ.)

Rainforest
See: *Tropical forest*.

Recycling
Every day, thousands of tonnes of waste materials are thrown away by consumers and industrial installations – New York City alone discards 24,000 tonnes of domestic waste every day. Much of that "waste" could be re-used – either directly or after relatively simple treatment – and as such it represents a potentially valuable resource. Indeed, according to David Morris of the Washington-based Institute for Local Self-reliance, "A city the size of San Francisco disposes of more aluminium than is produced by a small bauxite mine, more copper than a medium copper mine and more paper than a good-sized timber stand."

The ecological benefits of re-using waste materials extend beyond good resource management: recycling also cuts energy consumption and reduces pollution. A 1987 study by the Worldwatch Institute found that the energy equivalent of half a can of petrol is saved every time an aluminium can is recycled. In addition, "One tonne of remelted aluminium eliminates the need for four tonnes of bauxite and

British schoolchildren let off steam and energy recycling aluminium cans.

700kg (1,540lb) of petroleum coke and pitch, while reducing emissions of air polluting aluminium fluoride by 35kg (77lb)." The report calculates that, by doubling worldwide aluminium recovery rates, "over a million tonnes of air pollutants – including toxic fluoride – would be eliminated."

Several countries now operate successful recycling projects. In the USA, the amount of paper collected for recycling doubled every year between 1975 and 1980, while in Switzerland more than 40 per cent of glass is recovered, with recycled glass now supplying the material for 60 per cent of glass production.

Recycling has also been adopted by a number of industries. In the electroplating industry, for example, electrolysis has been used to recover gold, silver, tin, copper, zinc, solder alloy and cadmium. Equally, in the motor industry, many companies now recover the polyvinyl chloride in scraps of car-seat fabric by washing the material in a solvent. Previously, such scraps had been simply incinerated, causing vinyl chloride a potent carcinogen (qv), to be released into the atmosphere.

In both Holland and Britain, waste exchange networks have been operating since the 1970s, more than 150 wastes being listed for exchange. In the USA, the recycling of industrial solvents is already a $200 million-a-year business which is expected to reach $1,000 million a year by the end of the decade. (See also: *Hazardous waste*℗, *Waste reduction*℗.)

Reforestation

Deforestation (qv) has deprived many countries of much of their tree cover, and there is now an urgent worldwide need to plant trees to restore ecological stability and combat erosion (qv), desertification (qv), groundwater depletion, droughts and floods.

The need for reforestation is clearly greatest in the tropical countries of the Third World and in those areas most prone to desertification. But many temperate zone countries also need to increase their tree cover. Britain, for example, is only nine per cent wooded, relying on imports for 98 per cent of its timber. According to the eminent US ecologist Professor Eugene Odum, the optimum tree cover for countries in temperate areas is 50 per cent. Below that level, ecosystems no longer benefit from the full range of "services" provided by trees – from the absorption of pollutants to soil conservation, flood control and groundwater recharge.

At present, most reforestation projects are little more than commercial plantations under a different name. The World Bank's (qv) social forestry (qv) programme, currently being promoted throughout the Third World, is a case in point: ostensibly intended to provide villagers with trees for firewood, it has primarily served to supply industry with trees for pulping or rayon manufacture.

The near universal choice of fast-growing trees that yield a high return on investment – notably eucalyptus (qv) and conifer – reflects the commercial orientation of most reforestation projects. The result has often been the progressive degradation of soils, with conifers causing an acid pan to build up beneath the surface and eucalypts depleting available nutrients. The problem is not restricted to the Third World: in Europe, the Czechs have learnt from bitter experience that sandy soils used to grow more than seven generations of pines are soon so degraded that they can no longer support commercial forestry.

But successful reforestation schemes do exist. Villagers in many parts of the Third World have mobilized themselves – without the aid of international agencies – to replant degraded lands, with remarkable results. Undoubtedly, one of the keys to their success lies in the fact that the villagers identify with the project, looking after the trees and ensuring their protection. In India, for example, the Chipko (*qv*) movement, initiated by village women, has inspired numerous reforestation projects throughout India, while similar movements have achieved the same in North and East Africa. (See also: *Fuelwood crisis*© ③.)

Regional seas

The world's regional seas – most notably the Mediterranean, the Baltic, the Caribbean and the North Sea (*qv*) – have all been hard hit by pollution. Being enclosed or semi-enclosed, and often having slow rates of water renewal (it takes between 80 and 100 years for the Mediterranean to renew its waters), regional seas do not have the same cleansing capacity as the open oceans. Until recently, several tottered on the brink of ecological disaster as a result of industrial and municipal discharges, direct dumping from ships, oil pollution and agricultural run-off. Though a series of international conventions have now been signed in order to clean up the world's regional seas, the pollution threat has by no means vanished.

In the Baltic, the largest area of brackish water in the world, eutrophication (*qv*), combined with industrial pollution, has so degraded the marine ecosystem that only a few hardy species of worm survive. An estimated 100,000sq km (38,600sq miles) are affected – half of the Baltic's deep waters. Currently, the sea receives some 1,100,000 tonnes of nitrogen and 77,000 tonnes of phosphorus a year, mainly in the form of agricultural run-off. Nonetheless, some progress has been made in reducing pollution. Over the past decade, the levels of mercury in fish have been reduced by 66 per cent in some coastal waters, while a ban on DDT by all the Baltic states has cut levels of DDT in fish substantially. Levels of PCBs have not fallen, however, and are blamed for reducing reproductive rates of female grey seals from 80 per cent to 20 per cent.

Because of its high rates of evaporation and slow rate of water renewal, the Mediterranean is particularly vulnerable to pollution, the pollutants tending to accumulate without degrading. In 1976, the United Nations Environment Programme (UNEP) launched an Action Plan to clean up the Mediterranean. The plan was endorsed by 17 nations: but despite international agreement on the need to curb pollution, the Mediterranean remains one of the most polluted seas in the world. Though the direct dumping of wastes from ships is banned, the Mediterranean must still contend with an estimated 12,000 tonnes of mineral oils, 60,000 tonnes of detergents, 100 tonnes of mercury and 2,400 tonnes of chromium every year. Edible shellfish are deemed unsafe for human consumption in all but four per cent of recognized growing areas and levels of pesticides and heavy metals continue to rise in many marine organisms. In 1983, the cost of cleaning up the Mediterranean was put at $10,000 to $15,000 million.

The principal threats to the Caribbean lie in pollution from pesticide run-off and industry. Of all the world's regional seas, the Caribbean is thought to be the most damaged by pesticides. Many of the pesticides that enter the Caribbean via the 16 South and Central American states that border the sea are banned in the USA, which itself discharges prodigious quantities of pesticides and other chemicals via the Mississippi, which drains 41 per cent of the land area of the USA. Industrial pollution, particularly from sugar refineries, mining, offshore oil drilling, and the dumping of dredgings and industrial waste, has also wrought havoc with the fragile ecosystem of the region. Discharges of industrial waste have badly polluted the Gulf of Paria, between Trinidad and Venezuela. Tourism, too, poses a threat to the Caribbean, particularly to the region's coral reefs (*qv*), which are being depleted of their fish and coral for sale to tourists.

Through its Regional Seas Programme, UNEP has drawn up action plans for the world's major regional seas. However, their implementation has been patchy and much remains to be done if the ecological health of regional seas is to be ensured. (See also: *Fish stocks*Ⓟ, *Ocean dumping*Ⓟ, *Ocean incineration*Ⓟ.)

Reprocessing

The extraction of plutonium (*qv*) and unused uranium (*qv*) from nuclear fuel after it has been irradiated in a reactor.

Reprocessing is a fairly straightforward chemical process. Fuel rods are stripped of their cladding and then dissolved in a hot concentrated solution of nitric acid and an organic solvent, usually tri-butyl phosphate (TBP). The uranium and plutonium cross over into the TBP, and subsequent chemical operations separate the two elements. They are eventually stored in either liquid (nitrate) or solid (oxide) form.

Problems do not in the main arise from the plutonium and uranium, but from the mass of fission products that remain dissolved in the nitric acid. These fission products are a range of isotopes of middle-order elements, and are intensely radioactive with varied half-lives. They constitute high-level waste (HLW) or, as it is sometimes called, heat-generating liquid waste. HLW, by definition, is created solely by reprocessing, and in the UK it is stored in 16 stainless steel tanks at Sellafield (*qv*), each containing some 130 million curies of fission products. The tanks must be constantly cooled and stirred.

Reprocessing to extract plutonium for military purposes is relatively uncomplicated because fuel is resident in the reactor for a relatively short period, which minimizes the general level of radioactivity throughout the reprocessing system. The residence of uranium fuel in power reactors is much longer, because the requirement is for maximum heat extraction per fuel loading. Irradiated fuel from the civil reactors is thus more radioactive, and its reprocessing more difficult. That of fuel from second-generation reactors, which use enriched fuel and achieve much higher burn-ups, is still more difficult and costly to reprocess.

The assumption that civil fuel should be reprocessed is increasingly being questioned. It has been practised most enthusiastically in the UK and France, for three main reasons. First, fuel for the Magnox reactors adopted in both countries could not, it was thought, be stored for long under water; secondly, recovered plutonium and uranium were expected to have commercial value as reactor fuel; and thirdly, reprocessing was thought to minimize waste problems.

But Britain's Central Electricity Generating Board (CEGB) has demonstrated that Magnox (and any other type) fuel can be kept for many decades in dry stores, and since 1977 the price of uranium has fallen far below the economic cost of recycling it. Fast breeder reactors (qv), which can use plutonium as fuel, are still some decades away from commercial exploitation. Finally, reprocessing creates high-level waste, and increases the quantities of other categories of nuclear waste by a factor of 100.

Public disquiet in Europe centres primarily on the discharges from Britain's Sellafield reprocessing plant. The discharges are higher than those from all other European nuclear installations added together, and have turned the Irish Sea into the most radioactively-contaminated sea in the world. Further, the practice of Magnox reprocessing has made the CEGB the owner of the biggest stockpile of separated plutonium in the West, growing by 2.5 tonnes a year.

The cost of reprocessing has been rising steadily – by 100 per cent in real terms from 1978 to 1983 – so that it is now some ten times greater than the cost of long-term dry storage. In 1989, the CEGB's chairman admitted that the problems of reprocessing has been "underestimated" and that opting for dry storage "would have eased future difficulties considerably." In 1991, however, the CEGB's successor, Nuclear Electric, signed a contract with British Nuclear Fuels, operators of the Sellafield plant, for the reprocessing of two-thirds of the fuel from its second-generation Advanced Gas-Cooled Reactors (AGRS) (qv). The contract was underwritten by the government against unexpected cost increases. Nuclear Electric's counterpart in Scotland, Scottish Nuclear, has announced its intention to place AGR fuel in a dry store.

In 1977, the US administration withdrew support for civil reprocessing, and the practice, never technically successful in that country, has not been resumed. The main reason was concern that civil plutonium could be diverted for military or terrorist purposes. Other countries – notably Canada, Sweden and most other European countries – have also renounced the practice, clearly demonstrating that a limited nuclear power programme can be operated without reprocessing, and that the only way to limit international nuclear proliferation (qv) is to stop separating plutonium from irradiated reactor fuel. France, the UK and Japan are now in the minority. It seems likely that reprocessing in these countries, too, will prove to have been a temporary practice – for economic, if not for ecological and health reasons.

Resettlement programmes

Since World War II, millions of people have been uprooted from their homes and relocated, often forcibly, elsewhere. Some have been moved to make way for highways and roads, some for urban renewal projects, and still others for large dams (qv) or agricultural and industrial projects.

In the industrialized world, the numbers involved in resettlement schemes are generally small. By contrast, in Third World countries, resettlement programmes can involve thousands of people. The World Bank (qv) alone estimates that between 1979 and 1983, it funded projects that caused the forced resettlement of almost 500,000 people.

Few resettlement schemes in the Third World have proved successful. Where tribal peoples are involved, as often happens, the move from their traditional lands is often enough to provoke the total disintegration of their culture.

The emotional wrench of resettlement is frequently compounded by problems over compensation. In many instances, tribal people have been denied compensation altogether because they lack legal title to land. The same applies to landless squatters, some 10,000 of whom were denied compensation for land lost to Brazil's Tucurui Dam Project.

Even where compensation is paid, it is generally inadequate: the 45,000 people uprooted by Sri Lanka's Victoria Dam, part of the five-dam Mahawelli Project, received just £90 for the loss of their homes and land. Similarly, where land is offered in return for land lost, it is generally available only because it is of inferior quality. In all too many instances, relocees have been forced to exchange their fertile valley land for little more than scrub.

Clashes between rival ethnic groups have dogged many resettlement programmes and inadequate or inappropriate housing is also a common problem. In Ghana, where polygamy is the rule and men frequently have several wives, the houses provided for those displaced by the Volta Dam only had one bedroom. Instead of having their own room, as in a traditional house, the wives were expected to share the same room – with disastrous results. In Indonesia, those resettled under the country's Transmigration (qv) Programme have complained that their new houses lack even a place to cook.

Since 1980, the World Bank has laid down guidelines for resettlement in bank-sponsored projects. However, a 1986 review conducted by the bank reveals that those guidelines are frequently broken or ignored. Twenty-five projects were surveyed: in nine of them, the authorities had not even identified the areas where the displaced populations were to be resettled.

Many resettlement programmes have been carried out with great brutality, with whole villages being bulldozed and inhabitants being moved at gunpoint. The most notorious example in recent times comes from Ethiopia, where 800,000 people were moved between 1982 and 1986 from the north of the country to the south. Ostensibly, the programme (which was backed by the major Western aid agencies) was to relieve famine in the north. However, critics argue that its real aim was to break the back of local separatist movements with whom the Ethiopian Government have been fighting a long-drawn-out civil war.

Few of those who moved did so voluntarily. Indeed, refugees report that government troops burned their crops and poisoned their land with insecticides to force them into feeding centres, where they were then packed into transport planes for the flight to the resettlement camps. An estimated 100,000 people died as a result of the programme, which was eventually halted after the EC refused to grant further aid. (See also: *Development*③, *Narmada Valley Project*③.)

Rhine

The largest, and dirtiest, of Europe's rivers.

Even before the 1986 Sandoz fire (*qv*) disaster rendered a 100-200km (60-70 mile) stretch of the river lifeless through a major spill of chemicals, the Rhine was little more than an open chemical sewer – polluted in the main by perfectly legal everyday discharges.

In 1987, the governments of the five countries through which the Rhine flows announced a major clean-up programme. The intention is to make the river clean enough for humans to drink and salmon to spawn in by the year 2000. It remains to be seen whether the programme will achieve that aim, previous action plans having had a limited impact. (See also: *North Sea*Ⓟ.)

Rocky Mountain Arsenal

Eighty sq km (30sq mile) site near Denver, Colorado, used by the US Army and various commercial companies, notably Shell Chemicals, to manufacture chemical warfare agents and pesticides. It is now thought to be the most contaminated industrial area in North America.

Chemical and biological waste from the military and commercial activities at Rocky Mountain Arsenal were dumped at various locations throughout the site. They included TX wheat-killing viruses; scrap metal and manganese sludge; pesticide wastes; and mustard gas, nerve gas, and other chemical warfare agents.

The first signs of trouble came in 1951, when farmers complained of damage to their crops as a result of groundwater contamination. In 1968, an explosion occurred at one of the nerve gas plants. Earthquakes also increased in the area, the result of disposing of wastes via deep well (*qv*) injection. By the mid-1970s, groundwater in the region was found to be heavily contaminated with a wide range of pesticides, solvents and other wastes, including PCBS (*qv*), DDT (*qv*), trichlorethylene and DCPP.

In 1975, the Department of Defense announced a $300 million clean-up programme, to be completed in 1991. The programme is massively behind schedule: despite numerous studies, little had been done in practice to decontaminate the site. The costs of a clean-up are now conservatively estimated at $4 billion, with some experts putting the final bill at more than $6 billion.

Technical problems make it likely that the site will remain contaminated for decades to come. Some 16 million cubic metres (565 million cu ft) of soil are required to be moved from the area. The US Environmental Protection Agency estimate that a single dump truck working 24 hours a day would take two and a half years to remove all the contaminated earth. In addition, there is a 37ha (93-acre) lagoon containing two million gallons of highly toxic wastes, which are leaking into local groundwaters, and threaten to contaminate the South Platte River.

The US Army, the Federal Government and Shell Chemicals (which leased a part of the site from the Army to produce pesticides) have all been sued by the State of Colorado for "damages to natural resources." Shell is also involved in a major legal battle with its insurers over who should pay for its share of the clean-up, estimated at $380 million. Many underwriters fear that if Shell win the case, the insurance industry could be faced with the costs of cleaning up tens of thousands of other hazardous waste (*qv*) sites in the US. The bill is likely to amount to a minimum of $100 billion.

Should the insurance industry have to pay out, the repercussions could be severe. Unlike previous "environmental settlements," such as the damages paid to asbestos victims, the industry would be unable to spread payments over several years. The money would be required immediately.

Shell is not alone in suing its insurers. Westinghouse Electric is also attempting to recover the costs of cleaning up 74 of the sites for which it is responsible. Other lawsuits have been taken out by other companies – six in California alone.

The insurers argue that under standard comprehensive general liability policies taken out prior to 1973, they are only liable for pollution from hazardous waste sites if the pollution was "sudden and accidental." Policies written after 1973 make this explicit. But lawyers for the litigating companies accuse the insurance companies of "rewriting" history. They cite letters and other documents from the 1960s showing that the industry accepted it had a liability under standard pre-1973 policies. (See also *Hazardous wastes*Ⓟ.)

Routine radioactive discharges

All nuclear installations, including reactors and reprocessing plants, discharge radioactivity into the environment. Regular checks are made by the operators and other agencies on the air, grass, milk, water and animal life in the immediate vicinity of such installations. However, there is increasing concern that the discharges, though within the limits set by government agencies, such as the Department of the Environment and the Ministry of Agriculture, Fisheries and Food in the UK, have caused extra cancers and disease.

In the early days of nuclear power, radioactive releases were high, as were the permitted levels. For instance, the Dresden boiling water reactor, located 50 miles from Chicago, emitted one-quarter of a million curies of radioactive gases in 1967, the permissible level, set by the US Atomic Energy Commission, then being 22 million curies. The corrosion of the steel cladding used to encase the fuel was a major factor in the release of gases and equally in rapidly rising levels of radioactive iodine, strontium and caesium, as well as other elements, in the cooling water. The decision was then taken to replace the steel cladding with zircalloy which was much more resistant to corrosion. Meanwhile a study by Professor Ernest Sternglass, a radiological physicist at the University of Pittsburgh Medical School, indicated that infant mortality rates in the counties around the Dresden reactor more than doubled during the period of peak emissions. Equally, a study by the Bremen Institute for Biological Safety indicated that leukemia deaths among children shot up more than sevenfold in the decade following the start-up of the Lingen nuclear reactor in West Germany compared to the decade prior to operation. Today, there is increasing evidence of higher cancer rates and premature death in the areas in the near vicinity of nuclear installations.

Noble gases such as krypton-85, as well as water containing tritium and carbon-14, cannot be easily contained within a reactor or reprocessing plant and tend to escape in their entirety. Tritium, for instance, a weak beta emitter with a half-life of 12.35 years, is formed naturally by the action of cosmic radiation on water vapour, some two million curies being formed each year, leading to a global inventory of about 36 million curies. Today, depending on type, a commercial reactor will discharge up to five per cent of its tritium inventory, hence between 1,250 and 2,500 curies per gigawatt per year, in the form of vapour and liquid. Even so, much higher releases occur from ageing reactors, the pressurized water reactor (PWR) at Chooz in France releasing approximately 31,700 and 21,800 curies in 1971 and 1972 respectively, equivalent to as much as 100,000 curies per gigawatt per year. The emissions of tritium from all commercial reactors in use throughout the world amounts to more than one million curies; hence 50 per cent of naturally produced tritium.

Routine discharges are, however, potentially the largest from reprocessing plants. Krypton-85 is discharged in its entirety, approximately 11,000 curies per tonne for PWR fuel, some 30 tonnes per year of spent fuel being generated each year for one gigawatt of electricity. As for tritium, up to 100,000 curies per gigawatt per year are discharged during reprocessing, amounting to 85 per cent of the total tritium in the spent fuel. The two new reprocessing plants to come on line in the 1990s at Cap de la Hague (qv) in France, namely the UP2-800 and UP3-A, will release up to one million curies of tritium per year, according to current official estimates. Thus the UK and French reprocessing plants alone will release as much tritium as is now generated naturally.

During the years of their operation since World War II the large nuclear complexes at Hanford (qv) in Washington State and at the Savannah River Plant in South Carolina have had large discharges of waste containing tritium. The Savannah River Plant, for instance, has five military production reactors, and reprocessing plants. In the mid-1970s, the plant was routinely discharging 300,000 curies per year from the reactors – 75 per cent to the atmosphere – and 400,000 curies per year from the reprocessing facilities – 90 per cent to the atmosphere. The activities then increased, by 1983 the annual tritium release reaching one million curies.

Other radioactive wastes are routinely discharged from nuclear installations, the world's largest discharger being British Nuclear Fuels (BNF) at the Sellafield (qv) site in Cumbria in the UK. Between 1968 and 1979, some 180 kilogrammes (400lb) of plutonium were discharged into the Irish Sea, the operators of the site, first the UK Atomic Energy Authority, and then BNF, having had authorizations to discharge up to 6,000 curies of alpha-contaminated waste into the sea each year. During the 1970s BNF also discharged more than 120,000 curies per year of caesium-137 in addition to other beta-emitting radionuclides. By the early 1980s, BNF managed to reduce annual discharges of beta activity – including caesium-137 – to just under half the peak value of 250,000 curies discharged into the Irish Sea during the mid-1970s. The aim after a multi-million-pound investment programme was to reduce alpha emitters to 20 curies per year and beta to 8,000 curies per year, compared with 67,000 in 1983.

The principle being applied in the UK to bring discharges down, despite large authorizations, is known as ALARP – As Low As Reasonably Practicable – or ALARA – As Low As Reasonably Achievable. Critics, meanwhile, have argued that discharges should be "As Low As Technically Achievable" and, in 1986, the European Parliament's Committee on the Environment, Public Health and Consumer Protection put forward a resolution demanding zero discharges of radioactive wastes into the Irish Sea and that gaseous emissions of radioactive substances, including krypton-85, carbon-14 and tritium be controlled in accordance with available technology. Public exposure to radioactive substances around Sellafield has consistently been ten to 100 times greater compared with French, German and US plants. (See also: *Radiation and health*①ⓝ, *Radioactivity*①ⓝ.)

Saccharin
Sahel famine
Salinization
Sandoz fire
Schistosomiasis
Scrubber
Seal deaths
Sedimentation
Seed-pesticide
    connection
Sellafield
Seveso
Shifting cultivators
Sievert
Sizewell
Slash and burn
    agriculture
Social forestry
Soft energy paths
Solar collector
Stabilizers
Stockholm
    Conference
Sub-lethal pollution
Subsistence
    agriculture
Superfund
Super-Phénix
Sustainable
    development
Swidden agriculture
Symbiosis
Synergy
Synthetic organic
    chemicals

Saccharin
A synthetic sweetener, discovered in 1879 and used in a wide range of products, including soft drinks, ice creams, fruit preserves, chewing gums and cider. It is also used as a table-top sweetener.

By the mid-1970s there was clear and consistent evidence from at least four feeding studies in rats that saccharin causes bladder cancer. In April 1977, the US Food and Drugs Administration (FDA) proposed a ban on the use of saccharin in all processed food, in soft drinks, and as a table-top sweetener. The ban has never been implemented, despite the explicit provisions of the Delaney Amendment (qv), which obliges the FDA to ban all known carcinogens. As a result of intense lobbying by the US food, drink and additive industries, Congress passed a temporary moratorium in 1977 preventing the FDA from banning saccharin, but requiring all products containing the chemical to carry a health warning. The moratorium has been renewed four times.

The British official attitude has been to accept that saccharin is an animal carcinogen, but to argue that carcinogenic effects in humans remain to be proved. The only precaution adopted in Britain has been to ban the use of saccharin in foods intended for babies and young children. Paradoxically, its use is still permitted in some "infant formula" pharmaceutical products.

In 1982, the British government's expert advisory committee recommended that a survey should be conducted to establish the quantities of saccharin and other artificial sweeteners that the British public were ingesting. A study was conducted, which revealed that as many as 17 per cent of British children aged from two to five years old were consuming saccharin at levels greater than the Acceptable Daily Intake (ADI) (qv) agreed by the World Health Organization and the EC's Scientific Committee for Food. The same study also revealed that approximately 30 per cent of diabetics were also exceeding the ADI for saccharin. The response was not to restrict the use of saccharin but to invite the Committee on Toxicity to set an ADI for saccharin at 5 milligrammes per kilogramme body weight, which is twice the figure accepted everywhere else. The effect of that adjustment was to bring the majority of UK consumers within the new ADI. Saccharin is banned entirely in Canada, but there is no evidence that the UK, the EC or the USA are likely to ban this known carcinogen from our foods.

Sahel famine
See: *Cash crops.*

Salinization
When land is too salty to support plant life, it is said to be salinized. Worldwide, an estimated 200,000sq km (73,000sq miles) are thought to be naturally saline – wetland and coastal areas in arid regions being particularly susceptible. But, increasingly, land is being rendered saline through man's activities, the chief culprit being perennial irrigation schemes.

All soils contain minute quantities of salt. In areas of regular rainfall, those salts are flushed out of the soil into underlying groundwaters, or carried away to the sea by local streams and rivers. Either way, the salts do not accumulate in the soil. In arid areas of the world, however, where rainfall is minimal and evaporation rates high, soil tends to have a naturally high salt content, with salt making up 12 per cent of the soil profile in badly affected areas. Groundwaters, too, tend to be more saline in arid and semi-arid areas.

Salinization occurs when the delicate salt balance of the soil is upset, thus allowing salts to build up in the root zone of crops or, worse still, to form a saline crust on the surface. Where the water contains sodium or sodium bicarbonate salts – of volcanic origin – the process of salinization goes one step further and the lands become "alkalinized." The soil loses its structure and eventually turns hard as rock, rendering it barren and useless for agriculture. Some 900sq km (350sq miles) are affected by alkalinization in the Soviet Union, whilst Australia tops the world league with 3,000sq km (1,200sq miles) affected.

Perennial irrigation schemes – where land is irrigated year after year without ever being left fallow – are a major cause of salinization in arid areas. Unless the land is well drained, irrigation inevitably causes the water-table to rise, bringing the salt in the soil to the surface. Worldwide, according to the United Nations Conference on Desertification, 220,000sq km (85,000 sq miles) of irrigated land – one-tenth of the world total – are waterlogged.

The evapo-transpiration of irrigation waters also adds directly to the salt load of soils. Studies in the USA suggest that as much as three-quarters of the irrigation water applied each year in America is lost to evapo-transpiration. The result is a fourfold concentration of the salts in the remaining water. Such water often contains more than 2,000ppm of salt. Not surprisingly, the salinity of irrigation water is now itself a factor in causing the salinization of lands.

According to the United Nations Environment Programme (UNEP), between 30 and 80 per cent of the 2,200 million sq km (850 million sq miles) of irrigated land in the world suffers to some degree from salinization, alkalinization and waterlogging. Countries that are badly affected include the following:

Pakistan Some 100,000sq km (38,600sq miles) out of the 150,000sq km (58,000 sq miles) under irrigation suffer from salinization, waterlogging or both. All told, an estimated 100,000 acres are lost annually to waterlogging and salinization – more than 250 acres a day.

Egypt The problems of salinization and waterlogging have been described as "grave." A 1976 survey, undertaken by USAID, found that more than 17,000sq km (6,560sq miles) were undergoing slight to severe salinization. According to the FAO, 90 per cent of Egypt's farmland suffers from waterlogging, with 35 per cent experiencing salinity problems.

Iraq More than 50 per cent of the 36,000sq km (13,900sq miles) under irrigation suffers from salinization and waterlogging. Vast areas in South Iraq are reported by the environmental writer Erik Eckholm to "glisten like fields of freshly fallen snow."

India The amount of land degraded by salinization and waterlogging has variously been estimated at between 60,000 and 100,000sq km (23,000 to 37,000sq miles). If the higher figure is correct, then a quarter of the 430,000sq km (166,000sq miles) under irrigation is affected.

Argentina 20,000sq km (7,700sq miles) of irrigated land are affected by waterlogging, salinization or alkalinization.

Peru According to the Global 2000 Report, 3,000 out of the 8,000sq km (3,100sq miles) of coastal lands under irrigation are salinized, waterlogged or both.

USA According to the US Salinity Laboratory, 25 to 35 per cent of all the irrigated land in the country has salinity problems – and the problem is getting worse. If no remedial measures are taken, the highly productive San Joaquin Valley could lose over a million acres of farmland in the next hundred years.

It is rare to find perennial irrigation schemes which have not experienced some degree of salinization or waterlogging.

Certain measures can be taken to minimize salinization at the local level. However, such measures are extremely expensive. By and large, their aim is to ensure that saline water is flushed out of the soil before it has time to accumulate. But the flushed salts must go somewhere. Generally, they end up in the nearest river, thus increasing its salt content. For farmers downstream of irrigation schemes, the problem is obvious. They are forced to irrigate their fields with increasingly saline water. In many arid areas, the problem is now acute. In South Australia, for example, the salinity of the Murray River (*qv*) is twice the average for Australian rivers. Other rivers affected include the Euphrates, the Indus, the Rio Grande and the Colorado. (See also: *Dams*③.)

Sandoz fire

A fire in a warehouse at the Sandoz chemical factory near Basel, Switzerland. As firemen played their hoses on the warehouse, chemicals released by exploding drums were washed into the River Rhine. More than 30 tonnes of pesticides, fungicides, and chemical dyes entered the river rendering it lifeless for 100-200km (60-120 miles). (See also: *Rhine*ⓟ.)

Schistosomiasis

A disease caused by parasitic flatworms, known as "schistosomes." Three common species infect humans: *S. haematobium, S. mansoni* and *S. japont.*

In 1947, an estimated 114 million people suffered from schistosomiasis, the symptoms of which are fever, cough, muscle pains and skin irritation. Today, 200 million people are affected – the equivalent of the entire population of the USA.

The larvae of the schistosomes develop within the bodies of freshwater snails. When people swim or wade in water contaminated by infected snails, the larvae bore through their skin and enter their bloodstream. From there, they move to the liver, where they mature in a few weeks and mate. The resulting eggs leave the human body via urine or faeces.

The dramatic spread of schistosomiasis over the past 35 years is largely the result of large-scale water development projects. Such projects provide ideal habitats for both freshwater snails and the schistosome parasite.

The connection between schistosomiasis and water projects is well established. Not only is the snail vector's habitat greatly extended by water development projects but the conditions are also created for much longer breeding periods. In Kenya, schistosomiasis now affects almost 100 per cent of those children living in irrigated areas near Lake Victoria. In the Sudan, the massive Gezira irrigation scheme had a general infection rate of 60-70 per cent in 1979, with the rate amongst school-children reaching over 90 per cent. All in all,

1,400,000 people were affected. After the building of the Aswan High Dam (qv) in Egypt, the infection rate rose to 100 per cent in some communities.

Few doubt that the disease is on the increase. Dr. Letitia Obeng of the United Nations Environment Programme warns that the current incidence of schistosomiasis is "only the thin end of the wedge." (See also: *Dams*①③, *Waterborne diseases*①③.)

Scrubber

A piece of equipment designed to remove toxic gases from chimney emissions. The term scrubbing is mainly used to describe processes that use a liquid to absorb the gases though there are other techniques, involving the use of materials that adsorb gases onto solid particles, which are sometimes referred to as dry scrubbing.

Battersea and Bankside power stations on London's River Thames were among the first to scrub their stack gases to remove sulphur dioxide. The resulting gypsum slurry was easily disposed of in the Thames, which was highly polluted at the time. This option is no longer available and such wastes are now often landfilled, which may cause pollution problems in the long term.

Another problem with wet scrubbing is that in some weather conditions wet, smelly mists are created. This problem can be dealt with by re-heating the stack gases, but this is expensive in terms of energy.

Scrubbing is an important technique for controlling air pollution by industrially generated gases. Other methods, such as electrostatic precipitators and bag filters, are capable of removing particulate matter such as grit and smoke, but will not affect gaseous emissions from chimneys. (See also: *Acid rain*℗, *Coal*℮℗, *Incineration*℗, *Landfill*℗.)

Seal deaths

In 1988, seal colonies in the Baltic and the North Sea (qv) were struck by an epidemic which caused 18,000 deaths, 1,500 of them in Britain. In Sweden, 73 per cent of the country's common seal population died, and in Denmark 80 per cent. Lake Baikal's unique freshwater seals were also affected and about 1,000 died.

The overt cause of the epidemic has been established as canine distemper. However, many scientists believe that pollution was at the roots of the disaster. According to Dr. Albert Osterhaus, from the National Institute of Public Health and Environmental Hygiene in the Netherlands, PCBS (qv) and other persistent chemicals had undermined the seals' resistance, making them more vulnerable to viruses. The average daily intake of PCBs by seals in the North Sea is 1.5 milligrams, as compared to 0.22 milligrams in the cleaner North Atlantic. It has also been suggested that the dramatic spread of the virus may have been helped by the microbial activity caused by algal blooms (qv) in the North Sea.

Sedimentation

According to one estimate, as much as 24,000 million tonnes of sediment are carried each year to the sea by the world's rivers. Of that total, only 9,300 million tonnes are thought to be of natural origin: the rest – some 14,700 million tonnes – results from man's activities. In China the three major rivers of Sichuan carry an annual silt load of 250 million tonnes – enough to cover an area of 1,600sq km (620sq miles) with a good 5cm (2in) of topsoil.

Some of the material carried downstream is deposited on flood plains, some on the beds of rivers and streams, and still more ends up on the ocean floor. Where rivers have been dammed, sedimentation can cause major problems. Prevented from travelling freely downstream, the silt simply accumulates in the reservoirs behind the dams, thus reducing their capacity and, hence, their effective lives.

In temperate areas, the sedimentation of reservoirs is usually a slow process and the average annual loss of capacity not serious. In the tropics, however, the story is very different. The problem lies in the fragile nature of tropical soils – and in the sheer scale of deforestation in tropical areas. Where the catchment area of a dam is forested, the rate of soil erosion (qv) is very low: even steep slopes are protected.

Where the forest has been destroyed, however, the rate of soil erosion is dramatic: India alone loses an estimated 12,000 million tonnes of soil each year to erosion. In the Himalayas, the foothills of Nepal, once covered in rhododendron, oak and pine, have been stripped of 40 per cent of their forest cover since 1952. Each acre (4,000sq m) of the now denuded hills loses an estimated 10 tonnes of soil a year. Such is the volume of silt carried downstream by the Ganges and the Brahmaputra that whole new islands have been formed in the Bay of Bengal.

Predictably, dams (qv) in the tropics have experienced high rates of sedimentation:

In India, the expected siltation rate at the Nizamsagar Dam in Andhra Pradesh was 530 acre-feet a year. The actual rate was closer to 8,700 acre-feet a year.

In Haiti, the Peligre Dam on the Artibonite River was built to last 50 years. Excessive sedimentation threatens the dam with decommissioning after just 30 years in service.

In China, the Sanmexia Dam, commissioned in 1960, had to be decommissioned in 1964, due to premature sedimentation. Worse still, the reservoir of the Laoying Dam actually silted up before the dam was fully operational.

Once silted up, a dam is next to useless. Even when the last waters of the decommissioned reservoir have eventually drained away, the land beneath will not be suitable for agriculture. Only a small strip of land close to the dam, where the coarser – and therefore less compacted – particles of silt accumulate, will be cultivable.

Excessive sedimentation can also cause floods. Ironically, the problem is often most acute in those areas where embankments have been built to control them. Under normal circumstances, the silt carried by rivers is deposited on the river's flood plains. But where embankments have been built, this is no longer possible. The silt therefore accumulates on the river bed, raising its height until – eventually – it is higher than the surrounding land. Where China's massive Yellow River crosses the Yellow Plains, the bed of the river is now five metres (16ft) above ground level – and, in some places, ten metres higher. Raising the height of the embankments is only a partial solution: the higher the embankments, the greater the volume of water carried through them, and, consequently, the more severe the damage from flooding should a breach occur. (See also: *Deforestation*③, *Drought flood cycle*③, *Flood control*③, *Hydro-electricity*⑦, *Tehri Dam*③, *Three Gorges Dam*③.)

Seed-pesticide connection
Recently, the world's major chemical companies have started buying up seed companies on a major scale. One reason for this is that the seeds business has become much more commercially attractive as a result of new legislation that permits the patenting of seeds. Also the industry has now hit on the idea of making high-yielding varieties (HYVs) infertile, which means that farmers are forced to buy new seeds every year, thereby massively increasing sales. HYVs are also of interest to chemical companies because they are specifically designed to respond to fertilizer applications, which correspondingly increases fertilizer sales. They also tend to be particularly vulnerable to pests, thereby increasing pesticide sales.

Pesticides and seeds are complementary businesses, and chemical companies have learned to cash in on the pesticide/seed market in a number of ways. The first is by coating seeds with chemical protectants, forcing farmers and horticulturalists to buy the chemicals and seeds as a package.

The second method is by designing advertising packages that provide particular combinations of pesticides and seeds.

The third is by gearing research towards the development of seed pesticide combinations that are designed to be used together.

The seed pellet business is being increasingly refined. Growth regulators have been added to the coating, and fluorescent materials have also been included, allowing farmers to plant at night. More and more chemicals are added to the coating so that, in the words of Patrick Mooney, author of *Seeds of the Earth*, the seed is "wrapped in a swarm of special chemicals protecting it from everything from rot to weeds."

Ciba-Geigy includes three chemicals in the coating of its sorghum grains. Two are to protect the seed from encroaching grasses, but the third is there to protect it from Ciba-Geigy's own herbicide "dual", which is normally toxic to grain sorghum. As a result, Ciba-Geigy can now sell much more of that herbicide.

A 1982 EC report notes that breeders had three goals: to maximize yields, to make the crops easy to harvest by machine and easy to process, and to make them disease-resistant. It then says that breeders were willing to "sacrifice disease control if the pesticides effective against the disease were available." As Patrick Mooney notes "if the breeder is also the pesticide manufacturer, that sacrifice hardly hurts at all."

One consequence of these trends is that the new varieties are designed less and less for their nutritional qualities. A survey in the USA in the early 1970s concluded that only one or two breeders even possessed the facilities for determining the nutritional quality of their new varieties.

A further consequence of these trends is that small farmers must spend more and more money on chemicals. This puts many of them into debt and eventually forces them out of business. In the Third World many become landless labourers and slum dwellers. (See also: *Green Revolution, HYVs, Patented seeds, Pesticides*.)

Sellafield
Major nuclear complex, including Britain's principal reprocessing (*qv*) plant.

The complex is located on the coast of Cumbria, 24km (15 miles) south of Whitehaven. Construction began in September 1947, and the first plutonium-production pile, or reactor, began operating in October 1950. A second pile started up eight months later, and in January 1952 the first reprocessing plant, B204, was commissioned. In March, the first metallic plutonium was made at Windscale, and in October the first British atomic bomb was tested at Monte Bello.

The original piles were closed following the Windscale fire (*qv*) in 1957, but by that time their successors, the four Calder Hall reactors, were supplying the increased demand for plutonium. These, with four more reactors at Chapelcross in Dumfriesshire, were the prototypes of the Magnox reactors (*qv*) that were used for the first British civil nuclear power programme.

Nine twin-reactor Magnox power stations had been built by 1972; and a new reprocessing plant went operational in 1964 to cope with the irradiated fuel from these and the eight military reactors. Management of Windscale was transferred from the United Kingdom Atomic Energy Authority (AEA) to British Nuclear Fuels (BNF) in 1971, and in 1976 the company applied for permission to build a further reprocessing plant – the Thermal Oxide Reprocessing Plant or THORP – to handle uranium oxide fuel from the UK's advanced gas-cooled reactors (AGR) (*qv*) and foreign pressurized water reactors (PWR) (*qv*). After the Windscale Inquiry of 1977, consent was granted, but construction of THORP did not begin until 1984.

Between 1952 and 1987 there have been more than 700 reported incidents at Sellafield; incidents involving the contamination of workers have increased as the Magnox reprocessing plant has aged. Up until 1990, the families of 20 workers who had died or suffered serious illness had been paid over £500,000 in compensation by BNF (but without the company formally admitting liability). Many more claims are outstanding. Abnormal discharges to sea have also occurred regularly; BNF was found guilty on four counts, and fined £10,000 ($16,000), in connection with one such discharge in November 1983. The spill was discovered when Greenpeace divers tried to plug the main discharge pipe. Another attempt to plug the pipe was made by Greenpeace in 1987. A quarter to half a tonne of plutonium has been discharged into the Irish sea, and there is a higher-than-normal incidence of childhood cancer in the area surrounding Sellafield.

New, more stringent, discharge authorizations were imposed on the Sellafield plant in January 1985, with annual limits of 600 curies of alpha emitters, and 200,000 curies of beta. But the authorizations for the French reprocessing plant at Cap de la Hague (qv), comparable in age and throughput, have been 90 curies of alpha and 45,000 of beta emitters since 1980. The actual discharge of alpha emitters from Sellafield between 1967 and 1981 totalled 31,583 curies, and from la Hague 141.5 curies. Doses to workers per unit of Magnox electricity generated are more than double those at la Hague, despite the lower discharges to sea.

In December 1983, a £150 million ($240 million) programme was announced, to reduce discharges to levels comparable with those from Cap de la Hague. This programme was largely complete by 1986, but Magnox reprocessing will continue to provide the bulk of the discharges and doses at Sellafield until those reactors cease operation and the last of their fuel is reprocessed in 2000 or soon afterwards.

Sellafield is also the site of a prototype 30MW AGR which operted for 15 years and which is now being decommissioned as an exercise in "proving" the economic feasibility of dismantling old reactors. Recent controversy has surrounded the scheduled opening of the £1.8 billion THORP plant in 1992. Although BNF claims it has enough contracts from overseas (mainly Japanese) and UK nuclear stations to keep it going, critics predict that the plant will be a white elephant. They also point to the hazards of a growing international traffic in spent nuclear fuel. BNF has tried to counter the bad image of Sellafield as Britain's "nuclear dustbin" by opening a £5 million multimedia exhibition centre. In 1989, the centre attracted over 150,000 visitors and won a major tourism award. (See also: *Decommissioning*Ⓝ, *Leukemia clusters*Ⓝ, *Nuclear accidents*Ⓝ, *Routine radioactive discharges.*)

Seveso

Site of a major chemical accident in 1976. The accident occurred when a reactor used in the manufacture of trichlorophenol exploded at a chemical plant owned by Givaudan, a subsidiary of the Swiss pharmaceuticals giant Hoffman-La Roche.

A cloud of dioxin (qv) was released in the explosion, contaminating 18sq km (7sq miles) of surrounding countryside and necessitating the evacuation of more than 900 people. In the year following the accident, the rate of birth defects increased by more than 40 per cent.

The soil in the most heavily contaminated area was so polluted that the top 20cm (8in) had to be removed and buried in a massive plastic-lined pit. The clean-up has proved only a partial success, however. Recent soil samples from the "decontaminated" land have proved "dioxin-positive."

The factory itself was dismantled after the accident, some two tonnes of dioxin-contaminated waste being removed for disposal. In 1984, a major scandal broke when 41 barrels of dioxin waste went missing in France. The barrels were eventually found in an abandoned abattoir at Anguilcourt-Le-Sart in northern France. They were subsequently incinerated at a Hoffman-La Roche plant in Basel.

Shifting cultivators

Farmers who use slash-and-burn techniques to clear forested land for cultivation and who regularly move to new lands as soon as the fertility of their plots begins to decline. (See also: *Deforestation*③, *Encroaching cultivators*Ⓐ③, *Swidden agriculture*Ⓐ③.)

Sievert

The unit of radiation dose absorbed by tissue; being the dose in grays (qv) multiplied by a quality factor to account for differences in damage to tissue caused by different kinds of radiation, such as alpha and gamma radiation (qv). The sievert (Sv) is replacing the rem: 1 Sv = 100 rem.

Sizewell

Located on England's Suffolk coast immediately to the south of a world-famous water bird reserve at Minsmere, Sizewell Beach is an officially designated area of outstanding natural beauty. Nevertheless, a Magnox (qv) nuclear power station, Sizewell A, began operating there early in 1966, the sixth in the Central Electricity Generating Board's (CEGB) programme of eight such stations. The CEGB owns about 2.5sq km (600 acres) of Sizewell Beach.

The British government, advised by the UK Atomic Energy Authority, has traditionally dictated its choice of reactor type to the CEGB. In the early 1960s, the CEGB wanted no nuclear stations at all, considering them to be uneconomic, but the Magnox programme was imposed. The government's choice to follow the Magnox was the AGR, which had been developed by the UKAEA, but by 1975 the CEGB had experienced severe difficulties in building these reactors. It decided that the best course was to abandon the AGR and buy the American pressurized water reactor (PWR) (qv) instead. But such was the prestige invested in the AGR project that the CEGB was not allowed to apply for permission to build its first PWR until 1980.

The public inquiry into whether the CEGB should be granted planning permission for a PWR at Sizewell B sat for 340 days, the longest public inquiry so far held in the UK, and took detailed evidence on the need for the proposed station, its economics, its design and operational safety, and local environmental issues.

The Inspector, Sir Frank

Layfield, recommended that planning permission should be granted. After a brief parliamentary debate, permission was granted in March 1987, despite the fact that in the meantime coal prices had fallen dramatically and the Chernobyl (qv) accident had taken place.

By October 1988, when the second PWR inquiry opened at Hinkley Point (qv), the CEGB no longer argued that a new nuclear station would be economic as compared with a coal station. Instead, the CEGB's case rested on the need for a diversity of fuel supplies as imposed by the Government's White Paper of February 1988. The White Paper requires that, after the privatization of the electricity supply industry in 1989, 18 per cent of electricity must be generated from non-fossil fuels. Although alternative energy sources (chiefly wind, tidal and wave power) would count towards the percentage, the new requirement constitutes a "distortion in the market" (in the Minister's words) in favour of nuclear power, and is an implicit admission that nuclear power cannot compete in the free market without subsidy.

Critics argue that the Sizewell inquiry was nothing but a formality, rubber stamping a foregone conclusion. They point out that construction work on the PWR was already under way – with more than £200 million ($320 million) already spent – even before the inquiry opened. The Sizewell B station is scheduled to generate its first electricity in 1994. After the British government failed to privatize nuclear power in 1989 and shelved plans for further stations, Sizewell B is the only PWR under construction in the UK. Largely because of this, its building costs alone have risen to over £2.6 billion. Environmental groups claim that it will cost £1 million a day more to operate than equivalent gas-fired stations. (See also: *Nuclear economics*Ⓝ.)

Slash and burn agriculture
See: *Swidden agriculture.*

Social forestry
Many of the reforestation (qv) programmes being promoted by the World Bank (qv) and other development agencies are intended to encourage "social forestry" – described by the Forest Department of Gujarat, India, as "the creation of forests for the benefit of the community through the active involvement and participation of the community." The aims are both to increase village self-sufficiency in firewood and other forest products, thus reducing the pressure on existing forests, and to reduce rural migration and unemployment.

But contrary to the aims of the programme, few social forestry projects are owned communally: instead most are in the hands of relatively large landowners – a recent study in Karnataka, India, showed that 80 per cent of the plantations are on private land.

The same study revealed that 92 per cent of the trees that had been planted were eucalyptus (qv), a tree which in dry areas has a disastrous impact on both the soil and water supplies. It is of little use to villagers, since it provides no fodder for animals, no green leaves for manure, and timber that is unsuitable for many traditional uses.

The choice of eucalyptus reflects the commercial nature of most social forestry projects. In India, where social forestry is most widely practised, little of the wood grown under the programme is even available to villagers. In one district of Karnataka, 80 per cent of the timber grown went to local pulp mills or to rayon manufacturers.

To make matters worse, much of the land used for social forestry was previously used to grow food crops for local consumption. By 1988, an estimated 2,200sq km (850sq miles) of farmland in Karnataka alone will have been lost to social forestry projects, greatly exacerbating the problem of malnutrition.

Rural unemployment has also increased: unlike farming, growing trees requires little labour once the initial planting has been undertaken. Many of the displaced workers have no option but to strip trees for sale to the cities as fuelwood (qv), thus increasing the pressure on remaining forests.

Despite the failure of social forestry to achieve its stated aims, the programme is still heavily funded and promoted by the World Bank. (See also: *Deforestation*Ⓒ③, *Reforestation*Ⓒ③, *Tropical forests*Ⓒ③.)

Soft energy paths
A term coined by the US energy consultant Amory B. Lovins and used as the title of his influential book published in 1977. It refers to a complex of industrial, commercial and political strategies designed to reduce the dependence of industrial societies on conventional sources of energy. These call for an intensive energy conservation programme and for a shift from nuclear power and fossil fuel combustion to renewable sources of energy such as wind or wave power.

Lovins' argument is that conventional forms of energy production provide electricity but are uneconomic in providing heat for cooking and space-heating, for which much of the energy generated in our society is required. Such "end use services," Lovins argues, "are best provided by a sophisticated energy conservation programme, which would include draught-proofing, thermal insulation, window shutters and shades and coatings, greenhouses, heat-exchangers and the like."

It is only when all energy conservation measures have been taken that a country should even consider generating more power. In such an event, the cheapest and most appropriate methods of generation would be combined-heat-and-power (qv) stations, low-temperature heat engines run by industrial waste heat or by solar ponds, modern wind machines and small-scale hydro in good sites, and solar cells. (See also: *Alternative technology*Ⓔ.)

Solar collector
A device for the extraction of useful heat from the warmth of sunshine, to heat water or provide space heating.

In arid climates solar collectors

are used to power stills for evaporating saline water, the vapour being condensed and collected as fresh water. Focusing mirrors have been used in low latitudes to intensify the heat falling on the receiving surface, allowing solar heat to be used directly to boil water or cook food and, on a much larger scale, to produce steam for power generation.

At the present time, however, solar collectors make a limited contribution to our energy requirements, largely because there has been little government support for research. Unquestionably, however, they must have an important role to play if a soft energy path (*qv*) is adopted.

Stabilizers
Compounds added to food products to stabilize emulsions that might otherwise separate out into a water-based and an oil-based segment. They are, therefore, invariably used in combination with emulsifiers (*qv*), to which they are often chemically similar. Frequently they work by thickening one of the segments and so making the mixture less likely to separate. (See also: *Additives*Ⓛ.)

Stockholm Conference
Conference held on June 15-16 1972 in Stockholm and attended by representatives of 113 nations. It is considered to be a landmark in the development of global environmental concern. It resulted in the setting up of the United Nations Environment Programme, but the programme's achievements have been limited by its inability to make pronouncements, or take actions, that are likely to offend the governments that fund it.

Sub-lethal pollution
Even at levels too low to kill outright, many toxic pollutants cause severe biological damage. Indeed, in some cases, exposure to "sub-lethal" levels of a pollutant over a long period can be as damaging, if not more damaging, than exposure to high levels over a brief period.

The clinical effects of sub-lethal pollution are many and varied.

For example, very low levels of organophosphate (*qv*) pesticides (*qv*) have been shown to inhibit enzyme activity in humans and to impair hormone functions. Exposure to low levels of oil can cause serious chromosomal damage to fish eggs, while DDT (*qv*) disrupts the ability of some fish species to return to their home streams, thus breaking a critical phase in their reproductive cycle. Low levels of DDT also cause fish to become hyper-active.

All organisms are weakened by sub-lethal levels of pollution and are therefore more vulnerable to disease. Sub-lethal pollutants have played a key role in the spread of tree diseases (*qv*).

The sub-lethal effects of pollution have generally been played down or ignored when setting safe exposure standards. By the time the damage becomes obvious, remedial action is often too late.

Subsistence agriculture
See: *Traditional agriculture.*

Superfund
The reckless disposal of hazardous wastes has caused the contamination of both land and water at many sites throughout the industrialized world. As a result, massive sums of money are now required to clean up old dumps.

In the USA, a "superfund" – bankrolled largely by industry – has been set up to pay for the clean-up. Known formally as the Comprehensive Environmental Response, Compensation and Liability Act (CERCLA), the superfund legislation was passed in 1980 – the last bill that President Carter signed.

As originally conceived, the superfund was to raise $4,200 million – but this sum was reduced to $1,600 million under pressure from industry, which is required to provide 88 per cent of the cash. Clauses in the Act that would have enabled private citizens to sue the fund for any damage caused by improper dumping were also scrapped before CERCLA passed through Congress.

In 1986 the original $1,600 million was raised to $8,500 million, but even that seems nowhere near

sufficient to clean up all of America's abandoned "toxic time bombs." Some 1,200 "priority" sites have now been identified, but the Environmental Protection Agency (EPA) expects the number to rise to 2,000 by the end of the century. A 1983 report by the Office of Technology Assessment (OTA), however, estimated that "10,000 sites (or more) may require clean-up by Superfund." OTA went on to comment: "With Superfund's existing resources, it is not technically or economically possible to permanently clean up even 2,000 sites in less than several decades." Some of the polluting wastes removed from superfund sites have been found to be contaminating the supposedly "safe" disposal sites where they have now been deposited. (See also: *Drinking water*Ⓟ, *Hazardous wastes*Ⓟ.)

Super-Phénix: See: *Creys Malville*Ⓝ, *Fast reactor*Ⓝ.)

Sustainable development
Public disquiet over the ruinous social and ecological consequences of current development (*qv*) policies throughout the Third World has led the development industry, on several occasions, to announce new strategies which, it is claimed, will minimize the destructiveness of the development process. Unfortunately, few of these strategies have ever come to anything.

The current buzz word is "sustainable development," which has been talked about since the early 1970s.

The World Conservation Strategy argues that, for development to be sustainable, it must not interfere with the functioning of critical ecological processes and life support systems. This means, above all, that food cropland must be used for growing crops rather than for cattle ranching, that crops must be managed in an ecologically sound manner, that watershed forests must be protected, and that genetic diversity must be preserved.

Though the rhetoric has changed, however, development policies have not. Large dams (*qv*) continue to be built, vast plantations and livestock-rearing projects continue to be set up, colonization projects continue to occur in virgin forests – all undertakings which are known to be highly destructive and totally unsustainable in tropical conditions. By putting pressure on the Third World to export crops, ore and timber, moreover, the First World deprives peasants of the land they need for subsistence, forcing them to clear forests and swell city slums. Yet few governments or international agencies advocating "sustainable development" seriously address the First World lifestyles causing such suffering.

It is not certain that sustainable development is even possible. To begin with, in the competitive world in which we live, only those development projects are undertaken that maximize political advantages and short-term economic returns; socially benign projects rarely satisfy such conditions. In addition, economic development (*qv*) means increased consumption and production. Inevitably, the impact of human activities on already highly degraded ecosystems must also increase. Sustainability *and* development thus appear contradictory. (See also: *Cash crops*Ⓐ③, *Green Revolution*Ⓐ③, *Tropical agriculture*Ⓐ③, *Tropical timber trade*Ⓐ③.)

Swidden agriculture

Swidden or "shifting" agriculture is an ecologically sound system of farming used in the tropics.

Widely practised in tropical forests and throughout the savannahs of North and East Africa, swidden agriculture involves clearing small areas of bush and forest for cultivation on a rotational basis. Smaller trees are burned, unlocking the nutrients in the vegetation by providing the soil with fertilizer in the form of ash, which can readily be taken up by plants.

After two or three years of cultivation, the soil of an area is almost exhausted and yields begin to decline. The farmer then abandons the plot and opens a new clearing some distance away. The original plot is left fallow –

traditionally for 15 years or more – so that the forest can regenerate. In the savannah, the cycle is longer, with plots being left fallow for 20-30 years.

Development agencies such as the UN Food and Agriculture Organization and the World Bank charge that swidden agriculture is both "unproductive" and "environmentally destructive." In particular, it is singled out as a major cause of deforestation (*qv*). The charge is unfounded.

Insofar as shifting cultivators are a cause of deforestation, the threat lies not with traditional swidden farmers but with landless peasant colonists – many themselves "environmental refugees" (*qv*) – who are totally unversed in the skills of forest farming.

Many experts in tropical agriculture are now convinced that swiddening represents the only sustainable method of farming a rainforest. For, despite their lush canopy and profusion of plants, tropical rainforests grow on some of the most fragile and infertile soils in the world.

Traditional swidden systems ensure that the soils beneath cleared areas are kept protected at all times. Every plot grows an extraordinarily wide variety of edible plants, each maturing at different times and growing to different heights. The effect is to create a multi-layered garden which, in many respects, mimics the natural forest.

Anthropologists report that traditional swidden cultivators are acutely aware of the need to maintain fallow periods, thus allowing the cleared forest to regenerate. Among the Tsembaga of New Guinea, for example, it is estimated that 90 per cent of clearings eventually revert to mature rainforest. The Tsembaga revere sapling trees as "Duk Mi" – the mother of gardens – and assiduous care is taken not to uproot them while weeding.

Anthropologists also attest to the productivity of swidden systems. Indeed, almost all the food consumed and marketed in Tropical Africa is produced by shifting cultivators using swidden techniques. (See also: *Deforestation*③, *Tropical timber trade*Ⓐ③.)

Symbiosis

Permanent union between organisms. See: *Mutualism*.

Synergy

The process whereby two or more chemicals acting in combination produce an effect that is far greater than that achieved by the parent chemicals separately – or which is entirely new and unexpected.

Thus, the solubility in water of the carcinogenic pesticide DDT (*qv*) is increased 10,000 times by the presence of oil, greatly enhancing its dangers to aquatic organisms. Similarly, a study by Professor Irving Selikoff of Mount Sinai Hospital, New York, has shown that whilst asbestos (*qv*) workers who smoke have an eight times higher chance of contracting lung cancer than other smokers, by virtue of their exposure to asbestos, their chances when compared to non-smokers are 92 times higher.

Modern toxicology rarely takes account of synergic effects. Few of the 1,000 new chemical products entering the market every year are tested for their synergic effects, nor are synergic effects taken into account when setting safety standards. Permissible levels for pesticides in food, for example, are set individually, each pesticide being treated separately. Yet most foodstuffs contain a cocktail of chemicals, the combined effects of which are not even considered by the authorities. (See also: *Additives*①, *Cancer*①, *Cancer research*①, *Carcinogen*①.)

Synthetic organic chemicals

The modern chemical industry produces many thousands of synthetic organic chemicals that affect our daily lives in almost every aspect. Fibres, plastics, drugs, pesticides, dyes, food additives and fuels are just a few of the products involved.

All these organic chemicals are compounds of carbon and the skill of the organic chemist lies in shaping the molecules, by heat, pressure and reaction with other chemicals, into the desired end product.

In some cases the compounds produced may be identical with natural products – acetic acid, for example, is produced synthetically but is more familiar as the natural product vinegar – while in other cases – the pesticide DDT (*qv*), for example – the result may be very different from any naturally occurring substance.

Several characteristics make them dangerous. Many – notably the chlorinated hydrocarbons (*qv*) – tend to accumulate in fatty tissues, with all the attendant problems of bioconcentration (*qv*). Secondly, many have the ability to mimic the characteristics of naturally occurring substances, with the result that they are readily taken up by living organisms – often, as with pesticides like DDT, with fatal results. In addition, synthetic organic compounds are often resistant to degradation by natural processes, with the result that they persist in the environment and pose major disposal problems.

The majority of synthetic organic chemicals have never been tested for their effects on human health or on the environment. Nonetheless, as the US Environmental Protection Agency notes, synthetic organic chemicals account for "a disproportionately large number of recognized carcinogens." (See also: *Additives*Ⓛ, *Cancer*Ⓛ, *Carcinogen*ⒻⓁ, *Hazardous wastes*Ⓟ, *Pesticides*ⒶⓅ.)

Tartrazine
Taste additives
Tehri Dam
Teratogen
Third World debt
Threatened species
Three Gorges Dam
Three Mile Island
Tidal power
Tobacco
Tourism
Tradable emissions
Traditional
    agriculture
Transmigration
Tree diseases
Tribal people
Tropical agriculture
Tropical forests
Tropical Forest Action
    Plan
Tropical timber trade
2,4,5-T
2,4-D

Underground nuclear
    tests
Uranium
Uranium enrichment
Uranium mining
Urbanization

Tartrazine

A bright yellow coal-tar dye (*qv*), also known in the USA as FD&C Yellow No. 5, and throughout the EC as E102.

It is used unmixed to give a lemon yellow colour, but often mixed with other dyes to provide a variety of shades from cream to orange. Tartrazine has been in use since the late 19th century and remains one of the most widely used coal-tar dyes. It is found, for example, in many soft drinks and confectionery products.

Tartrazine is generally recognized to be responsible for a wide range of allergies and symptoms of intolerance, including child hyperactivity, asthma, migraine, and skin rashes. It has also been suggested that it may cause cancer, though the evidence is inconclusive.

Tartrazine is permitted in the UK, much of the EC, and the USA, but it is banned in Norway and Finland. There are severe restrictions on its use in Austria, Sweden and France. (See also: *Additives*Ⓛ, *Food dyes*Ⓛ.)

Taste additives

The largest single group of food additives, measured both in terms of the number used and their cost. The European and North American industries are probably using about 3,500 different additives, and that figure does not include the artificial sweeteners (*qv*). The UK industrial market is alone worth more than $88 million a year; the EC as a whole accounts for about $320 million; and the US market has been valued at $500 million annually.

Though taste additives are the largest single group of additives, they are also the least regulated. Neither Britain, the USA, nor any of the EC countries has a comprehensive positive list of those permitted. They do not possess E numbers (*qv*) and their identities do not have to be declared to consumers or even to governments. At most, product labels have to list them as part of the ingredients. The food and chemical industries have often argued that regulation is unnecessary and impractical, but consumer groups do not agree. Since they are not regulated, taste additives have hardly been tested at all for their safety or toxicity; taste additives are merely presumed to be safe until evidence to the contrary is provided.

They are sometimes divided into those that are natural, those that are "nature-identical" and those that are synthetic. Those classed as natural occur in, and are extracted from, foods. Those classed as "nature-identical" occur in foods, but, when used commercially, are synthesized in the laboratory. "Nature-identical" additives can thus be incorporated into products that would not naturally contain them. The synthetics are not known to occur in nature.

Some countries, such as Germany, do have positive lists for the synthetics, but they are untypical. British labelling regulations make a distinction between the meaning of the terms "flavour" and "flavoured." A product that relies on synthetics should be labelled, for example, "strawberry flavour," while a product may be called "strawberry flavoured" as long as it uses either naturals or "nature-identical" flavours. (See also: *Additives*①, *Colourings*①, *Convenience food*①, *E numbers*①.)

Tehri Dam
Once commissioned, the Tehri Dam – now being built near the confluence of the Bhagirathi and Bhilangna rivers in the Himalayas – will flood some 45sq km (17sq miles). The town of Tehri and 23 villages will be completely submerged, and 72 other villages will be partially submerged. More than 70,000 people will be displaced by the dam.

Numerous geologists have warned that the dam is sited in an area of intense seismic activity.

In April 1986, Indian environmentalists took the Government of India and the State of Uttar Pradesh to court in an attempt to cancel the project. One point raised was that high sedimentation rates (*qv*) could render the dam useless within 25 years. Engineers for the hydro-electricity board, however, insist that the dam will last 100 years or more.

The environmentalists were supported in their case by a government-appointed committee charged with assessing the likely environmental effects of the dam.

After six years of deliberation, the committee concluded: "The serious adverse environmental effects of the Tehri reservoir scheme are not commensurate with the potential benefits." The committee recommended that a series of small hydro-electric plants be built instead of a single giant dam.

Despite this recommendation, the government of India continued with the project. In December 1985, the USSR announced that it would finance the dam, the cost of which was then estimated at about £500 million. Latest estimates ranged between £1,000 million and over £2,000 million.

In July 1991, however, Mr Kamal Nath, Minister of State for Environment and Forests, moved to suspend work on the dam because the contractors had not conformed to certain safety conditions. This may prove to be a temporary setback. More important in the long run may be the collapse of the Soviet Union; any new administration might well be happy to find an excuse to withdraw funding. (See also: *Dams*③, *Development*③.)

Teratogen
A substance that causes defects in the offspring of a parent exposed to it. The most notorious teratogen is the drug thalidomide, which deformed the babies of many women who were prescribed it in pregnancy.

Organic mercury (*qv*) compounds have been found to be teratogenic in humans, while dioxins (*qv*) are known teratogens in laboratory animals and suspected of having this effect in people. The herbicide ioxynil has also been found to be teratogenic in animals.

Women are advised to avoid taking drugs in pregnancy, but few warnings are given about avoiding exposure to industrial and agricultural chemicals – despite the fact that many substances to which people are frequently exposed have not been tested for teratogenicity.

Third World debt
Between them, the nations of the Third World owe approximately $1,000,000 million to the banks and lending agencies of the industrialized world. The interest on the debts is now so high that the Third World is paying more money to the West in interest payments than it is receiving in aid – a negative transfer which in 1989 amounted to $20,000 million. Some countries are now borrowing money simply to service past debts.

Most debtor nations have called for some form of debt relief. Some have defaulted on their interest repayments, but they have found it difficult to unite and negotiate collectively with their creditors. When in the late 1980s Peru, under President Garcia, limited debt repayment to a maximum 10 per cent of its income from exports, it soon found itself economically isolated and entered a spiral of impoverishment that precipitated Garcia's downfall.

A large proportion of the debts incurred by Third World governments has been spent on environmentally and socially destructive development programmes, from large dams to massive highway schemes and livestock rearing programmes.

Many of those projects have proved totally uneconomic. A 1987 study by the Asian Development Bank of 40 large irrigation schemes, for example, concluded that financial returns were typically less than 30 per cent of those expected. In India, according to a recent report, every single large dam built since World War II has been an economic disaster: not only have the dams cost more than estimated, but they have failed to provide the expected benefits. In South America, the Guatemalan government is now forced to sell electricity at four times the competitive rate in order to service the debts incurred on its massive hydro-electricity programme. Many farmers and small businesses have simply switched to using diesel and gas.

Other projects have been just as disastrous. In Brazil, it can cost as much as $50 a head to move cattle from the new ranches which have been set up in Amazonia (*qv*) to the nearest railhead, with the animals losing up to ten per cent of their weight en route. Not surprisingly, many livestock projects have proved totally unviable. Other white elephants that have contributed to Brazil's massive debt include its nuclear power programme and its highway development projects.

Corruption has further increased losses, some authorities suggesting that as much as one-third of the money borrowed has been siphoned off by businessmen, bureaucrats and politicians, much of it going into numbered accounts in Switzerland. A study of 18 debtor countries by the Morgan Guaranty Trust Company estimated that some US $200,000 million of loans had been lost to such "capital flight."

To service the loans on debts, Third World countries have been forced to plunder their natural resources for all they are worth, thus adding to the environmental and social costs of the debt crisis. In particular, the amount of land under cash crops (*qv*) has been increased, while the exploitation of forest and mineral resources has accelerated.

Several Western banks, led by Citicorp, have now made provisions against countries defaulting on their debts. The Toronto agreement of 1988 and the Trinidad initiative launched at the London G7 conference in 1991 have provided some debt relief for poorer African countries. But at present this relief amounts to only $100 million out of annual payments totalling some $10,000 million.

Debt-for-nature (*qv*) swaps are being discussed as a possible means of reducing debt. In such arrangements, Third World countries undertake to protect environmentally important areas – such as tropical forests – in return for debt being written off or re-

duced. However, unless fundamental changes are made in the world economy, measures to reduce debt are likely to be temporary. As economist Cheryl Payer explains in her incisive book on the subject, *Lent and Lost: Foreign Credit and Third World Development*, the present Third World debt crisis is "the direct result of the ideology which insists that poor countries require large and sustained inflows of foreign capital for their development." Payer shows that the belief that the debt crisis was caused by the OPEC price rises of the 1970s is pure myth. In fact, the crisis was around long before oil prices rose and is a direct result of aid (*qv*) policies followed by the Western powers after the Second World War. According to Payer, "International flows of funds must be subjected to stringent controls of a strictly non-political nature if the disaster of the 1980s is not to be repeated." (See also: *Aid*③, *Dams*③, *Deforestation*©③, *Development*③, *Hamburger connection*Ⓐ③, *World Bank*③.)

Threatened species
See: *Extinction, Genetic diversity.*

Three Gorges Dam
If built, China's Three Gorges Dam on the Chiang Jiang River (formerly the Yangtze) will be the world's largest dam. Two kilometres (2,166yd) long and 175m (574ft) high, the dam will produce 14,700MW of electricity – the equivalent output of several large nuclear power stations. It is estimated that the final cost will be between $16,000 million and $20,000 million.

Critics of the dam, both within China and abroad, are concerned at its probable ecological and social effects. The dam's reservoir will extend 500km (310 miles) upstream, completely flooding ten cities and partially flooding eight others, in addition to some 440sq km (170sq miles) of fertile farmland. As many as 860,000 people will require resettlement. Many factories, roads and railways will also be flooded if the dam is built: replacing them could cost as much as $3,500 million.

Landslides are common in the area and could threaten the dam. Hou Xueyu of the Chinese Academy of Sciences has argued that the weight of the dam and its reservoir could trigger an earthquake. The army is concerned that the dam might provide an easy target for enemy bombers in some future conflict.

Experts are also worried that the dam could have a disastrous effect on fisheries. Eighty species of fish could be adversely affected by the reduced flow of the Chiang Jiang, and by salt water intrusion into the delta region. By trapping silt, the dam will also deprive downstream fisheries of nutrients. Upstream, the accumulated sediment could cause the port of Chongqing to silt up.

Early in 1989, in response to growing criticism, the Chinese government announced that the project was to be suspended. But after the Tiananmen massacre in June, Dai Quing, a leading critic of the plan, was jailed and the project was revived. In June 1991, vice premier Zou Jiahua spoke favourably of the dam, and the following month the governor of Hubei province announced that he thought a positive decision would be made later in the year. Meanwhile the World Bank (*qv*) remains firmly committed to the project, despite an independent review of the Bank's own feasibility study condemning the Bank's study as being deeply flawed. The review found that the study had "glossed over serious technical and environmental problems, ignored safety risks and significant project costs and exaggerated the flood control and navigation benefits of the dam." (See also: *Dams*③, *Sedimentation*③.)

Three Mile Island
An island in the Susquehanna River near Harrisburg, Pennsylvania, famous as the site of a power station containing two pressurized water reactors (PWRs) (*qv*), one of which almost suffered a catastrophic accident. In the early morning of March 28 1979 several water-coolant feed pumps failed in TMI-2. The reactor closed itself down eight seconds

later, but both emergency water supply lines were blocked by closed valves. Though the reactor had closed, the "decay heat" from the nuclear reaction was still causing the core temperature to rise sharply, and no new cooling water was arriving.

To compound the problem, a relief valve in the reactor which opened in the first few seconds of the accident, failed to close, despite a control room indication that it had. This valve bled off much of what little water was in the core. The emergency core-cooling system came into operation, but the operators closed it. The increasing core temperature caused steam bubbles to form in the coolant, accelerating the rate of water loss. Within two hours the water level in the reactor vessel fell below the top of the fuel rods, and their temperature increased drastically. The fuel cladding melted, and reacted with the water to form hydrogen. Later TV pictures indicate that the uranium fuel itself may well have started to melt.

The remaining coolant pumps started to shake violently, because they were trying to pump steam; not realizing the cause, the operators closed the pumps. Soon afterwards help arrived from the reactor manufacturer, and the core was flooded and brought slowly under control. For several days experts tried to calculate the risk of a hydrogen explosion – in fact, one occurred on the afternoon of the accident – and the amounts of radioactivity released during the accident. In the face of conflicting advice, the Pennsylvania Governor recommended that children and pregnant women within a five-mile radius should be evacuated.

Though the containment (qv) held and little radioactivity was released at the time of the accident, the stricken reactor was itself highly contaminated. Six months after the accident, the containment was 2m (6ft) deep in radioactive water, which was leaking in at a rate of 3,800 litres (1,000 US gallons) a day from the primary circuit. The water contained 250 curies per cubic metre,

including a total of 3,000 curies of tritium, a radioactive isotope of hydrogen. Meanwhile, 57 curies of krypton-85 were trapped in the reactor dome and subsequently, more than a year after the accident, the authorities agreed to it being vented into the atmosphere, despite public protests.

The plant could not be entered for two years, and the first TV pictures, taken a year later, showed a completely collapsed core. The clean-up is not yet complete but, by 1987, its cost was put at more than $1,000 million. At the end of 1986, the plant's owners, General Public Utilities, reported intractable problems in extracting chunks of disintegrated fuel from the reactor. Large quantities of nuclear waste (qv) have had to be removed by train, some of it being transported for over 2,900km (1,800 miles) to a dump at Idaho Falls. The reactor will be entombed in concrete when adequately decontaminated. In 1986, its companion reactor TMI-1 was restarted, despite vociferous local opposition.

In 1987, a rise in the death rate among old people living in states neighbouring Three Mile Island was blamed on the accident. Between 1979 and 1982, at least 50,000 (and possibly 130,000) more elderly people died in the affected states than expected, the death rate in Pennsylvania, for example, being 3.6 times higher than the national average. Dr. Jay Gould of Public Data Access, the group that undertook the study, argues that low-level radiation released during and after the Three Mile Island accident may have damaged the immune system of elderly people, thus hastening their deaths from apparently "normal" causes. There have also been many claims that the accident has seriously affected the health of farm animals, crops and people in the agricultural area round the plant. By 1985, the power station company's insurers had already paid out $40 million in damages, and 2,000 lawsuits were still outstanding in 1989.

The Three Mile Island accident resulted in a re-assessment of

safety standards, and the retrofitting of safety devices to many stations. It also brought a disenchantment with nuclear power in the USA, the view among electricity utility executives that nuclear power was too expensive being reinforced by the accident. (See also: *Nuclear accidents*Ⓝ, *Containment*Ⓝ, *Radiation and health*ⒸⓃ.)

Tidal power

The use of sea tides to provide energy to do useful work, most commonly to generate electricity. A large tidal movement is necessary, restricting sites to semi-enclosed bays or estuaries on ocean coasts.

A dam (qv) built at a saltwater site allows tidal water to enter but prevents it from leaving. A lake forms behind the dam, the tide is allowed to ebb, and then the water is released, turning turbines as it flows downstream. In some designs there are two sets of turbines, one operated by the rising tide, the other by the water released at low tide.

The capital cost of tidal power projects is high, but operating costs are low. They can generate large amounts of power, and should enjoy long operating lives provided the bed behind the barrage is dredged regularly to control the accumulation of silt.

Little is known of the long-term ecological effects of tidal barrages. However, by interrupting the flow of water downstream and trapping silt that is disposed of elsewhere, rates and patterns of estuarine sedimentation (qv) are inevitably altered. This may affect populations of invertebrates on which wading birds feed, but the lake behind the barrage may increase the total area of open water to the benefit of other aquatic organisms, including waterfowl.

The best known installation is at La Rance in Brittany, France, but schemes have also been proposed for the Severn Estuary and other rivers in the West of England. The planned Severn barrage would stretch for 16 kilometres between Weston-super-Mare and the South Wales coast, and include more than 200 turbine generators as well as locks for shipping. With a capacity of 8,600MW, it would produce over 16 million megawatt hours of electricity per year, about 7 per cent of current total usage in Britain. However, its probable construction cost of over £8,000 million is thought prohibitive without major government support. A smaller barrage scheme across the river Mersey with a capacity of 700MW is being actively promoted by a private company. According to the Department of Energy, if all reasonably practical estuaries were exploited, tidal energy could provide at least 20 per cent of the electricity consumption in England and Wales. There are also small-scale experiments in Norway and the Hebrides, which generate electricity by channelling waves into rock gullies. (See also: *Alternative technology*Ⓔ, *Energy*Ⓔ, *Soft energy paths*Ⓔ.)

Tobacco

The adverse medical effects of smoking tobacco are well established. Less well known are the ecological effects of growing tobacco.

Worldwide, tobacco accounts for 1.5 per cent of total agricultural exports. For some countries it is the main export crop; Malawi, for example, earns 55 per cent of its foreign exchange from tobacco. More than 100 Third World countries export tobacco, which is inevitably grown on land that could otherwise be used to grow food.

Tobacco is a crop that is ruinous to the soil. When compared to cassava (a food crop that it often displaces in Africa) it takes 11 times more nitrogen, 36 times more phosphorus and 24 times more potassium from the ground.

But the heaviest environmental cost of tobacco production lies in the sheer volume of wood needed to fuel tobacco-curing barns. Every year, the trees from an estimated 12,000sq km (4,600sq miles) are cut down, with 55 cubic metres of cut wood being burned for every tonne of tobacco cured.

Some experts put the figure even higher – at 50,000sq km (19,000sq miles).

Tobacco production uses up 0.3 per cent of the world's available arable land – land that could be used to grow food crops.

Tradable emissions

Many environmental economists agree that the surest way to reduce the world's carbon emissions to a sustainable level is to apply some form of economic instrument, the most obvious being an international carbon tax (*qv*). However, with carbon or energy taxes, it is difficult to predict the size of the reductions that will be achieved. Considerable attention is therefore being given to a system of tradable emission permits, or licences. A global quota of carbon dioxide (CO_2) emissions would be set, and each country would be given its own allocation of emission permits, which would be tradable internationally at market price.

The proposal has three main advantages over a carbon tax. Firstly, if all nations complied, a target level of CO_2 emissions could be guaranteed. Secondly, the system would be much fairer because poor countries with a low CO_2 output, who would be disproportionately penalized by a carbon tax, could sell their surplus emission permits to rich countries that were unable to bring their output down to prescribed levels. Finally, economists anticipate that the global cost of reducing emissions would be lower because countries where CO_2 reduction would be a more expensive process would be prepared to offer a higher price for additional permits than countries that could cut emissions cheaply.

Before any such system could be introduced, there would have to be agreement on a number of questions. For example, opinions diverge as to whether the permits should apply to all greenhouse gases, or simply to CO_2. Another problem would be allocation of quotas, although the most commonly preferred option is distribution according to population. There are also many difficulties

associated with implementing such a scheme, in particular how to monitor emissions and how to stop fraud. But most of these problems are not unique to tradable emissions, and would apply to other forms of global regulation, such as carbon taxes (*qv*).

The greatest difficulty by far would be to persuade the majority of nations to join such a scheme. It is unlikely that the wealthy industrialized nations, particularly the USA, would be keen to enter an arrangement that involved the flow of an enormous and unspecified sum of money to the Third World. Even if the scheme were agreed in principle, the haggling over detail might continue indefinitely.

In sum, there are so many variables and problems associated with tradable emissions that they are unlikely to be applied at an international level. Their most enthusiastic proponents are those who see the market as a mechanism for overcoming pollution and redressing the enormous imbalances between the poor and rich nations. But others see them as a means of legitimizing overconsumption in the North, and of avoiding the question of whether the polluting industries are needed in the first place.

Tourism

The tourist industry is now, or soon will be, the biggest industry in the world, with receipts of over $2,000,000 million amounting to about 5 per cent of the total global economy. The industry is expected to be worth $3,000,000 million in 1996. Much of the recent growth has been in the developing world, where tourism offers wealthy visitors exotic experiences and gives poor host countries a unique opportunity to acquire foreign exchange. There were 6 million visitors to developing countries in 1962 and over 40 million in 1978; the number has continued to grow throughout the 1980s. It is hardly surprising that such sudden expansion has brought with it an enormous variety of environmental and social problems.

International tourism is inextricably linked with international air travel. Seventy-six per cent of all passenger aircraft journeys are undertaken for leisure purposes. The environmental effects of aircraft are still partly undiscovered. It is known, however, that air traffic contributes 2.3 per cent of total emissions of carbon dioxide, and hence about 1.3 per cent of the gases that cause global warming (qv). The effect of the release by aircraft of nitrogen oxide into the atmosphere at a height of 10,000 metres has yet to be analysed in any detail.

In many poor nations, tourism holds first or second place as a foreign exchange earner. Unfortunately only a percentage of the profits are kept by the host country, much of the money going to foreign companies who owned and controlled the industry. The jobs held by locals tended to be of low status and poorly paid, while the better positions are occupied by outsiders.

Even when tourism brings money into the community, it frequently disrupts the local economy and the way of life. The price of land rises steeply, agricultural production is undervalued, and there may be moments of acute labour shortage alternating with periods of unemployment. The influx of thousands of wealthy visitors tends to create a two-tier economy, which distorts social relations and undermines traditional values.

Pressure upon local inhabitants to become "commodities" is seen nowhere more clearly than in the sex-tourism industry that now flourishes in many countries in South East Asia and Africa. In Thailand, more than a million women are involved in the industry, some of them children under 14 years of age.

The effect of tourism upon the natural environment can be just as disastrous as it can be upon communities. When a small village is transformed within a few years into an artificial metropolis the pressures upon the surroundings are sudden and violent. Hillsides are razed for development, land is bulldozed for golf courses

and camping sites, beaches are concreted for marinas, and the seas become a sewage and trash depository. The sudden increase in population strains the natural resources, depleting timber supplies in a cold country such as Nepal, or water supplies in dry areas such as the Mediterranean. Ignorant and inquisitive visitors trample plants and frighten wild animals, while individual species are poached for sale as souvenirs.

Concern about these problems has led to the development of what is known as "ecotourism." In its simpler form, this means simply that tour operators undertake to conform to a code that respects the environment and local people. In its more ambitious form, ecotourism aims to bring in tourists in order to encourage awareness of fragile environments, and raise money for conservation.

Many of the problems raised by the tourist industry are a reflection of the disparities that exist between the First World and the Third. Governments in the Third World might do well to note the attitude taken by the King of Bhutan. In 1988, he drastically reduced the number of annual tourist entry visas to 2,400; as he explained to World Bank representatives at a Tourism conference in Bangkok, he was less interested in improving the country's gross national product than in maintaining its "gross national happiness."

Traditional agriculture

The systems of agriculture practised by tribal and peasant societies.

Though such systems are frequently portrayed as backward, inefficient and unproductive, the reality is quite different. Indeed, traditional agriculture cannot be judged by the same criteria as are used to judge modern intensive agriculture, since the goals of the two systems are by and large antithetical.

Traditional farmers do not aim to produce food for sale but to produce food for consumption by their own families and to fulfil such social obligations as distributing food to relations and giv-

ing feasts. This latter goal is very important since it plays a vital part in maintaining the social cohesion which alone makes possible the social co-operation required for fulfilling many essential traditional practices – such as maintaining irrigation canals, desilting storage ponds, weeding plots and maintaining terracing. A further feature of traditional agricultural practices is often the joint responsibility of women and men. When agricultural "experts" moved into rural areas, this feature was ignored, resulting in disruptions to the relative status of women's and men's agricultural work.

Unlike modern intensive agriculture, the goal of traditional agriculture is not to maximize yields but rather to maximize security by minimizing risks. To quote the anthropologist Dr. James Scott, "Typically, the peasant seeks to avoid the failure that will ruin him rather than attempting a big, but risky, killing. In decision-making parlance, his behaviour is risk-averse. He minimizes the subjected possibility of maximum loss."

To achieve this, traditional farmers exploit a whole range of strategies. In particular, they practise polyculture, as opposed to monoculture (qv), growing not only many different crops in the same plot, but also many different strains of the same crop. In Sri Lanka, for instance, farmers would grow up to 400 different varieties of rice, in India, more than 10,000. Each had different qualities: some were useful when the rain was poor, others were resistant to certain pests, others were cultivated because they were highly nutritive and therefore good for pregnant women, or simply for their taste and fragrance. This extraordinary diversity of cultivated crops confers great stability on traditional forms of agriculture.

Great care is also taken to maintain the fertility of the soil. This is achieved by returning to it all the organic matter possible, by cultivating leguminous crops which maintain the soil's necessary nitrogen content, by terrac-

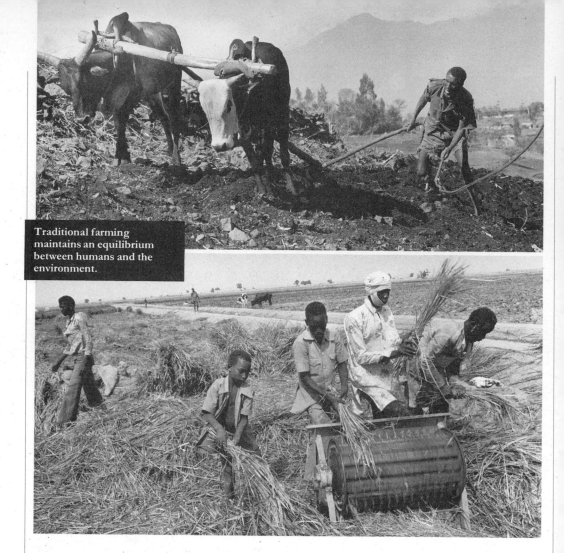

Traditional farming
maintains an equilibrium
between humans and the
environment.

ing mountain slopes, and by allowing land to remain fallow for often lengthy periods.

Though high yields are not a primary consideration, they are rarely as low as is made out by the development industry. Indeed, contrary to received wisdom, traditional agriculture is highly productive. According to Susan George, author of *How the Other Half Dies*, "Indigenous cropping systems use labour more efficiently, give more stable yields from year to year and are intrinsically higher yielding than monoculture." She considers that "the subsistence farmer has developed a highly sophisticated system . . . based on good economic sense."

The World Bank also acknowledges the efficiency of traditional farmers. In a report on New Guinea, it notes: "A characteristic of Papua New Guinea's subsistence agriculture is its relative richness. Over much of the country, nature's bounty produces enough to eat with relatively little expenditure of effort."

Yet, despite the productivity of traditional agricultural systems, the development industry is intent on replacing them by intensive farming regimes. One reason is that traditional farmers are unwilling to grow the export crops (*qv*) that provide Third World countries with the foreign exchange to import western goods. Another is that traditional agriculture does not provide a market for the capital-intensive goods and services – tractors, pesticides, dams and so on – that the development industry is geared to

marketing and selling.

Though a minority of agronomists now argues that the Third World would benefit from a return to traditional techniques, it seems unlikely that this will come about while the development industry remains committed to its present goals. (See also: *Development*③, *Green Revolution*④③, *Post harvest losses*④③, *Sustainable development*③, *Tropical agriculture*③.)

Transmigration

An Indonesian colonization programme, the largest in the world, which aims to resettle inhabitants from the densely populated central islands of Java, Lombok, Bali and Madura to the sparsely populated outer islands of the Indonesian archipelago, Sumatra, Borneo and West Papua. Some 3,600,000 people had already been moved by 1984 and, if the Government of Indonesia has its way, a further 65 million will be moved in the next 20 years. The programme is heavily funded by the World Bank (*qv*) and other Western multilateral development banks. By June 1985, nearly $800 million had been provided to the Indonesian government, with a further $750 million promised.

The programme has been heavily criticized by environmental and human rights organizations. The colonization programme is being implemented at the expense of the tropical rainforest, which covered 1,480,000sq km (571,000sq miles) of Indonesia in 1950. It is estimated that as much as one-third of the forest cover has been lost since then, and further transmigration will put an intolerable burden on what is left.

Settlement schemes in tropical rainforest areas are rarely capable of supporting sustained agricultural exploitation, due to the poor rainforest soils. According to one study, more than 5,000sq km (1,900sq miles) of lowland development projects in Indonesia were located in forests judged unsuitable for the type of exploitation planned under transmigration. The same study estimated that only about 750sq km (290sq miles) of Central Kalimantan were suitable for development. Indonesian Government targets, however, involve the clearance of nearly 17 times that amount of forest in the period from 1979 to 1989. The figure gives some measure of the extent to which the programme is ill-conceived and environmentally destructive.

One of the reasons for transmigration is the need to resettle peasants who have been deprived of their land to accommodate large development projects. It is clear also that transmigration fulfils many of the ambitions of Indonesian nationalism. The military component of the programme is quite evident, especially in sensitive areas such as West Papua and East Timor. The programme also has a part to play in the government's plans to "assimilate" the large tribal population on the outer islands into mainstream Javanese society.

In December 1986, in the face of falling oil prices and widespread opposition to transmigration, the government announced a 65 per cent cut in the programme's budget. The target for the numbers to be relocated in 1987 was reduced from a planned 100,000 people to just 1,000. In 1989, however, more than 30 environmental and human rights groups from 10 countries wrote to the World Bank expressing concern over the continuing environmental and social impact of transmigration, which they reported was continuing apace. The groups charged that "over the last year, reports from Indonesia have revealed that protection for indigenous peoples continues to be deficient and improvements in comprehensive environmental protection are not progressing at a satisfactory rate." In response to this criticism, the World Bank has restricted its funding to "Second Stage Development," that is, offering further financial help for established migrants who have encountered problems. The flow of new migrants has dropped, but there is still a steady stream. The Indonesian government predicts the arrival of another 555,000 families between 1989 and 1994 – compared to 750,000 between 1984 and 1989. (See also: *Deforestation*③, *Development*③, *Resettlement*, *Tribal peoples*③, *Tropical rainforest*.)

Tree diseases
Even before acid rain (*qv*) began to wreak havoc among forests in northern Europe and the east coast of North America, trees were already succumbing in ever greater numbers to various virulent diseases.

From New England to south-west Australia, various diseases have, since the beginning of the century, attacked chestnuts, elms, oaks, maples, coconut palms and eucalyptus.

The most obvious cause of such tree epidemics is the introduction of alien parasites against which native trees have no defence. Thus the fungus associated with chestnut blight was imported from China, while that associated with Dutch elm disease came from Asia via Europe. The elm bark beetle, without whose help the fungus could not have caused so much damage, also came from Europe.

Unfortunately, modern society favours such ecological invasions by encouraging a high level of mobility and international trade.

Diseases, however, cannot be regarded as being solely caused by a pathogen. The factors that reduce the host's resistance to them must also be considered.

One such factor is the planting of trees in conditions – soil, climatic and biotic – to which they have not been adapted by their evolution. Another is pollution. Damage by smoke, for instance, has been shown to increase susceptibility to pests such as bark beetles, weevils and fir lice. Smoke also tends to reduce resistance to frost. Pollution by cement dust has been found to reduce photosynthesis on lime and elm trees. Sulphur dioxide from blast furnaces, coke plants, fertilizers, soda, cellulose, sulphuric acid plants and thermal power stations, has, for a long time, been known to increase susceptibility to pests, as has fluorine from aluminium foundries, and fertilizer factories.

What makes matters still more complicated is that the various factors leading to ecological maladjustment, and hence to the reduced resistance of trees to disease, rarely occur independently. Very often trees are affected by various combinations of these factors which have, at best, an additive effect, at worst, a synergic effect (*qv*).

This makes tree diseases particularly difficult to treat. To spray affected forests with pesticides is merely to treat the symptoms, and in a very crude way. The only real solution is to correct whatever maladjustments are involved. Ideally, evolution would do the work, but that takes time. To speed up the process of adaptation, we can plant soil-improving trees such as the rowan or the silver birch. However, their timber is of little value, so this is not generally regarded as being economically viable.

Planting different species from the appropriate strains to replace a single monoculture (qv) must also reduce vulnerability, but unfortunately it may also reduce immediate financial returns, which may not be regarded as acceptable. When it comes to dealing with a maladjustment caused by a destructive imported parasite, more adventurous remedies such as biological control (qv) are clearly required, even though this may well mean taking certain risks.

When pollution is an important factor, then there can be no satisfactory solution but to reduce emissions of the offending pollutants. Because of present priorities, however, this is difficult. It is also difficult to cut down on the mobility and the trade in wood products that leads to the importation of alien parasites.

Tribal peoples
According to the human rights group, Survival International, there are some 200 million people worldwide who can be described as "tribal." Such people live in small cohesive communities that are economically self-sufficient and are themselves usually part of larger, culturally distinct groups, which may or may not be capable of acting as political units.

Tribal peoples, among whom are numbered hunters and gatherers, shifting cultivators, herders, subsistence farmers and fisherfolk, can also be defined by the absence of some of the characteristics common to state-based societies. They may not use money. They may have no systems of writing. Leadership patterns and decision-making processes are complex and power is diffuse. They may have deeprooted traditions to ensure material equality, though not necessarily social equality, and they have strong ties to their traditional lands. Unfortunately, such lands often lie in territory that can be profitably logged, mined,

farmed, ranched, dammed or otherwise "developed." Consequently, tribal lands are increasingly being expropriated for development projects, with numerous tribal groups being forcibly dispossessed in the "national interest." This is often rationalized on the grounds that tribal people are poor, malnourished and disease-ridden, and that it is the duty of governments and international agencies to assure that for their own benefit they are integrated into mainstream society.

In Indonesian-occupied West Papua, for example, the Indonesian Government has embarked on a project entitled "Total Development of Indonesian People" and aimed at re-educating West Papuans, whom it described as "still living in a stone-age-like era." To bring these peoples "up to par with the rest of the country", it was decided that the children would be "separated from their parents to keep them from settling into their parents' lifestyles."

Tribal people are also accused of environmentally destructive behaviour. Because they are so "poor," we are told, they cannot afford to take long-term considerations such as resource conservation into account. In particular, the slash and burn agriculture (qv) that many forest peoples practise is portrayed as destructive, as are many other time-honoured agricultural practices.

The reality is very different. Tribal peoples are poor only if poverty is identified with material deprivation. Certainly, many have few material goods, but then these are of little value to people who often lead a nomadic way of life. In fact, they do very well without them and there is no evidence that they feel in any way materially deprived.

On the other hand, their biological, social, spiritual and aesthetic needs – which could be regarded as much more important than their material needs – are well satisfied. The diet of tribal peoples, consisting of a rich variety of fresh and uncontaminated foods, is generally excellent; their

health status also seems very good; and their extended families and cohesive communities admirably satisfy their basic social needs. As for their agricultural practices, time has proved these to be not only environmentally benign, but also sustainable.

If tribal peoples are to be protected against cultural imperialism, the key to survival lies in the recognition of their rights; their rights to the inalienable collective ownership of their traditional territories; their right to self-determination; and their right to an acceptance of the legitimacy of their own institutions and systems of decision making. (See also: *Environmental refugees*③, *Resettlement schemes*③, *Subsistence agriculture*Ⓐ③.)

Tropical agriculture
A consequence of Third World development has been the introduction of agricultural techniques developed in temperate areas into the tropics – where, for many reasons, they are totally inappropriate. In particular, they have proved unsuited to the local climate and soils.

The heat in the tropics is both intense and continuous. Winter, which elsewhere restrains the growth of weeds, insects, fungi, etc., is absent. The result is an ideal and permanent habitat for potential pests, which often prove almost impossible to control.

Livestock, too, is afflicted by a wide variety of internal parasites that seriously reduce yields, typically to as little as a quarter of the yield in temperate areas.

The intense heat also kills off soil microorganisms. The consequent low organic content of the soil reduces its water-retaining capacity and makes it particularly vulnerable to erosion, since all the rain falls during the annual monsoons, while during the rest of the year the soil can be dust-dry.

This means that agriculture in the tropics has to be carried out sensitively, and on a small scale, by people whose goal is to provide food for themselves and their families rather than for export. It cannot be carried out on a massive scale for very long.

Not surprisingly, attempts to intensify agricultural practices in the tropics have led to widespread environmental degradation and declining yields. Nonetheless, intensive cropping techniques are still being systematically encouraged by the World Bank (*qv*), bilateral aid agencies, and the specialized agencies of the United Nations. Unless they are abandoned and replaced by others that better satisfy the particular exigencies of tropical soils and climate, environmental degradation and famine can only increase. (See also: *Cash crops*Ⓐ③, *Development*③, *Green Revolution* Ⓐ③.)

Tropical forests
Running like a girdle around the equator, tropical forests encompass some 9,500,000sq km (3,670,000sq miles), the greatest forested area by far being in South America, particularly in the Brazilian part of the Amazon, but stretching into Peru, Ecuador, Colombia, Venezuela and French Guyana. The remaining tropical forests, some five million sq km (two million sq miles), are found in 16 countries of tropical Asia and in Central Africa. The tropical forests of the Ivory Coast and of Nigeria are now virtually gone, cut down over the past 40 years.

In 1981, the United Nations Food and Agricultural Organization (FAO) estimated that 100,000sq km (62,000sq miles) of tropical forest were being lost every year, although the US Academy of Sciences put the figure for primary tropical forest alone at double that area. The FAO's 1991 figures show an annual loss of 168,000sq km (105,000sq miles). At this rate, nearly all tropical forests will have been removed from the planet by the middle of next century. The overall global rate has increased, despite a significant decline in Brazil's deforestation level after 1987 resulting from unusually wet weather and the suspension of ranching subsidies.

The destruction of the tropical forests has been variously described as "the greatest natural calamity since the Ice Age," "the greatest biological disaster ever perpetrated by man", and "a threat to civilization second only to thermonuclear war." If the destruction continues, the consequences for the future are likely to be devastating.

Tropical forests generally grow on extremely poor soils, and most of the essential nutrients are locked away within the plants themselves. Once the trees are cut down, the fragile soils soon erode away, silting up rivers and disrupting the downstream ecology. Rainwater is no longer retained in the soil, causing rivers to flood in the rainy season and streams to dry up during the dry season. Deforestation also leads to the cultural death of tribal peoples who depend upon the forests and threatens to condemn 50-90 per cent of the world's species of plants and animals to extinction. The burning of forests is also an important factor in global warming because of the large volumes of carbon dioxide that are released into the atmosphere. (See also: *Amazonia*③ⓒ, *Dams*③, *Deforestation*, *Drought-flood cycle*③, *Genetic diversity* ⓒ, *Greenhouse Effect*Ⓟ, *World Bank*③, *Reforestation*③, *Tropical timber trade*③.)

Tropical Forest Action Plan
The Tropical Forest Action Plan (TFAP), launched in 1987 by the World Bank, the UN Food and Agriculture Organization, the UN Development Programme (UNDP) and the World Resources Institute, puts forward a five-year programme – to cost $8,000 million – aimed at "addressing deforestation issues on a broad front." Under the plan, $1,600 million will be invested each year in forestry and related agricultural projects. Sixty-one developing countries are participating in the plan, which has financial support from the World Bank, UNDP and the US Agency for International Development. In that the TFAP was drawn up by the major international development agencies and has the support of national governments, its programme may be said to constitute the "official" response to the deforestation crisis in the world.

The TFAP has five principal components: to increase the supply of firewood; to promote agroforestry; to reforest upland watersheds; to conserve tropical forest ecosystems; and to strengthen the Third World's institutional framework for forestry research, training and extension work.

However, despite these laudable aims, the plan itself is deeply flawed. Indeed, in the view of many environmental groups, particularly in the Third World, the policies it proposes will in fact exacerbate the problems of deforestation, in addition to having grave negative consequences for those who depend on the forests for their livelihood. The main criticisms of the TFAP are:

● First, that its diagnosis of the causes of tropical deforestation trivializes the pre-eminent role played by dams, plantations and other development practices in the destruction of forests, and instead blames the victims of the development process – landless peasants and firewood collectors, for example – for causing deforestation. Inevitably, no measures are put forward to curtail, let alone halt, such projects, despite their having been responsible for most of the deforestation that has occurred over the last 40 years. Having failed to address the primary causes, the TFAP thus effectively ensures that the destruction can only continue unchecked.

● Secondly, the plan pays only lip-service to the rights of these forest dwellers and indigenous peoples who have lived in tropical forests since time immemorial.

● Thirdly, the plan is a classic example of "top-down" development planning. It was drawn up without consulting grassroots groups, and although certain non-governmental organizations were drawn for discussions in a later stage, the choice of groups was highly selective. Grassroots groups which expressed strong opposition to conventional development policies were gradually excluded as "extremist" or "emotional." By contrast, those without links to the grassroots have been paraded as representatives of the people of the Third World, and their endorsement of the TFAP is often taken to prove that "consultation" has taken place.

• Fourthly, despite the avowed commitment to ecological restoration, a 1988 report by UNDP itself reveals that of the 42 countries which have drawn up national TFAP plans, none intended to engage in ecosystem restoration. Most of the countries' plans have been criticized for giving inadequate consideration to the multipurpose use of natural forests. The UNDP report states that wildlife conservation and utilization, forest grazing, the propagation of medicinal and other plants, small-scale food production, and non-consumptive use of the forest have received little attention by national governments. The use of natural forests by indigenous forest peoples is hardly addressed at all in most national plans.

• Fifthly, the plan is less concerned with the preservation of forests than with the setting up of commercial plantations of fast-growing species, such as eucalyptus, which not only have a serious adverse effect on the environment, but which also do little to benefit the poor. Control over the forests would be taken away from local forest-based communities and instead vested in external agencies, whose prime concern is the rate of return on their investment. Indeed, if implemented, the TFAP would quickly result in the large-scale transformation of natural forests – as well as prime agricultural land – into industrialized plantations producing "commercial" timber for sale.

The Forestry Action Plan for Latin America and the Caribbean, for example, aims to invest between $2,000 million and $2,800 million a year for the next decade in the industrial development of the region's forests. The plan spells almost certain destruction and degradation for the forests of Amazonia, where the bulk of the forests lie. Financing will come largely from the multilateral banks, with the World Bank playing a central role, and from the private sector. Significantly, Japan's Official Development Assistance Programme and Japanese companies are already accelerating their investments in Brazil.

In 1990, National Forest Action Plans (NFAP) were published for nine separate countries. In Cameroon, Peru, Guyana, Papua New Guinea, and the Philippines, the plans actually advocate further logging of primary forests. The Cameroon NFAP proposes a new 600km (375-mile) road, linking the virgin forests of the south, home to an estimated 50,000 pygmies, to the Atlantic seaboard so that logs can be delivered to the international market.

The TFAP justifies support for commercial logging by claiming that the overriding cause of deforestation is the uncontrolled spread of landless settlers. Yet most of the NFAPS make no attempt to deal with the root causes of this colonization, such as the displacement of peasants by large-scale agricultural export projects, and the international debts that prompt such projects. The vital questions of land tenure and land reform are ignored.

These are, of course, politically sensitive issues. Financing for the TFAP will come from national governments, the World Bank, and the private sector. Many of its consultants are large forestry firms. In South East Asia, Jaoko Powry, a leading Finnish pulp and paper company, was consultant for the NFAPS of Sri Lanka, Nepal and probably Thailand; the consultants for the plans for the Philippines, Pakistan, Laos, Bhutan, Bangladesh and China have been primed by the Asian Development Bank. Such institutions are more accustomed to dealing with short-term economic returns than with long-term social and environmental problems.

Worldwide criticism of the TFAP has caused concern, even among its sponsors. A meeting in March 1990 agreed to establish an independent "consultative group," composed of governments from North and South, international agencies, NGOs, and local people's organizations. Its brief would be to ensure that TFAP became more accountable and self-critical. For a time it seemed that there was a possibility of genuine reform. But a subsequent meeting in September 1991 disintegrated into an unseemly squabble between the various interests. The imposition of environmental standards and the empowerment of local communities were seen by some Third World governments as a threat to national sovereignty.

The TFAP now seems to be a sinking ship. The USA has already withdrawn some of its promised funding. It appears that the impetus to save the forests can now only spring from those who live in them and depend on them, and that their voice will never be heard in a multilateral initiative like the TFAP while it is dominated by powerful contending international vested interests. (See also: *Deforestation*③, *Eucalyptus*©, *Reforestation*©③, *Social forestry*③, *Tropical timber trade*③, *World Bank*③.)

Tropical timber trade

For many tropical countries, the export of tropical timber represents a major source of income. However, the impact of commercial logging on tropical forest environments and their peoples has been devastating.

Worldwide the tropical timber industry is responsible for degrading some 5 million hectares (12 million acres) of primary rainforest annually. Much of the wood is used to make cheap, throwaway goods. Eight out of every 10 logs imported into Japan, for example, are made into cheap plywood, much of which is used by the building industry to make frames and scaffolding which are burned when the building is finished. Tropical hardwood chips are also used to make throwaway chopsticks and paper.

The tropical timber industry is particularly sensitive to accusations of causing deforestation, arguing that it is only responsible for some 10 per cent of forest destruction worldwide. However, that global average obscures the pre-eminence of logging as *the* major cause of primary rainforest destruction in both South-East Asia and Africa. Moreover, the industry's figure does not take account of the widespread forest loss caused *indirectly* by logging, primarily through opening up previously inaccessible areas to landless peasants. If that subsequent forest loss is taken into account, the timber industry is probably responsible for 40 per cent of forest destruction. The true figure could be even higher, according to the international Union for the Conservation of Nature: for example, more than 75 per cent of the forest land that is cleared annually by peasant farmers in Africa had previously been logged over.

The damage caused by logging is extensive. Current logging practices in Sarawak, Malaysia, leave 33 trees damaged for every 26 trees removed as timber: in some areas, up to 70 per cent of the remaining trees die from their injuries. Although several governments require loggers to replant the areas they deforest, such replanting is rarely carried out. Much of the forest which has been logged is never replanted, reforestation rates lagging behind cut-

ting by a ratio of 1 to 4 in Asia and 1 to 29 in Africa. A World Bank study has estimated that of the 33 countries which currently export tropical timber, all but 10 will be logged out by the year 2000.

The loss of biodiversity in logged areas has been severe. According to Patrick Anderson of the Rainforest Information Centre, Australia, "It will never be known how many species have become extinct to provide luxury rainforest timber for the consumer countries, but a study in Kalimantan comparing primary rainforest and 30-year-old secondary rainforest showed a 20 per cent decline in tree species." Even in areas where "selective" logging is practised, the impact on wildlife can be devastating: one study in Uganda reveals that 70 per cent of the primate species living in an area subjected to "low intensity" logging were seriously affected, their numbers being significantly reduced. Inevitably, the loss of wildlife means the loss of an important source of protein for local forest peoples.

The extensive network of roads

and skid trails needed to get the logged timber out of the forest and onto the international market are a major source of erosion, as are the denuded slopes of the forest itself. Such erosion adds appreciably to the silt and sedimentation load of rivers, reducing the populations of fish and other aquatic organisms. According to official statistics, 59 per cent of Sarawak's rivers are now "polluted" due to soil erosion and siltation, leading to a dramatic reduction in fish catches. Fish provide a major part of the native people's diet.

The recent floods in Bangladesh (at one point, two-thirds of the country was under water), in the Sudan and in Thailand are directly attributable to deforestation of upland watersheds. In 1989, under pressure from environmentalists and local villagers, the Thai Government banned all commercial logging as a direct outcome of the deforestation-related mudslides that killed hundreds and left whole villages buried beneath tonnes of logs, uprooted trees and earth. The ban

Mahogany from the Amazon is loaded on trucks; about 10% of the timber is exported.

has only shifted the problem elsewhere, however: logging companies are now seeking new sources of timber in Myanmar and Indo-China. The Philippines have also instituted a ban on the export of logs.

Logging operations have had a devastating impact on those indigenous peoples who have traditionally lived in the world's tropical forests. Such peoples rely entirely on the forest for their livelihood: they derive their food from it; the building materials for their houses; the wood for their agricultural implements; the herbs for their traditional medicines; the fibres and dyes for their clothes; and the materials for their traditional artefacts. The loss or degradation of the forests can thus spell cultural death. In Sarawak, for example, timber operations have destroyed ancestral graves, flattened traditional forest gardens and fruit trees, reduced the availability of wildlife and forest products and polluted rivers. Yet, in many cases, no compensation has been paid for the damage caused by logging. Applications by indigenous groups to have their lands declared communal forest reserves have been ignored or turned down.

In 1987, the continuing destruction caused by logging caused some local Penan groups in Sarawak to blockade logging roads. Such action was the only course left open to them, official channels having proved unhelpful, biased and obstructive. The government reacted to the blockades by arresting many of those involved and charging them with trespass and obstruction. In April 1989, the charges were dismissed "due to lack of evidence." It is widely thought that the government dropped the case because its prosecution would have allowed the Penan to bring into question the legality of the process by which logging concessions are awarded on land which is rightfully theirs. Meanwhile, the granting of logging concessions continues and further arrests of protestors have been made.

In response to the devastation caused by logging – and the accompanying abuse of human rights – many Western environmental groups have called for a boycott of tropical timber unless it comes from a "sustainable" source. Although opposed to such boycotts, the International Tropical Timber Organization (ITTO) (*qv*) is now committed to promoting "sustainable rainforest logging." In Britain, the Timber Trade Federation has called for a levy to be raised on all imports of tropical timber, the moneys raised being ploughed back into "better forest management."

But is the commercial logging of tropical forests possible on a sustainable basis? Certainly, current logging practices could be made more efficient and less destructive, but to date, there is scarcely a single example of sustainable industrial timber extraction in the rainforests. Indeed, a recent study carried out for the ITTO itself concluded that sustainable tropical timber operations cover less than one-eighth of one per cent of rainforest lands – and even that minute figure has been criticized as being inflated.

Moreover, current definitions of "sustainability" are unacceptably narrow. For most commercial companies, the term is equated with sustaining the *yield* of timber – and takes no account of other factors. The ITTO definition is broader – taking on board ecological and biological considerations – but still takes no account of ensuring the sustainability of non-timber forest products, and thus the local communities which rely on them, or of other activities (fisheries, for example) which take place outside the forest but which are nonetheless affected by the logging industry.

Indeed, under present political and economic circumstances, sustainable commercial timber extraction in the rainforests is impracticable. Corruption, commercial pressures, the high rate of return expected on capital and the ravages of heavy machinery make it a pipedream. It is for that reason that several environmental organizations – notably those from rainforest countries – have called for a moratorium on all commercial timber extraction in primary rainforests.

Such groups point out that forests have greatest value when exploited as "extractive reserves" for their non-timber resources, recent research in Peruvian Amazonia showing the net economic value of such products per hectare of forest to be twice that from logging. Research from South-East Asia draws similar conclusions. Using the forests as extractive reserves would not only maintain the integrity of the forest but would also leave their management in the hands of those forest peoples who currently suffer most from the impact of deforestation, and who have centuries of experience of sustainable forest management. (See also: *Deforestation*③, *Tropical forests*③, *Drought-flood cycle*③.)

2,4,5-T

A phenoxy herbicide (*qv*) which first gained notoriety as one of the ingredients in a defoliant – codenamed Agent Orange (*qv*) – used widely in the Vietnam War. During its manufacture, 2,4,5-T becomes contaminated by small amounts of dioxins (*qv*) which are highly toxic and known to cause birth defects and cancers in laboratory animals.

In many areas other than Vietnam 2,4,5-T has been blamed for birth defects, cancers and a variety of other illnesses. Proving that 2,4,5-T – or its dioxin contaminants – caused the damage has been difficult and many experts disagree over the evidence. Some countries have taken action, however. Sweden has banned 2,4,5-T and, as an environmental protection measure, the USA has greatly restricted its use. Commenting on the evidence against 2,4,5-T, the US Environmental Protection Agency (EPA) stated, "The quality, quantity and variety of data demonstrating that the continued use of 2,4,5-T contaminated with dioxin presents risks to human health is unprecedented and overwhelming." 2,4,5-T is also banned in India, Norway and the USSR.

In Britain, 2,4,5-T is still in widespread use since the official government view is that it is not harmful so long as it is used according to the instructions and provided that the dioxin content remains below 0.01 parts per million – twice the limit recommended by the EC. Union officials argue that "the instructions" take little account of the realities of spraying under field conditions. One hundred local authorities and several major trades unions have banned its use.

2,4,5-T, however, is still sprayed in large quantities in the Third World with no restrictions.

The manufacture of 2,4,5-T has now ceased in every country of the world. Until 1987 it was still manufactured in New Zealand, but the plant suffered a serious accident and was closed. The manufacturer has now produced a new pesticide, with similar characteristics, but little is known about its health effects.

2,4-D

A phenoxy herbicide (*qv*) used as a general weedkiller. It was originally thought to be fairly harmless to humans. However, in 1969, a US commission concluded that 2,4-D was likely to cause birth defects and recommended that it "should immediately be restricted to prevent the risk of human exposure." That recommendation was contested by the US manufacturers, Dow Chemicals, and today 2,4-D remains one of the most widely used herbicides in the industrial world. Recent research suggests that 2,4-D may also be a carcinogen (*qv*). (See also: *Agent Orange*Ⓛ Ⓟ, *Biocides*Ⓛ Ⓟ, *Cancer*Ⓛ Ⓟ, *Dioxin*Ⓟ, *Pesticides*Ⓛ Ⓟ, *Phenoxy herbicides*Ⓟ, *Teratogens*Ⓛ.)

Underground nuclear tests

Since the signing of the Partial Test Ban Treaty (PTBT) (*qv*) in 1963, the atomic tests of the USSR, the UK and the USA have been conducted underground. Bowing to international diplomatic and legal pressure, France, a non-signatory of the PTBT, followed suit in 1975. China, also a non-signatory, has conducted only underground tests since 1980. The sole Indian test was conducted underground in 1974.

Underground tests are intended to limit the amounts of radioactivity released into the environment – unlike the previous, much more damaging, atmospheric tests. However, numerous leaks of radioactivity from underground tests have been documented at the US Nevada and French Mururoa (*qv*) test sites. In 1970, for example, a test code-named "Banebury" resulted in a cloud of radioactive dust being vented into the atmosphere. (See also: *Atomic tests*Ⓝ Ⓛ.)

Uranium

The heaviest naturally occurring element. Most uranium (99.3 per cent) consists of the 238 isotope. The rare (0.7 per cent) 235 isotope is more unstable and liable to fission (*qv*), either spontaneously or under neutron bombardment. All nuclear reactors generate heat by uranium fission.

The 238 isotope is fertile, that is, it can absorb a neutron and transmute to plutonium-239 (*qv*), which is fissile. It is possible to run a nuclear reactor using as fuel uranium containing the natural proportions of the two isotopes – the Magnox (*qv*) is an example – but most modern reactors use fuel in which the proportion of U-235 has been increased to two or three per cent by means of uranium enrichment (*qv*).

Uranium enrichment

Techniques that increase the proportion of fissile uranium-235 in the natural metal. The natural proportion of fissile uranium-235 to non-fissile uranium-238 in the natural metal is 0.7: 99.3. Highly enriched uranium contains 90 per cent or more U-235, and is required for uranium fission bombs, and as fuel for the small pressurized water reactors (PWRs) that power nuclear submarines. Uranium enriched to 2.5-3 per cent U-235 is used as fuel in many power reactors including advanced gas-cooled reactors (*qv*) and commercial PWRs (*qv*). British supplies of highly enriched uranium are obtained from the USA in exchange for plutonium from the UK military stockpile, under the 1958 US/UK Mutual Defence Agreement (*qv*).

A British low-separation plant began operation at Capenhurst in 1953, initially to enrich the depleted uranium obtained from reprocessing (*qv*) to levels suitable for re-use in Magnox reactors (*qv*). Enrichment is difficult to achieve on a commercial scale, as different isotopes of the same element are chemically identical; separation depends on the tiny difference in the atomic weights between them.

A gaseous diffusion technique was developed by the wartime Manhattan Project, and is still used in the USA, but this method consumes huge amounts of electricity. A consortium of British, West German and Dutch interests formed Urenco in 1970 to develop enrichment using a centrifuge technique; production began at Capenhurst in the mid-1970s, and Urenco now competes successfully on world markets.

A new enrichment technique is under development in the USA and Europe, based on laser isotope separation. This promises to be a much more efficient method, providing low-cost fissile material at any required purity. It may provide a means of extracting plutonium and uranium from irradiated reactor fuel without conventional reprocessing, and to any required degree of purity. (See also: *Uranium*Ⓝ.)

Uranium mining

There is no doubt that uranium miners receive far higher exposures to radiation than any other nuclear workers.

Uranium ore contains 0.1-0.2 per cent uranium metal. The tailings, 99.8 per cent of the mass and 85 per cent of the radioactivity, are left at the mine location. Tailings continue to emit radon for many hundreds of thousands of years. Nonetheless, in the USA, thousands of houses have been built on or near tailing sites. Since the early 1970s the practice has been to cover the tailing heaps with either clay or water, a procedure of limited effectiveness. In Colorado, a centre of uranium mining, over 40 per cent of houses have radon levels above safe limits.

Better mine ventilation and improved health care facilities are beginning to cut the high cancer rate among uranium miners. Other factors are the sharp reduction in demand for uranium, which has brought employment in mines down by 30 per cent of 1978 levels.

Lung cancer is the most prevalent occupational disease, with an incidence among American and Canadian miners of 4.8 times that found in the general population, with those who smoke suffering the highest rates. A US Nuclear Regulatory Commission (NRC) report showed that uranium mining in the USA produces 4,000 extra lung cancers every year; this translates to between 15,000 and 30,000 lung cancer deaths caused in the process of supplying uranium for a large modern nuclear station, such as a pressurized water reactor (qv), in Britain, over its 35-year life.

Several early US mines were located in Navajo reservations, and the incidence of lung cancer among Navajo miners (who do not smoke) has been found to be 14 times greater than normal. Navajo miners have also suffered from a higher-than-normal level of birth malformations and adverse pregnancies because of the presence of the tailing heaps close to residential areas. Other statistics, from the 1930s, indicate that about half of those employed as uranium miners eventually died of lung cancer.

Canada is now the West's largest producer of uranium, followed by the USA. The other producers are South Africa, Namibia, France and Australia. Uranium has also been mined in large quantities in the Soviet Union, China and Eastern Europe. Following the series of democratic "revolutions" throughout Eastern Europe during 1989 and 1990, there were moves to close down some of the uranium mines in East Germany, Czechoslovakia and Hungary because of the risk they pose to health. (See also: *Radiation and health*Ⓝ Ⓛ, *Uranium*Ⓝ.)

Urbanization

One of the most critical developments of the last decades, as critical as the population explosion, is the vast shift of population from the countryside to the cities. The urban population of the Third World was about 100 million in 1920; it is 1,000 million today. Between 1985 and the year 2000, Third World cities are likely to grow by another 750 million people. Almost half the world's population will then live in cities.

The most obvious implication of this change is that there must be a massive increase in the physical infrastructure in the world's cities to accommodate all these new city dwellers. No country can conceivably afford this. The richest countries of the world cannot even afford to maintain their existing urban infrastructure, which in both the USA and the UK is disintegrating fast. In the UK more than £27,000 million ($43,000 million) is required to rebuild the disintegrating sewage system, and more than £5,000 million ($8,000 million) to renew the gas mains, while billions of pounds are needed to modernize the country's crumbling stock of local government houses.

In the Third World the situation is very much worse. Half the population of Delhi already lives in slums and the Delhi Planning Authority admits that by the end of the century the figure will be closer to 85 per cent. In the main Third World cities, slums attain a degree of squalor that people in the West cannot imagine.

The second implication is that food production has to be reorganized. In particular, small farms that are not geared to achieving surpluses must be replaced by big capital-intensive farms, just to produce the amount of food required for city dwellers. A massive transport and distribution system is clearly also required. Facilities for providing clean water must also be expanded – this is a massive problem that few cities have overcome. There is also an almost insoluble problem of waste disposal, particularly in Third World countries.

A further implication is health.

If we take into account pollution, the tremendous density of population, the lack of facilities, the contamination of drinking water and so on, conditions in the massive Third World slums could not be less propitious.

Officially, migration occurs because of poverty and overpopulation in the countryside, and the search for jobs and the amenities of city life. But the main reason for the growth of the slums (other than natural urban population growth) is the displacement of peasants from their lands as a natural consequence of the modernization of agriculture and the setting up of large-scale development schemes. For instance, if India goes ahead with its ambitious dam-building plans, the programme will inevitably lead to the displacement of tens of millions of rural people from their land. The Narmada Valley Project alone will lead to the displacement of a million people. (See also: *Green Revolution*Ⓐ Ⓧ, *Resettlement programmes*, *World Bank*Ⓧ.)

WX YZ

Wakersdorf
Waste reduction
Water quality
Water transfer
    projects
Waterborne disease
Wave power
Wetlands
Whales
Wind power
Windscale
Windscale fire
Wood preservatives
World Bank
World Commission on
    Environment and
    Development

X-ray

Zero population
    growth

Wakersdorf

Site, in Bavaria, Germany, of a controversial reprocessing (qv) plant for used nuclear fuel. Under German law, arrangements have to be made for irradiated fuel management and disposal before a reactor is permitted to begin operation. Plans were therefore drawn up in 1969 for a huge federal reprocessing plant and vitrification and disposal facility, to handle fuel from all the country's reactors. However, in 1974 the consortium formed to build the plant decided abruptly to withdraw on commercial grounds.

The federal government decided to press ahead, and chose a site in Lower Saxony called Gorleben for the reprocessing complex. Though very near the East German border, the site was chosen because it is a salt mine and thus an extremely stable geological feature, considered suitable for the disposal of vitrified waste. After vociferous local opposition, hearings into the proposal were arranged, which opened at almost the same instant as the feedwater pumps failed at Three Mile Island (qv) on March 28 1979. Two months later the state premier announced that Gorleben would not go ahead.

The idea of a vast central facility was abandoned, and Wakersdorf was chosen as the site for a relatively modest (350 tonnes a year) reprocessing plant. Construction began in May 1986 but was shadowed by large and violent demonstrations during which there were repeated confrontations between riot police and antinuclear protesters. In 1989, construction was abandoned and a deal signed to consign spent fuel from German reactors to the French and British reprocessing plants. The Wakersdorf plant has since been converted into a factory for, among other things, the production of solar cells. (See also: *Cap de la Hague*®, *Fast reactor*®, *Sellafield*®.)

Waste reduction

The best solution to the problem of hazardous wastes (qv) lies in reducing (or, better still, eliminating) their production. Radical as that proposal might sound, it can often be achieved relatively simply through a variety of strategies, including minor changes in manufacturing processes, or by substituting polluting products for nonpolluting products.

By 1986, INFORM, a New Yorkbased research organization, had identified 44 waste reduction practices. Of these, "11 achieved reductions of individual waste streams that ranged from 80 per cent to 100 per cent."

Already several companies have cut considerably the amount of waste they generate. The most celebrated example involves the Minnesota Mining and Manufacturing Corporation (3M) which began its "Pollution Prevention Pays" programme in 1975. By 1984, the company had eliminated 10,000 tonnes of water pollutants, 90,000 tonnes of air pollutants and 140,000 tonnes of sludge. The rewards were not only ecological but also financial: according to 3M, the programme saved $192 million in less than ten years.

The scope for waste reduction is enormous but it has still to be widely practised. A survey by INFORM of 29 major US companies found that only 12 had waste production programmes – and that these were being applied only to a minute fraction of the wastes generated. Significantly, nine out of the 12 companies had adopted waste reduction as a last resort, generally "only after regulatory and/or operational pressures forced management to focus on waste reduction opportunities." Once in practice, however, the waste reduction measures saved money at five out of those nine plants. (See also: *Hazardous waste*®, *Recycling*®.)

Water quality

See *Drinking water*.

Water transfer projects

Already many regions of the world – including China, India, Canada and the USA – are having difficulties meeting even their present-day requirements for water. Forecasts predict severe shortages (with attendant economic loss) by the year 2000. The conventional answer to regional water shortages has been to build storage reservoirs. But there are only a limited number of sites where reservoirs can be built – and many of these have already been exploited or are under development. Several countries are now looking to large-scale water transfer projects to provide their future water requirements, the idea being to transport water from water-rich areas to drought-prone regions.

Some of the proposed projects are mind-boggling in their sheer scale and complexity. One scheme, the North American Water and Power Alliance (NAWAPA), would involve transferring water from northwest Canada, Alaska and the northwestern United States to Mexico, south-central Canada, the Great Lakes area and the southwestern United States. In China, another such project (already under construction) will transfer 14,000 million cubic metres of water over 1,150km (715 miles) from Chang Jiang in the south-east of China to the North China Plain.

In April 1986, the Soviet Union cancelled a proposed water diversion scheme that would have reversed the flow of Russia's northern rivers to channel water to the arid lands of Central Asia. President Gorbachev's personal economic adviser, Professor Abel Aganbegyan, criticized the plan as unnecessary and ill-conceived. "The idea of redistribution was based on the strategy of endlessly bringing new land under the plough, and on forecasts of the progressive fall in the water levels of our rivers, leading to a catastrophic fall in the level of the Caspian Sea. These forecasts have proved incorrect." (See also: *Drinking water*℗, *Dams*③.)

Waterborne disease
Diseases transmitted by bacteria, insects and other organisms that live or breed in water. Examples include cholera, schistosomiasis (*qv*), malaria (*qv*), river blindness, diarrhoea, leprosy, yellow fever, trachoma, scabies, polio and elephantiasis, a monstrous swelling of the limbs.

Such diseases kill an estimated 25,000 people a day – millions every year. More than 160 million people suffer from malaria; 200 million from schistosomiasis; and 250 million people – the equivalent of the entire population of the USSR – from elephantiasis. In 1980, according to the Washington-based World Resources Institute, five million children under the age of five died from diarrhoea – "about ten every minute of the day."

In urban areas, lack of pollution controls, particularly from sewage outlets and industrial plants, are a major cause of gastro-intestinal disease in Third World countries, particularly in slum areas. In rural areas, dams and other water projects, notably irrigation (*qv*) programmes, have played a major role in spreading schistosomiasis, malaria and other diseases.

In 1978, the United Nations launched its International Drinking Water Supply and Sanitation Decade 1980-90, the aim being to supply piped water and latrines to more than 1,000 million people at a cost of $140,000 million. Lack of funding (the UN raised less than a quarter of its target figure) and inadequate maintenance have dogged the programme. In many rural areas, pumps corroded or simply broke down, never to be repaired.

Nonetheless, by 1985, the UN claimed to have supplied 345 million people in the Third World, most in rural areas, with a clean supply of water. Some 140 million had received new waste disposal facilities. In 1987, a full seven years after the Water Decade was initiated, 1,200 million people were still without reasonable access to safe water, with 1,900 million lacking basic sanitation.

Though laudable in its aims, the drinking water decade has itself created many problems. By providing piped water to rural and urban areas, it has increased dramatically the consumption of water, thus depleting water supplies. As a result, according to N.D. Jayal, former adviser to the Planning Commission of India, fewer people in South-East Asia now have access to clean and

adequate water than they did in the 1970s – this despite heavy expenditure on drinking water programmes. In Maharastra, India, groundwater depletion has increased the number of villages lacking a source of water from 112 in the mid-1970s to 23,000 in 1985. Attempts to increase water supplies through dam projects will inevitably exacerbate the problem by increasing the prevalence of waterborne disease. (See also: *Development*③, *Urbanization*③.)

Wave power
The harnessing of the vertical motion of sea waves to generate electricity.

Wave power devices have been tested in Britain and other countries, and one has been built off Bergen, Norway, but in Britain, where much of the early development took place, the wave power programme was closed down in 1982 after a series of critical reports from the Energy Technology Support Unit (ETSU), based at the Atomic Energy Authority laboratories at Harwell. Instead the government switched its renewable energy research funds into wind power (*qv*), which was deemed to be a more viable source of energy.

A number of promising wave power projects suffered from the decision to end wave research, most notably the "Salter Duck", a device developed by Stephen Salter at the University of Edinburgh. Although the "duck," which relies on exploiting the up and down movement of waves to generate electricity, had received high praise from the Department of Energy's own consultants, the British government nonetheless refused to back the project.

Electricity from the "duck" would have been competitive with that from nuclear power stations, if not cheaper, and it has since emerged that ETSU's damning reports on the project distorted the figures in an attempt to convince the government that wave power was less economic than nuclear energy. A subsequent report from ETSU, published in 1991, finally conceded that wave power together with other forms of renewable energy could, in theory, supply half Britain's electricity by 2010. (See also: *Alternative technology*③, *Energy*Ⓔ.)

Wetlands

Wetlands are among the most productive ecosystems in the world. Covering six per cent of the Earth's land surface, these marshlands, swamps and bogs play a vital role in cleansing water of pollutants, regulating floods, and providing a habitat for numerous species of plants and animals. An estimated 60-70 per cent of fish in US coastal waters and two-thirds of shellfish rely on wetlands for food or for spawning grounds and nurseries. In Europe, the coastal waters of the Wadden Sea help to support almost 60 per cent of the North Sea's brown shrimp, 50 per cent of the sole, 80 per cent of the plaice and nearly all of the herring population.

Wetlands provide other benefits, acting as buffers against storms and playing a significant role in filtering out pollutants. In tidal wetlands, the rich soils of the floodplains have been exploited by numerous societies. In West Africa, as many as 1,500,000 people rely on floodplains for grazing cattle, sheep and goats, or for growing seasonal crops. Yet, throughout the world, wetlands are menaced by drainage schemes, land reclamation, tourism, pollution and the reservoirs of large dams (*qv*).

The major threat to wetlands comes from drainage and development schemes. More than half of the original 870,000sq km (335,000sq miles) of wetlands in the USA have been lost, 87 per cent of them being converted to farmland or rangelands.

In Africa, the giant Okovango swamp in Botswana is threatened with drainage, the plan being to develop the area for mining and agriculture. In the Sudan, work is already well advanced on the Jonglei Canal, which will divert water from the marshlands of the Sudd swamps to Egypt and north Sudan. The project will reduce the grassland floodplains of the Sudd by an estimated 50 per cent, disrupting the traditional migration routes of the local pastoralists and depriving wildlife of vital habitats. Elsewhere, in Pakistan, the Farraka Barrage (*qv*) has wrought havoc with the wetland forests of the Ganges Delta.

Many wetlands have succumbed to pollution, particularly in areas where there is run-off of agricultural chemicals or a concentration of heavy industry. One wetland that has been badly polluted is the Wadden Sea, where many fish and marine mammals are contaminated with high levels of PCBS (*qv*) and chlorinated hydrocarbons.

Since 1971, wetlands have been "protected" by the Convention on Wetlands of International Importance especially as Waterfowl Habitats. Known less formally as The Ramsar Convention, after the Iranian town where it was signed, the convention is ratified by 43 nations, the most recent signatories being the United States, Ireland, Suriname and Belgium, all of which joined in 1986. To date, the convention has saved some 200,000sq km (77,000sq miles) of wetlands. Sadly, this is only a minute proportion of the 8,500,000sq km (3,280,000sq miles) of wetlands worldwide. (See also: *Development*③, *Pesticides*Ⓐ Ⓟ.)

Whales

The first records of commercial whaling date from the 10th century, when the Basques started hunting in the Bay of Biscay. By the 16th century, they had decimated the Biscayan right whales and had moved north to Greenland, Iceland and Newfoundland in pursuit of the bowhead whale. They were joined by Dutch and English whalers. Together the whalers hunted the bowhead to commercial extinction by 1680. The 18th and 19th centuries marked the period of the great American whalers. The sperm whale was their target, and at the peak of the period, between 1835 and 1846, 600 ships were hunting them in the Atlantic for their valuable oil. By the 1920s the stocks were practically exhausted. In the Pacific, the grey whale in Baja California was decimated within 45 years of the first kill.

By the turn of this century, interest had shifted to the Antarctic. There, the pillage was aided by the invention of the explosive harpoon and the development of steam vessels, which enabled the pursuit of faster whales. In 1904, the British established a whaling station on South Georgia, where thousands of blue whales were processed each year. In 1914, the Norwegians, in competition with the British, developed the first factory ship. Within ten years, such ships had stern slipways, allowing a whale to be hauled on board and cut up and processed within an hour.

As a result of these technological improvements, species after species has been hunted to the brink of extinction. In the 1930s, as the blue whale was getting rarer, attention was turned to the smaller fin whale. By 1960, the fin whale stocks had been commercially depleted and whalers concentrated on the minke whale, which until then had been left in peace.

The International Convention for the Regulation of Whaling, ratified in 1946, marked the first attempt to regulate the hunting of whales on an international basis. The International Whaling Commission (IWC), set up by the convention, voted in 1982 to impose a five-year moratorium on commercial whaling, starting in October 1985. But the commission has no power to enforce its decisions and, by the end of the 1985-1986 season, 4,969 minke whales had been killed. Several countries, notably the Soviet Union, Japan, South Korea, Norway and Iceland, have exploited loopholes in the IWC rules, which allow whales to be killed for scientific research. The label "scientific" is bogus: the data acquired has not been needed by the IWC, there are many non-lethal research techniques, and the dead whales end up as meat for the table. In 1987, the IWC passed a US resolution calling on governments not to issue licences for "scientific" whaling. None of the IWC nations has to abide by the decision but any nation that fails to do so will face stringent US sanctions on imports and will be barred from fishing in US waters. Iceland and Norway continued scientific whaling for a time. But by 1991, both countries had bowed to international pressure and, in Iceland's case, to an international boycott of its fish. Now only Japan, which is strong enough to resist economic pressure, has an active whaling fleet. In April 1991, the Japanese fleet returned from the Antarctic with the meat and oil of 327 minke whales. Japan, Norway and Iceland continue to argue that stocks have increased sufficiently to allow resumption of commercial whaling. If such whaling does resume, there seems little chance that these gentle and intelligent creatures will grace our seas in anything more than token quantities. (See also: *Krill©, Overfishing©*.)

Wind power

The wind has been used to turn sails and work grain mills and water pumps for centuries, but, since the 1940s, entirely new "windmills" have been developed for generating electricity. With rigid blades rather than sails

these bear little resemblance to their picturesque but less efficient ancestors, owing much instead to the introduction of new lightweight materials and advances in aerodynamics, especially in the design of their rotor blades.

Individual models range in size from those designed to produce a few kilowatts for domestic or farm use, to large models intended to serve entire communities or to feed power into a grid network and generating about one megawatt. Still larger generators, of up to three-megawatt capacity, have been built.

The environmental advantages of wind power, as with other sources of renewable energy, are that it is largely pollution-free and saves the burning of fossil fuels (such as coal and oil). The only objections come from the noise of the turning blades and the visual intrusion of large arrays of turbines in the countryside.

In California, grid-connected wind turbines installed over about the last 10 years (more than 15,000 individual machines) produce over 1,400MW of electricity. They provide 1 per cent of the state's electricity – enough for ab-

out 300,000 households. Denmark produces 190MW of wind generated power, with a target of 10 per cent of the country's electricity supply being wind-produced by the year 2000. The Danes were also the first country to develop a "wind farm" offshore – where the wind is stronger and more reliable. In other countries, wind power is used to supply remote communities and islands without the expense of bringing in outside supplies. In the UK it has been estimated that wind power could provide 54 terawatt hours of electricity – about a fifth of annual demand – more than the nuclear industry provides at present. This would mean 1,000 large (4MW) and 3,000 medium-sized (500KW) wind turbine generators (WTGS) on land and 2,000 very large (8MW) ones offshore. During 1990, a rush of schemes for wind farms were proposed in Britain, mainly in Wales, Cornwall and northern England, and with the benefit of a government subsidy originally designed to support nuclear power. The first farm was opened in late 1992. (See also: *Alternative technology©, Energy©, Soft energy paths©*.)

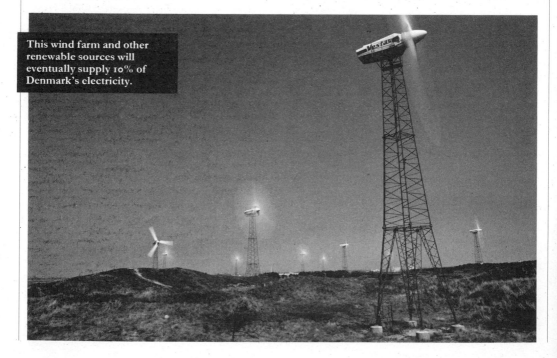

This wind farm and other renewable sources will eventually supply 10% of Denmark's electricity.

Windscale
See: *Sellafield*.

Windscale fire
Construction work on the first British plutonium-production piles (or reactors) began in September 1947 at Windscale. The first was operational in October 1950, the second eight months later. Their design did not allow the heat generated to be used for electricity production; instead they were air-cooled, and the heat dispersed by huge electric fans. On the morning of October 8 1957 the physicist operating the No 1 pile was involved in a series of routine procedures that involved raising and lowering the core temperature, but apparently without the Pile Operating Manual available to him. He allowed the core temperature to rise to the point at which fuel began to melt, unaware that the gauges did not take their readings from the hottest part of the core. There was no sign of trouble until, 42 hours later, instruments in the stack filters indicated that radioactivity was being uncontrollably released.

The reactor core was on fire, accelerated by the cooling fans. Flames shot out of the core from the fuel discharge face and, at the height of the accident, 11 tonnes of uranium and the graphite moderator were on fire. Carbon dioxide was used in the first attempt to put out the fire, but served only to intensify it. Despite the real possibility of a hydrogen explosion, fire hoses were coupled directly into a line of fuel channels and water poured onto the blazing core. During the morning of October 11 the fire, which had been out of control for more than 24 hours, finally subsided.

The stack's filters, which had only been incorporated into the pile design as an afterthought, probably prevented a major accident from becoming a disaster. Even so, huge quantities of radioactivity were released, the most dangerous of which were some 20,000 curies of iodine-131. (Only in 1983 was it admitted that polonium was also released, presumably because an earlier admission would have revealed that Britain was manufacturing a type of polonium-triggered hydrogen bomb that was already, by 1957, out of date.) Two million litres (528,000 US gallons) of milk were poured away from farms in the surrounding 500sq km (190sq miles), but the local health effects cannot be known in detail, because the identities of those people near the fire were not recorded. Subsequent assessments indicate that up to 100 people may have died as a result of the accident, making it the most serious nuclear incident prior to Chernobyl (*qv*).

After the fire it was obvious that No 1 pile would never operate again. Both it and the No 2 pile were shut down and filled with concrete – they had anyway been superseded. A year earlier the new Calder Hall reactors, the military precursors of the civil Magnox (*qv*) reactors, came on stream at Windscale and took over the function of supplying military plutonium. They had (and still have) the advantage over the air-cooled piles of producing electricity as a by-product, thus off-setting the costs of plutonium production. (See also: *Nuclear accident*®, *Sellafield*®.)

Wood preservatives
Mixtures of compounds designed to protect vulnerable timber from attack by insects, such as woodworm and death watch beetle, and fungi, such as wet and dry rot. A wood preservative will therefore often contain an insecticide and a fungicide, though woodworm killers and some anti-rot products can be bought separately.

Several toxic materials have been used as insecticides in these products. Dieldrin (*qv*) was popular but has been phased out for use in Britain and several other countries. Lindane HCH (*qv*) has also been used, but because of its lethal effects on bats it has been replaced in some products by permethrin, which is less toxic but also less long-lasting. Products used to preserve exterior timber, such as fences, do not usually contain a specific insecticide, but some of the chemicals used – notably creosote – are poisonous to insects as well as fungi. Where termite attack is expected, toxic insecticides may be used.

Some timbers are impregnated under pressure or vacuum with a copper/chromium/arsenic mixture that poses risks when the timber is burned or sanded down. Tributyl tin compounds are also often used to treat interior timbers such as joists and rafters. Probably the most harmful compound used in this way is pentachlorophenol (*qv*).

The World Bank
Established in 1944 at the Bretton Woods Conference, attended by 44 nations, the World Bank is now by far the biggest and most influential of the multilateral development banks (MDBS). Not only does it invest some $16,000 million a year in the Third World, but those development projects that it approves or partly funds have little difficulty in obtaining further funds from other MDBS and bilateral aid organizations.

The World Bank works in close association with its sister organization, the International Monetary Fund (IMF) (*qv*). Whereas the bank is responsible for long-term investments, the IMF's role is to provide bridging finance to countries with short-term balance of payments difficulties.

The World Bank is made up of three main bodies: the International Bank for Reconstruction and Development (IBRD), which raises money on international financial markets and lends at commercial rates of interest; the International Development Agency (IDA), which provides loans at concessional rates of interest to the poorest countries and which obtains its funds from member subscriptions, donations and grants from the IBRD; and the International Finance Corporation (IFC), which lends money to the private sector with government guarantees.

The bank is controlled by member countries whose votes are in accordance with the size of their respective donations. This means that the World Bank is largely controlled by the United States, the biggest donor. The World Bank is located in Washington and its director is invariably a US citizen.

The bank's policies reflect Western and, in particular, US foreign policies vis-à-vis the Third World, which is not altogether surprising since it and the IMF were set up largely to assure the continued expansion of the Western industrial economy. The bank is firmly committed to free trade and its policies help to promote the sale of Western manufactured goods to Third World countries, which, in turn, are encouraged to export agricultural produce and other raw materials needed in the West.

Since the bank is a commercial organization, and requires that its loans be repaid, it will lend money only for projects that have some chance of being profitable. A special department of the bank, the Operations Evaluation Department (OED), advises it on the likely economic viability of proposed schemes.

Social and environmental considerations have, up till now, been almost entirely ignored, in spite of continued assurances to the contrary. In 1984, the bank admitted in an internal memorandum, "As a matter of routine, environmental issues are not considered." It was also admitted that it "does not have the capacity to conduct sector work on environmental issues on a routine basis." At the time, the bank's Office of Environmental Affairs had just five members of staff, who were expected to evaluate the environmental impact of more than 300 new projects a year. Out of the 6,000 employees of the bank, there was just one professionally trained ecologist.

Projects funded by the bank that have had adverse effects on the environment and on local people include many large dams and other water development schemes; road construction programmes, particularly in forested areas; and many livestock rearing programmes.

In recent years, three of the bank's schemes have been subject to particularly strong criticisms:

the Polonoroeste project in Brazil; the Narmada Valley Project (qv) in India; and the Transmigration (qv) scheme in Indonesia.

In 1986, the bank's environmental record was severely criticized by the Appropriations Sub-Committee of the US Senate, chaired by Senator Kasten of Wisconsin. Kasten said that if people knew the truth about the projects that the World Bank and other multilateral development banks were financing, they would be "out on the streets" demanding why their money was "being spent on this kind of destruction." Kasten's committee refused to provide further US backing for the Polonoroeste project.

The bank received another blow when Hugh Foster, its alternate US Executive Director, voted against financing a series of hydro-electric projects in Brazil, describing them as "pure folly" and "environmental disasters."

The bank has now promised to mend its ways. Its development committee issued a report entitled "Environment: Growth and Development" in April 1987, in which it set out new environmental guidelines for its activities. Future projects will have to meet three criteria: "economic growth, poverty alleviation and environmental protection."

In 1987, the bank launched an initiative to "integrate women into development." Its focus is on "increasing women's productivity by investing in human capital and improving women's access to productive resources and the labour market." On the one hand, the bank could be commended for finally, if belatedly, recognizing the significant part women play in all economies. On the other hand, incorporating women into international markets is likely to prove more beneficial to the bank and its patrons than to the women. Working for large-scale businesses and selling through entrepreneurs usually translates into a loss of control over what is produced, for whom, and at what price to the producer.

It is clear that the bank has much to do before the rhetoric of environmental concern is trans-

lated into real action. Despite the devastation they are causing, the bank is continuing to fund such notorious projects as Indonesia's Transmigration (qv) Programme and India's Narmada (qv) project. Moreover, although it has withdrawn funding from several projects, it has done so only after protests from environmental and indigenous rights groups.

Indeed it is debatable whether or not the goals set out in the new guidelines are compatible. In particular, it is difficult to see how the pursuit of economic growth can be reconciled with environmental protection. (See also: *Grande Carajas*③, *Dams*③, *Development*③, *Sustainable development*③, *Third World debt*③.)

World Commission on Environment and Development
See: *Brundtland Report.*

X-ray
See: *Radiation and health.*

Zero population growth
State where the number of deaths in a population equals the number of births, with the result that there is no natural increase in the size of the population over time. However, populations which have achieved zero population growth may still increase as a result of immigration.

In the USA, concern over the environmental and social impact of overpopulation has spawned a powerful lobby in favour of zero population growth, including a pressure group of that name.

Despite the ecological imperative of reducing human numbers, however, population growth rates are only part of the problem. Levels of material consumption are also of critical importance. Even if the US population were to stabilize at its present level, for example, current standards of consumption could not be sustained for long without placing an intolerable burden on the environment. (See also: *Demographic transition*③, *Family planning*①③, *Population*③, *Population explosion*③.)

International

ECOROPA (European Ecological Action Group), International Secretariat, 42 Rue Sorbier, 75020, Paris, France

Environment Liaison Centre, PO Box 72461, Nairobi, Kenya *All issues*

Friends of the Earth International, 26-28 Underwood St., London N1 7JQ

Greenpeace International, Keizersgracht 176, 1016 OW Amsterdam, Netherlands *All issues*

Institute for European Environmental Policy (IEEP), 3 Endsleigh Street, London WC1H 0DD *All issues*

International Coalition on Development Action, 22 rue des Bollandistes, 1040 Brussels, Belgium *All issues*

International Rivers Network, 300 Broadway, Suite 28, San Francisco, California CA 94133, USA *Third World, conservation*

International Institute for Environment and Development (IIED), 3 Endsleigh Street, London WC1H 0DD *All issues*

(IOCU) International Organization of Consumer Unions, PO Box 1045, 10830 Penang, Malaysia *All issues*

International Union for the Conservation of Nature, 1196 Gland, Switzerland *All issues*

Pesticides Action Network, 22 rue des Bollandistes, 1040 Brussels, Belgium *All issues*

TRANET (Transnational Network for Appropriate Technology), Box 567, Rangeley, ME 04970, USA *Energy, Third World*

WISE (World Information Service on Energy), PO Box 5627, 1007 AP Amsterdam, The Netherlands *All issues*

World Rainforest Movement, International Secretariat, 87 Cantonment Rd., 10250 Penang, Malaysia *Third World, conservation*

World Wide Fund For Nature, 1196 Gland, Switzerland *All issues*

Australia and New Zealand

Albury-Wodonga Environment Centre, Shop 3, 608 Dean Street, Albury NSW 2640 *Conservation, pollution*

Australian Conservation Foundation, 672B Glenferrie Rd., Hawthorne, Victoria 3122 *All issues*

Barrier Environment Group, West Post Office, Broken Hill NSW 2880 *Conservation, pollution*

Cairns and Far North Environment Centre, 1st Floor, Andrejic Arcade, 55 Lake Street, Cairns QLD 4870 *Conservation, pollution*

Canberra and South East Region Environment Centre, Childers Street Buildings, Kingsley Street, Acton ACT 2601 *All issues*

Capricorn Conservation Council and Environment Centre, 135 William Street, Rockhampton QLD 4700 *Conservation, pollution*

Central Australia Conservation Council, PO Box 2796, Alice Springs NT 5750 *Conservation, pollution*

Conservation Council of Victoria, 247–251 Flinders Lane, Melbourne VIC 3000 *Conservation, pollution*

Conservation Centre and Conservation Council of SA Inc, 120 Wakefield Street, Adelaide SA 5000 *Conservation, pollution*

Conservation Council of the South East Region and Canberra, GPO Box 1875, Canberra ACT 2601 *Conservation, pollution*

Conservation Council of WA Inc, 1st Floor, 794 Hay Street, Perth WA 6000 *All issues*

Environment Centre (Victoria), 247–251 Flinders Lane, Melbourne VIC 3000 *All issues*

Friends of the Earth – Australia, PO Box 530E, Melbourne, Victoria 3001 *All issues*

Friends of the Earth – New Zealand, PO Box 39–065, Auckland West, New Zealand *All issues*

Geelong Environment Council, PO Box 639, Geelong VIC 3320 *All issues*

Greenpeace – New Zealand, Nagel House, 5th Floor, Courthouse Lane, Auckland, New Zealand *All issues*

Illawarra Environment Centre, Suite 11, 157 Crown Street, Wollongong NSW 2500 *Conservation, pollution*

Launceston Environment Centre Inc, 34 Patterson Street, Launceston TAS 7250 *Conservation, pollution*

Mid North Coast Environment Centre, "Coolenberg", 60 Lake Road, Port Macquarie NSW 2444 *Conservation, pollution*

Nature Conservation Council of NSW, NSW Environment Centre, 176 Cumberland Street, Sydney NSW 2000 *Conservation, pollution*

Newcastle Ecology Centre, Room 6, Trades Hall, Union Street, Newcastle NSW 2300 *All issues*

New Zealand Values Party, Box 116, New Plymouth, New Zealand *Political, all issues*

North Coast Environment Council, c/o J. Tedder, Pavans Road, Grassy Head, via Stuarts Point NSW 2441 *Conservation, pollution*

North Queensland Conservation Council Inc and Townsville Environment Centre, 477 Flinders Street, Townsville QLD 4810 *Conservation, pollution*

Rainforest Information Centre, PO Box 368, Lismore NSW 2480 *Conservation*

South Coast Environment Centre, Shop 5, Sams Market Arcade, Orient Street, Batemans Bay NSW 2500 *Conservation, pollution*

Tasmanian Conservation Trust Inc, 102 Bathurst Street, Hobart TAS 7000 *Conservation, pollution*

Tasmanian Environment Centre Inc, 102 Bathurst Street, Hobart TAS 7000 *All issues*

The Big Scrub Environment Centre, 88A Keen Street, Lismore NSW 2840 *Conservation, pollution*

The Environment Centre, Beaman Park, James Street, Yeppoon QLD 4703 *Conservation, pollution*

The Environment Centre (NT), Shop 8, The Track, Darwin NT 5794 *All issues*

The Environment Centre of NSW, 176 Cumberland Street, Sydney NSW 2000 *Conservation, pollution*

The Wilderness Society, 130 Davey Street, Hobart TAS 7000 *Conservation*

The Wilderness Society, PO Box 188, Civic Square ACT 2608 *Conservation*

Total Environment Centre, 18 Argyle Street, Sydney NSW 2000 *All issues*

Tweed Valley Conservation Trust, 35 Tweed Arcade, Queen Street, Murwillumbah NSW 2484 *Conservation, pollution*

Wide Bay/Burnett Conservation Council, 16 Alvie Street, Mayborough QLD 4650 *Conservation, pollution*

World Wide Fund for Nature – Australia, Level 17, St Martins Tower, 31 Market Street, GPO Box 528, Sydney NSW 2001 *All issues*

World Wide Fund for Nature – New Zealand, PO Box 6237, Wellington, New Zealand *All issues*

Canada

Alberta Environmental Law Centre, 202 10110–142 St, Edmonton, Alberta T5N 1P6 *All issues*

Alberta Wilderness Association, Box 6398, Station D, Calgary, Alberta T2P 2E1 *Conservation*

Canadian Arctic Resources Committee, 46 Elgin Street, Room 11, Ottawa, Ontario K1P 5K6 *Conservation*

Canadian Coalition on Acid Rain, 112 St Clair Avenue West, Toronto, Ontario M4V 2Y3 *Pollution*

Canadian Coalition for Nuclear Responsibility, CP 236, Saccursale, Snowden, Montreal, Québec H3X 3T4 *Nuclear*

Canadian Environmental Law Association, 234 Queen Street West, Toronto, Ontario M5V 1Z4 *All issues*

Canadians for Conservation of Tropical Nature (CCTN), Faculty of Environmental Studies, York University, 4700 Keele Street, Toronto, Ontario M3J 1P6 *Third World, conservation*

Conservation Council of New Brunswick, 180 St John Street, Fredericton, NB E3B 4A9 *All issues*

Consumers United to Stop Food Irradiation, RR £1, Illderton, Ontario NOM 2AO *Lifescan, pollution, nuclear*

Ecology Action Centre, 1657 Barrington Street, Suite 520, Halifax, Nova Scotia B3J 2A1 *All issues*

Energy Probe, 100 College Street, Toronto, Ontario M5G 1L5 *All issues*

Federation of Ontario Naturalists, 355 Lesmill Road, Don Mills, Ontario M3B 2W8 *Conservation*

Friends of the Earth, 251 Laurier Avenue West, Suite 701 Ottawa, Ontario K1P 5J6 *All issues*

Green Party, 831 Commercial Drive, Vancouver, British Colombia, Canada *All issues*

Greenpeace, 427 Bloor St West, Toronto, Ontario M5S 1X7 *All issues*

Institute of Concern for Public Health, Suite 343, 67 Mowat Avenue, Toronto, Ontario M6K 3E3 *All issues*

Manitoba Naturalists Society, 190 Rupert Avenue, Winnipeg, Manitoba R3B 0N2 *Conservation*

Nuclear Awareness Project, 730 Bathurst St, Toronto, Ontario M5S 2R4 *All issues*

Ontario Environment Network, PO Box 125 Station P, Toronto, Ontario M5S 2Z7 *All issues*

Ontario Public Interest Research Group, 229 College Street, Toronto, Ontario K1P 5C5 *All issues*

Operation Clean Niagara, 83 Gage Street, Niagara-on-the-Lake, Ontario M5S 2R4 *Pollution*

Pollution Probe, 12 Madison Avenue, Toronto, Ontario M5R 2S1 *Pollution*

Probe International, 225 Brunswick Avenue, Toronto, Ontario M5S 2M6 *All issues*

Recycling Council of Ontario, PO Box 310 Station P, Toronto, Ontario M8S 2S8 *Pollution, lifescan, conservation*

Société Pour Vaincre la Pollution, CP 65 Place d'Armes, Montreal, Québec H2Y 3E9 *All issues*

SPEC – The Society for the Promotion of Environment Conservation, 2150 Maple St, Vancouver BC. V6J 3T3 *All issues*

Taskforce on Churches and Corporate Responsibility, 129 St Clair, Avenue West, Toronto, Ontario M4V 1N5 *Pollution, lifescan, conservation*

Tomorrow Foundation, 10511 Saskatchewan Drive, Edmonton, Alberta T6E 4S1 *All issues*

West Coast Environmental Law Association, 1001–207 West Hastings Street, Vancouver BC V6B 1H7 *Nuclear, pollution, lifescan, conservation*

World Wide Fund for Nature (Canada), 60 St Clair Avenue East, Suite 201, Toronto, Ontario M4T 1N5 *All issues*

United Kingdom

British Society for Social Responsibility in Science, 25 Horsell Road, London N5 1XL *All issues*

British Organic Farmers, 86 Colston Street, Bristol BS1 5BB *Organic Farming*

Campaign for Freedom of Information, 3 Endsleigh Street, London WC1H 0DD *All issues*

Campaign for Lead-free Air (CLEAR), 3 Endsleigh Street, London WC1 0DD *Pollution*

Campaign for Nuclear Disarmament (CND), 22 Underwood Street, London N1 7JG *Nuclear*

Centre for Alternative Technology (CAT), Llwyngwern Quarry, Machynlleth, Wales *Energy*

Civic Trust, 17 Carlton House Terrace, London SW1Y 5AW *Conservation*

Climate Action Network – UK, 45 Shelton Street, London WC2 9HJ *Pollution*

Common Ground, 45 Shelton St., London WC2 9HJ *Conservation*

Commonwealth Human Ecology Council, 63 Cromwell Road, London SE7 7BL *All issues*

Compassion in World Farming, 20 Lavant Street, Petersfield, Hampshire *All issues*

Council for the Protection of Rural England, 4 Hobart Place, London SW1N 0HY *Conservation*

Council for the Protection of Rural Wales, Tŷ Gwyn, 31 High Street, Welshpool, Powys, Wales *Conservation*

Countryside Commission, John Dower House, Crescent Place, Cheltenham, Gloucestershire GL50 3RA *Conservation*

Earth Resources Research Ltd, 258 Pentonville Road, London N1 9JY *All issues*

Ecoropa (UK), Henbant, Crickhowell, Powys, Wales NP8 1TA *All issues*

Farm and Food Society, 4 Willifield Way, London NW11 7XT *All issues*

Fauna and Flora Preservation Society, 79-83 North Street, Brighton, Sussex BN1 1ZA

Food Additives Campaign Team, 25 Horsell Road, London N5 1XL *Lifescan*

Friends of the Earth, 26-28 Underwood Street, London N1 7JQ *All issues*

Friends of the Earth (Scotland), 15 Windsor Street, Edinburgh EH7 5LA *All issues*

Green Alliance, 60 Chandos Place, London WC2 *All issues*

Green Deserts, High Rougham, Bury St Edmonds, Suffolk *Third World, conservation*

Green Party, 10 Station Parade, Balham High Road, London SW12 9A2 *All issues*

Greenpeace, 30–31 Islington Green, London N1 *All issues*

Henry Doubleday Research Association, Ryton on Dunsmore, Coventry CV8 3LG *All issues*

Intermediate Technology Development Group, Myson House, Railway Terrace, Rugby, Warwickshire *All issues*

International Institute of Biological Husbandry, 9 Station Approach, Needham Market, Ipswich,

Suffolk *All issues*
League Against Cruel Sports, Sparling House, 83–87 Union Street, London SE1
London Food Commission, 88 Old Street, London EC1V 9AR *All issues*
Marine Conservation Society, 4 Gloucester Road, Ross-on-Wye, HR9 5BU *Pollution*
Men of the Trees, Turns Hill Road, Crawley Down, Crawley, West Sussex RH10 4HL *Conservation*
Nature Conservancy Council, Northminster House, Peterborough, Cambs PE1 1UA *Conservation*
National Society for Clean Air, 136 North Street, Brighton, Sussex *Pollution*
NATTA (Network for Appropriate Technology and Technology Assessment), C/o Faculty of Technology, Open University, Milton Keynes, Buckinghamshire *Research on alternate technologies*
National Tryst, 36 Queen Anne's Gate, London SW1H 9AS *Conservation*
Organic Growers Association, Aeron Park, Llangietho, Dyfed *All issues*
Oxfam, 274 Banbury Road, Oxford OX2 7DZ *All issues*
Panos Institute, 8 Alfred Place, London WC1E 7EB *Third World*
Parents for Safe Food, 102 Gloucester Place, London W1H 3DA *Food issues*
Pesticide Group, C/o Transport and General Workers Union, Transport House, Smith Square, London SW1P 3JB *All issues*
Pesticide Trust, C/o Earth Resources Research, 258 Pentonville Road, London N1 9JY *All issues*
Reforest the Earth, 48 Bethel Street, Norwich, Norfolk NR2 1NR *Action on global warming*
Royal Society for Nature Conservation, The Green, Nettleham, Lincoln LN2 2NR *Conservation*
Royal Society for Protection of Birds (RSPB), The Lodge, Sandy, Bedfordshire SE1 2DL *All issues*
SCRAM, 11 Forth Street, Edinburgh EH1 3LE *Nuclear*
SERA (Socialist Environment and Resources Association), 26-28 Underwood Street, London N1 7JQ *All issues*
Soil Association, 86 Colston Street, Bristol BS1 5BB *All issues*
Survival International, 310 Edgware Road, London W2 1DY

Third World
Sustainability, 1 Cambridge Street, London SW13 0PE *Consumerism*
The Ecologist, Worthyvale Manor, Camelford, Cornwell *All issues*
Town and Country Planning Association (TCPA), 17 Carlton House Terrace, London SW1 5AS *Conservation*
Transport 2000, 10 Melton Street, London NW1 2EJ *Transport*
Urban Centre for Appropriate Technology, 82 Colston Street, Bristol *Energy, conservation*
Urban Wildlife Group, 131-133 Sherlock Street, Birmingham B5 6NB *Conservation*
Vegetarian Society, 53 Marloes Road, London W8 6LA *All issues*
Woodland Trust, Autumn Park, Dysart Road, Grantham, Lincs NG31 6LL *Conservation*
World Food Assembly, 15 Devonshire Terrace, London WC2 3DW *All issues*
World Wide Fund for Nature (UK), Panda House, 11 Ockford Road, Godalming, Surrey *All issues*

United States

Citizens Party, 411 Esty Street, Ithaca, NY 14850 *All issues*
Cultural Survival, 11 Divinity Avenue, Cambridge MA 02178 *Third World*
Defenders of Wildlife, 1244 19th Street NW, Washington DC 20036 *Wildlife, conservation*
Earth Island Institute, 300 Broadway, Suite 28, San Francisco, CA 94133–9905 *All issues*
Environmental Defense Fund, 1616 P Street NW, Washington DC 20036 *All issues*
Environmental Law Institute, 1616 P Street NW, Washington DC 20036 *All issues*
Friends of the Earth, 530 7th Street SE, Washington DC 20003 *All issues*
Friends of the Trees, PO Box 1466, Chelan WA 98816, *Conservation*
Institute for Food and Development Policy, 145 Ninth Street, San Francisco, CA 94103 *Third World, agriculture*
Global Tomorrow Coalition, 1325 G Street NW, Suite 920, Washington DC 2005 *All issues*
Greenpeace, 1436 U Street, NW, Washington DC 20009 *All issues*
Intermediate Technology Development Group, 777 United

Nations Plaza, New York NY 10017 *Third World, energy*
Monitor Consortium, 1506 19th Street NW, Washington DC 20036 *All issues*
National Audubon Society, 801 Pennsylvania Avenue SE, Washington DC 20003 *Conservation, pollution*
National Wildlife Federation, 1412 16th Street, NW, Washington DC 20036 *Conservation, pollution*
Natural Resources Defense Council, 1350 New York Avenue NW, Washington DC 20005 *Conservation, wildlife*
New Alchemy Institute, 237 Hatchville Road, East Falmouth, MA 02536 *Energy, conservation*
Permaculture Institute of North America, 6488 S Maxwell Rd, Clinton, WA 98236 *Agriculture, conservation, pollution*
The Rachel Carson Council, 8940 Jones Mill Road, Chevy Chase, MA 20815, *Agriculture, pollution, conservation*
Rainforest Action Network, 466 Green Street, Suite 300, San Francisco, CA 94133 *Third World, conservation, agriculture*
Sierra Club, 330 Pennsylvania Avenue NW, Washington DC 20003 *Conservation, wildlife*
Survival International, 2121 Decatur Place, Washington DC 20008 *Third World*
The Wilderness Society, 1400 I Street NW, Washington DC 20005 *Conservation, wildlife*
World Resources Institute, 1735 New York Avenue NW, Suite 230 Washington DC 20006 *All issues*
Worldwatch Institute, 1776 Massachusetts Avenue NW, Washington DC 20036
World Wide Fund for Nature (USA), 1255 23rd Street NW, Washington DC 20037 *All issues*

Main entry headings are not indexed.

A
abortion, spontaneous 15, 85, 90
Acceptable Daily Intake 140
acetylcholinesterase 33, 123
acid rain 16, 81, 82
acrylonitrile 14
additives 22, 34, 55, 60–1, 63, 72, 97, 109, 132, 146, 148
adenocarcinoma (vaginal cancer 54, 85
advanced gas-cooled reactor (AGR 31, 43, 48–9, 91, 137, 143, 144, 161
aerosols 38, 39, 40
aflatoxins 72, 84
Aganbegyan, Professor Abel 164
Agent Orange 54, 160
AIDS 16, 37
air pollution 32, 44, 54, 80, 124, 142
albedo 82
aldicarb 33, 85
aldrin 41, 42, 53, 54, 61
algae, marine 33, 44
algal blooms 21, 65, 115, 142
alkalinization 140–1
alpha radiation 18, 75, 134, 139, 144
aluminium 12, 47, 57, 70, 71
amaranth 42
Amazonia 80, 87, 92, 106
aminotriazole 90
ammonia 20, 75, 101
anaemia 37, 90
Andreae, Meinrat 16
antioxidants 12
appropriate development 52
aquaculuture 70
Aroclor 130
artificial fertilizers see fertilizers
artificial sweeteners 13, 45, 140, 148
asbestos 147
asbestosis 21
ascorbates 19
asthma 13, 42, 63, 72, 86, 132, 148
atmospheric testing 23
Atomic Energy Authority (UK 36, 56, 116

B
bacterial blight (BB 90
Baker, Senator Howard 14
Barney, Dr Gerald O. 79
Basel Convention 66
bats 90, 167
Beni Biosphere Reserve 48
benzene 33, 107
Berg, Paul 77
Bergeret, Dr Anne 132
beri-beri 104
Bertell, Dr Rosalie 134
beta radiation 16, 36, 134, 139, 144
Bhopal 63, 65
biochemical oxygen demand (BOD 65, 100–1
bioconcentration 29, 38, 48, 54, 107, 127, 148
biodegradation 44
biogas machines 73
biological shield 43
biosphere 33, 62, 82
biotechnology 126
birdlife 15, 26, 48, 53, 56, 66, 78, 80, 87, 88, 90, 93, 115, 120, 151
birth control pill 86
birth defects 13, 55, 106, 133, 144, 160, 161, 162
bleached paper products 55–6
Blue Revolution 20
Bohm, David 49
boiling water reactors 28
Borgstrom, Georg 78
Borlaug, Dr Norbert 84, 127

Boucher, Professor *The Biology of Mutualism* 112
Boyer, Herbert 77
British Nuclear Fuels Ltd (BNFL 18, 102, 137, 139, 143
Brown, Lester 51, 60
Brundtland Report 10, 131
Bullard, Linda 78
Burkett, D.P. 55
Bush, President George 12, 15

C
cadmium 12, 14, 89, 102, 114, 115
caesium 36, 37, 72, 105, 134, 139
cancer 53, 70, 97, 100, 115, 128, 129, 133, 148
  in animals 38, 42, 45, 90, 160
  bladder 140
  brain 60
  breast 27, 43
  cervical 43
  in children 23, 38, 60, 101, 144
  Hodgkin's Disease 30
  leukemia see leukemia
  liver 13
  lung 22, 33, 87
  mesothelioma 21
  and radiation 23, 24, 36, 37, 72, 101, 102, 105, 111, 118, 134, 139, 144, 162
  skin 86, 124
  stomach 21
  throat 20
  thyroid 37
  vaginal (adenocarcinoma 54, 85
Candarel 22
Candu reactor 70
Cap de la Hague 118, 139, 144
captan 128
car emission see vehicle emissions
carbamates 15, 93
carbon dioxide 32, 41, 44, 82, 103, 124, 152, 153
  emissions 32, 41, 63, 82, 83
carbon monoxide 15, 32, 36
carbon taxes 33, 152
carbon tetrachloride 14, 39, 107
carcinogens 14, 15, 16, 27, 31, 32, 33, 38, 39, 48, 50, 53, 55, 72, 73, 85, 90, 91, 107, 111, 120, 127, 128, 129, 132, 133, 135, 140, 148, 161
carrying capacity 131
Carter, President Jimmy 79
cash crops 14, 52, 68, 95, 97, 131, 150
Castleman, Dr Barry 65
cattle ranching see livestock rearing
Caufield, Catherine 88, 92
Central Electricity Generating Board (CEGB 13, 91, 103, 104, 137, 144
CFCs see chlorofluorocarbons
chemotherapy 30
Chernobyl 13, 24, 62, 94, 103, 116, 118, 133
Chimane Indians 48, 95
Chinese Restaurant Syndrome 109
chloracne 13, 55
chlordane 41
chlorinated hydrocarbons 16, 38, 39, 53, 61, 90, 92, 93, 115, 126, 148, 165
chlorofluorocarbons (CFCs 38, 82, 83, 109, 123–4
chloroquine 104
chromium 30, 114
chromosome disorders 45, 72, 146
Clements, F.E. 23
climate 17, 33, 41, 57, 58, 68, 74, 81-2, 83, 88, 119–20, 124, 126, 156–7
Clophen 130
coal-fired power stations 13, 62, 103
coal-tar dyes 16, 34, 72, 148
cobalt–60 72, 118
Cohen, Stanley 77

combined heat and power energy systems 41–2
consumer groups 13, 27, 63, 81, 148–9
containment sites 100
coral reefs 75, 136
cot death 60
cotton growing 15, 20, 35, 50, 52, 68
Creutzfeldt-Jacobs disease 28
crop rotation 122
Cummins, Professor Joseph 130

D
daminazide 15
dams 18, 50, 53, 61, 63, 71, 84, 92, 97, 113, 142, 151, 157, 164, 165
Darmon, Dr Albert 55
DBCP 41, 85
DDT 18, 25, 38, 41, 42, 115, 128, 136, 138, 146, 147, 148
DDVP see dichlorvos debt bondage 35, 37
debt-for-nature 150
deforestation 10, 11, 17, 18, 35, 38, 47, 52, 57, 58, 61, 62, 63, 68, 73, 83, 85, 99, 135, 147, 155, 157, 158–9, 160
desertification 50, 62, 63, 123, 135
Deukmejian, George 133
deuterium 73, 74
Devall, Bill 49
development 61, 67, 131
development refugees 63
diabetes 55, 97
dichlorvos 111
dieldrin 16, 38, 40, 115, 123, 128, 167 diet 19, 55, 79, 89, 104, 133, 156
diethylstilbesterol (DES 34, 85, 91
Digby, Sir Kenelm 111
dilution and disperal 120
dilution and dispersal 100, 118
dimethyl sulphide 16
dimethylhydrazine (UDMH 15
dinoseb 90
dioxins 13, 39, 93, 103, 129, 144, 149, 160–1
diseases of civilization 29, 44, 97, 104
disposable nappies 54–5
DNA 124
DNOC 90
Dounreay 69, 98, 118
Dow Chemicals 161
Down's Syndrome 13, 60
DPCP 40
drins 54
drought 68, 81, 82, 109, 114
drought-flood cycle 50
dry cleaning 39
Duhl, Dr Garry 85
dumping 30, 48, 88, 89, 97, 98, 99, 102, 146
  at sea 29, 54, 89, 102, 115, 118, 123, 136
Dungeness B 13
Dutch Elm disease 155
dyes 13, 16, 34, 42

E
E-numbers 19, 60, 132, 148
earthworms 21
EBR–1 reactor 69
Eckholm, Erik 141
ecotourism 153
eczema 42, 63, 72
Egerton, Dr Frank 23
Ehrlich, Anne and Paul 25
electromagnetic (EM fields 60
Elkington, John 81
encroaching cultivators 49–50
endrin 42, 53, 54
energy conservation 62, 63, 94
energy tax 34, 82, 152
Enrico Fermi nuclear plant 69
Environmental Protection Agency (EPA (US 14, 15, 22, 30, 38, 53, 57, 82, 86, 88, 93,

121, 124, 127, 128, 138, 146, 160
environmental refugees 53, 82, 95, 147
Epstein, Professor Samuel 30
erosion 21, 22, 38, 47, 50, 62, 64, 73, 89, 109, 123, 135, 142, 156, 159
eucalyptus 135, 145, 158
EURATOM 117–18
eutrophication 16, 21, 47, 80, 113, 115, 129, 136
extinction 77, 78, 82, 125
Exxon Valdez 15
eye cataracts 124

F
family planning 131
famine 52, 95
Fansidar 104
fast breeder reactors 31, 37, 45, 56, 69, 70, 98, 129
fast-food industry 39, 40, 104
fertilizers 16, 20, 21, 22, 29, 65, 75, 83, 84, 85, 90, 109, 113, 126, 128, 132, 155
Finaplix 86
fish 10, 12, 16, 17, 18, 30, 47, 66, 84, 87, 90, 98, 101, 106, 107, 120, 121, 124, 127, 140, 150, 159, 160
fish acreage 78
fish farming 19, 53
fishing 18, 19, 22, 46, 56, 70
Flavin, Christopher 62
fluorine 155
fluorosis 70–1
foetal damage 43, 60, 90, 106
food contamination 21, 41, 42, 55, 65, 89, 101
    labelling 12, 63
Food and Agriculture Organization (FAO) 10, 19, 41, 42, 45, 49, 50, 52, 70, 84, 96, 122, 132, 147, 157
food chains 25, 26, 38, 53, 106, 120, 121, 127
food webs 90, 93
Forbes, E. 23
formaldehyde 25
formalin 73
fossil fuel power stations 10, 83, 115
fossil fuels 33, 41, 61, 82, 117
Foster, Hugh 168
Fox, Warwick 49
free market economics 33, 76
Freedom from Hunger Campaign 84
Friends of the Earth (FOE 14–15, 83, 94
fuel wood 145
fungicides 31, 33, 127

G
Gaia hypothesis 26, 82
gamma radiation 36, 72, 134
Gandhi
    Mahatma 38
    Rajiv 113
genetic diversity 84, 146
genetic patenting 72, 76, 77, 91
Geophysiology 75
George, Susan *How the Other Half Dies* 154
glass fibre 22
Gleason, Professor Herbert 59
Global Tomorrow Coalition 79
global warming 33, 40, 63, 79, 81, 82, 88, 153
glyphosate 90
Gould, Dr Jay 151
grassy stunt virus (GSV 90
Green Belt movement 73
Green Consumer Guide 81
Green Fund 79
green manures 122
green revolution 14, 20, 37, 90
greenhouse effect 21, 33, 40, 41, 63, 82, 100, 124
greenhouse gases 14, 32, 40, 62, 75, 81, 82, 83, 88, 97, 100, 124, 152

Greenpeace 90, 98, 110, 115, 144
Grenley, Dr Martin 132
groundwater 21, 38, 39, 57, 65, 88, 89, 99, 100, 101, 113, 121, 122, 127, 135, 138, 140
growth promoters 54, 91–2
Gulf War 1991 15, 94, 117

H
Hailes, Julia 81
Hall, Professor Ross Hume 97
halons 40, 109–10
Hansen, James 81
HAO nuclear plant 31
hazardous waste 27, 66, 85, 92, 99, 100, 103, 138, 146, 163
Hazardous Waste Inspectorate (HWI 100
heavy metals 12, 29, 30, 87, 93, 101, 106, 115, 120, 121
hedgerows 109
heptachlor 38, 42, 44
herbicides 13, 20, 25, 34, 54, 90, 125, 126, 127, 129, 143, 160, 161
hexachlorocyclohexane (HCH 38, 40
high-yielding varieties (HYVs 127, 128, 143
Hills, Lawrence 126
Hodgkin's Disease 30
holism 23, 59, 60, 112
Hooker Chemicals and Plastics Corporation 102–3
hormones 33, 34, 43, 78, 85, 86, 90
    in food 27, 42
Horowitz, Professor Michael 114
Hutton, James 75
hydrocarbons 10, 32, 33, 36, 39, 87, 114, 115, 124
hydrofluoric acid 71
hyperactivity 13, 42, 63, 72, 148

I
immune system 16, 27, 37, 124, 134, 151
in-vitro fertilization (IVF) 78
incineration 89, 102, 114, 115
infectious diseases 19
infra-red radiation 75, 83
insecticides 16, 25, 33, 38, 39, 44, 53, 61, 69, 90, 123, 125, 127
insulation 62
International Atomic Energy Agency (IAEA) 37, 102, 117, 133
International Commission on Radiological Protection (ICRP) 102, 134
International Monetary Fund (IMF) 167, 168
International Union for the Protection of Plant Varieties (UPOV) 126
ionizing radiation 72, 94, 111
irrigation 20, 22, 46–7, 51, 71–2, 84, 85, 128, 141
isomers 90
itai-itai disease 29

J
James, Dr 112
Jayal, N.D. 164
JET (European Torus Project) 73
Jiahua, Zou 150

K
Kahn, Herman 80
Karin B 65
Keller, Dr 112
Kent, Professor George 35
Khian Sea 98
krill fishing 18, 19
Kullenberg, Professor Gunnar 120–1

L
labelling 12, 63
Lacey, Professor Richard 27
landfill 39, 41, 83, 85, 88, 89, 130, 133

Layfield, Sir Frank 144–5
leachate 27, 41, 89, 100
lead 12, 29, 32, 36, 57, 89, 102
leukemia 23, 24, 30, 34, 37, 38, 90, 134, 139
light water reactors 45, 70, 74
lindane 41, 90, 128, 167
Linnaeus 111
Liss, Peter 16
livestock rearing 17, 18, 28, 35, 50, 52, 54, 61, 63, 69, 73, 83, 87, 88, 89, 91–2, 106, 114, 147, 149, 150
logging 17, 24, 38, 49, 50, 52, 79, 95, 158, 159, 160
London Dumping Convention (LDC) 118, 120, 121
Love, William T. 102
Lovelock, James 26, 74, 82
Lovins, Amory B. 145
Lutalyse 85, 91
Lutzenberger, Jose 17, 18

M
McCarrison, Sir Robert 55
McNamara, Robert 79
McNaughton, Professor 112
mad cow disease (BSE) 27
Magnox reactors 43, 49, 91, 111, 129, 137, 143, 144
malaria 46, 97, 164
malathion 105, 128
malnutrition 20, 52, 68, 72, 73, 95, 97, 145
Malthus, Thomas 131
Mannitol 21
Margulis, Lynn 26
marine life 66, 80, 87, 89, 90, 107, 136
Marsh, George Perkins 23
Marshall Islands 24
melengesterol acetate (MGA) 85
mercury 12, 44, 89, 102, 107, 114, 136, 149
mesothelioma 21, 22
methaemoglobinaemia 114
methane 44, 75, 83, 88, 97, 100, 124
methanol 32
methyl chloroform 85
methylene chloride 39, 85
migraine 42, 43, 63, 72, 148
milk 27, 36
miscarriage 43, 90, 107
monoculture 77, 127, 156
Montreal Protocol 40, 87
Mooney, Patrick *Seed of the Earth* 143
Moore, Barrington 59
Morris, David 134
mosquitoes 25, 69, 104
MOX (mixed oxide) fuels 31
multiple sclerosis 60
Muskie, Senator Edmond S. 79
mutagens 10, 16, 34, 127
mutations 31, 72, 111
mycorrhizae 112
Myers, Dr Norman *The Primary Resource* 87

N
Naess, Arne 49
Narmada Valley project 162, 168
National Forest Action Plans (NFAP) 158
Natural Environment Research Council 41, 100
nematocides 85
neohesperidin dihydrochalcone 21
New Reproductive Technologies 67
Nile River 20, 22, 58
NIREX 118
nitrates 27, 57, 65, 85, 114, 115, 129, 132
nitrogen 11, 16, 20–1, 33, 44, 64, 77, 109, 115, 122, 132, 136, 153
nitrogen oxide 10, 12, 32, 36, 41, 44, 75, 124, 153
nitrosamines 132
nitrous oxide 21, 83, 124
nomadic pastoralism 51

Non-Proliferation Treaty (NPT) 94, 111, 117
North Sea 16, 25, 30, 65, 89, 120, 123, 136, 142
Nuclear Electric 13, 104, 132, 137
nuclear reactors 18, 28, 31, 51, 70, 72, 88, 101, 132, 138
 advanced gas-cooled 31, 43, 48–9, 91, 137, 143, 144, 161
 fast breeder 31, 37, 45, 56, 69, 70, 98, 129
 light water 45, 70, 74
 Magnox 43, 49, 91, 111, 129, 137, 143, 144
 pressurized water 31, 43, 48, 118, 139, 143, 144, 145, 150, 161, 162
 RBMK 43, 69
nuclear reprocessing 143, 161, 163
nuclear waste 49, 56, 72, 74, 102, 116, 120, 151
nuclear weapons 73, 103, 114, 117–18
 testing 22–3, 24, 105, 110–11

O
ocean dumping 29, 102, 118, 123, 136
 incineration 102, 114, 115
Odum, Professor Eugene 135
oil 15, 19, 34, 60, 61, 86, 136, 147
Operation Smokey 23
organic farming 21, 83, 127
organochlorines 128
organophosphates 27, 33, 44, 53, 69, 93, 104, 125, 128, 146
organosilicon 102
Oslo Treaty 120, 121
Osterhaus, Dr Albert 142
oxidation catalysts 36
ozone 32, 44
 tropospheric 15, 83
ozone layer 21, 38, 39, 40, 79, 81, 87, 98, 110

P
packaging 39, 40, 55, 81
paper making 54, 65
parathion 128
Partial Test Ban Treaty (PTBT) 161
patenting of seeds 72, 76, 91, 143
Payer, Cheryl 150
PCBs see polychlorinated biphenyls
PCDFs 129, 130
pellagra 104
pentachlorophenol 108, 128, 167
perchlorethylene 39
permaculture 127
persistence in the environment 16, 38, 90, 93, 94, 102, 115, 123, 125, 126, 142
Pesticide Exposure Group of Sufferers (PEGS) 123
pesticides 40–1, 42, 77, 78, 84, 126, 132, 143, 146, 147, 148
Peto, Professor Julian 43
Phenoclor 130
phenoxy herbicides 54, 90, 160, 161
pheromones 26
phosphates 16, 65
phosphorus 16, 20–1, 136
phytoplankton 16, 98, 121
plutonium 18, 45, 69, 70, 88, 102, 103, 105, 118, 136, 137, 143, 144
Polonoroeste project 168
Polyani, Karl 68
polybrominated biphenyl (PBB) 106–7
polychlorinated biphenyls (PCBs) 25, 39, 54, 92, 115, 121, 130, 136, 138, 142, 165
polyculture 122
population 51, 52, 67, 68, 84
potassium 20, 21, 133
pregnancy 34, 38, 149, 153, 162
preservatives 12, 13
pressure tube reactors 31
pressurized water reactor (PWR) 31, 43, 48, 118, 139, 143, 144, 145, 150, 161, 162
Prior, Dr Ian 55

Products of Incomplete Combustion (PICs) 92
propellants 38
prostaglandins 91
purse-seining 56

Q
Quing, Dai 150

R
radiation and health 23, 24, 36, 37, 72, 91, 101, 102, 105, 111, 118, 134, 139, 144, 162
radioactive iodine 36, 37, 91
radon 30, 118, 162
rainforests see tropical forests
Ralgro 86
Ramsar Convention 165
Rasmussen Report 116
rayon manufacture 135, 145
RBMK reactors 43, 69
reforestation 145
refrigerants 39
Reilly, William 82
reprocessing 45, 69, 117
respiratory problems 15, 20, 24, 86
The Resourceful Earth 80
Rhodes, Cecil 52
rickets 104
Rickless, Professor 112
Rifkin, Jeremy 78
Rowland, Sherry 123
run-off 21, 41, 57, 89, 115, 129, 136
ruthenium 118

S
salinization 20, 22, 47, 97
schistosomiasis 22, 46, 97, 108, 164
Scott, Dr James 153
sea dumping see ocean dumping seals 19, 25, 93, 115, 136
seed patenting 72, 76, 91, 143
Selikoff, Professor Irving 147
Sellafield 18, 101, 102, 115, 134, 136, 137, 139
Sessions, Georg 49
sewage 56–7, 121, 129, 164
shallow ecology 49
Shapiro, Mark 40
sheep 18, 36, 37
shelf-life 13, 19, 72
Shelford, V.E. 23
Shell Chemicals 126, 138
shifting cultivators 147
silt 22, 47, 50, 120, 142–3, 150, 151, 159
simazine 57, 90
Simon, Professor Julian 80
Sizewell 132
slash and burn 49, 61, 144, 156
Snell, Peter 129
social ecology 59
social forestry 73, 135
sodium 140
soils 11, 18, 20, 21, 52, 53, 57, 58, 64, 65, 68, 73, 82, 89, 90, 109, 113, 114, 122, 123, 125, 135, 140, 142, 144, 147, 156
solvents 24, 39, 85, 100
Sorbitol 21
Southwood Report 1989 28
spray cans see aerosols steam generating heavy water reactor 31
Sternglass, Professor Ernest 139
Stockholm Conference 110
strontium–90 88, 105, 134
Suess, Edward 26
sulphur dioxide 10, 11, 12, 15, 16, 41, 54, 75, 142, 155
Super-Phaanix reactor 69
surface impoundment 99
Swaminathan, Dr M.A. 90
synergy 34, 50, 71, 121, 155
synthetic organic chemicals 127

T
Tansley, A. G. 60
Target 2000 95
tectonic plate movements 33
telodrin 53, 54
teratogens 16, 31, 34, 38, 43, 106, 127
tetrachlorodibenzo-paradioxin (TCDD) 134
tetrachloroethylene 39, 85
thalidomide 149
Thatcher, Margaret 81, 82
thermal expansion 82
Third World Debt 37, 48, 84, 95
thorium 134
30 per cent club 12
timber 17, 24, 38, 49, 50, 52, 79, 95, 158, 159, 160
Times Beach 54
trade acreage 78
traditional agriculture 68, 91
trees 10, 17, 49, 52, 82
trenbolen acetate (Finaplix) 86
tri-butyl phosphate (TBP) 136
tribal peoples 17, 18, 23, 29, 46, 48, 53, 78, 113, 137, 157, 160
tributyl tin 109, 167
trichlorethylene 39
trichlorethylene (TCE) 39, 85, 138
trichloroethane 39
trichlorophenol 144
trihalomethanes (THMS) 57, 107
tritium 74, 118, 139
tropical forest 17, 33, 47, 48, 50, 66, 78, 87–8, 95, 105, 106, 147, 155, 158
tsetse fly 114
tubewells 85
2,4-D 54, 129
2,4,5-T 54, 129
2,3,7,8-tetrtachlorodibenzo-para- dioxin 54

U
ultraviolet (UV) radiation 124
Union Carbide 24, 63
unity of nature 23
unleaded petrol 32–3, 36
unsymmetrical dimethylhydrazine (UDMH) 128
Upjohn Corporation 85, 91
uranium 31, 45, 70, 102, 103, 133, 134, 136, 137

V
vehicle emissions 10, 14, 62, 82, 101, 115, 124
Vernadsky, Vladimir The Biosphere 26
vinyl chloride 30, 55, 65, 135
Visual Display Units (VDUs) 60
vitrification 118
volcanic eruptions 11, 33

W
Waldsterben 10, 12
WASH 1400 Report 116
waste trade 66
waterborne diseases 22, 46, 47, 56, 84, 97, 141–2
Weir, David 40
White, Paul 44
Wigglesworth, Dr. V.B. 48
Wilkinson, Dr Richard 55
Wilson, Edward O. 66, 78
Windscale 101, 116, 143
women 38, 53, 131
 health 24, 27, 34, 43, 53, 54, 85, 86, 91, 106
 miscarriage 43, 90, 107
 pregnancy 34, 38, 149, 153, 162 work 35, 56, 73, 153, 168
wood fuel 62
wood pulp 54–5, 65, 135, 145
woodchipping 65
World Bank 14, 38, 46, 47, 61, 63, 67, 73, 79, 80, 104, 113, 114, 135, 137, 145,

147, 150, 154, 155, 157, 158
World Health Organization (WHO) 10, 15, 16,
    19, 25, 29, 39, 42, 45, 69, 104, 106, 107,
    127
World Heritage list 80
World Resources Institute 11, 50, 70, 124,
    157
World Wide Fund for Nature 48, 63
Worldwatch Institute 49, 51, 60, 62, 70, 121,
    134

X
X-rays 133
Xueyu, Hou 150
Xylitol 21

Y
Yanomami Indians 17

Z
Zeranol 86
zineb 33
Zooxanthellae 44

Acknowledgements

The General Editors wish to thank the editorial staff of Mitchell Beazley
    Publishers and the following contributors; Michael Allaby, Crispin
    Aubrey, Patrick Anderson, John Ballantine, Peter Bunyard, Marcus
    Colchester, Simon Fairlie, Bill Hare, Jackie Karas, Mick Kelly, Larry
    Lohmann, David Lomax, Patrick McCully, Robert Mann, Erik Millstone,
    Brian Price, Pam Simmons, Jonathan Spink, John Valentine; also Hilary
    Datchens and Helen Lamper for their help with the inputting.

Research
Hilary Bacon, Michael Clark, Chris Cooper, Clark Robinson Ltd.

Picture credits
Cover: John Garrett (background and torso). Text: Reuters/Bettmann, 86;
    Associated Press/Topham, 110; Mark Edwards/Still Pictures all other
    text photographs.